NEW YORK
D. Van Nostrand Company, Inc., 250 Fourth Avenue, New York 3

TORONTO
D. Van Nostrand Company (Canada), Ltd., 228 Bloor Street, Toronto

LONDON
Macmillan & Company, Ltd., St. Martin's Street, London, W.C. 2

PRINTED IN THE UNITED STATES OF AMERICA

Principles of
Nuclear Chemistry

BY

RUSSELL R. WILLIAMS, JR., PH.D.

*Assistant Professor, Department of Chemistry,
University of Notre Dame*

D. VAN NOSTRAND COMPANY, INC.

TORONTO   NEW YORK   LC

PREFACE

BEGINNING with the intensive war-time development of "atomic" energy, the scientific institutions of this country have devoted a considerable fraction of their effort to the study and application of nuclear phenomena. One consequence of this interest has been the appearance of courses entitled "Radiochemistry" or "Nuclear Chemistry" in the curricula of many universities. This book is an outgrowth of such a course given at Notre Dame during the past few years. It is intended to serve as the basis for a one-semester lecture course for advanced undergraduates and graduate students.

Although the main object of this work is the description and discussion of the chemical phenomena which are related to nuclear properties and processes, a considerable amount of material which would be more precisely titled "Nuclear Physics" must be presented in order to lay the proper foundation for consideration of more truly chemical problems. With the previous training and interests of the chemistry student in mind, this material is presented from an empirical rather than a theoretical point of view, and with somewhat less than complete mathematical treatment.

The chemical phenomena considered in this work and in similar courses may be divided into two broad groups. In the first, the main object is the study of nuclear phenomena and their chemical consequences. The student will learn that radiochemical analysis is an intriguing and sometimes peculiar combination of qualitative and quantitative analysis. He will hear of methods for separating and studying the sub-microscopic quantities of radioactive substances produced in nuclear reactions, and the importance of the methods may be emphasized by reference to the discovery of nuclear fission by Hahn

iii

and Strassmann. Aside from such preparative and analytical studies, chemical phenomena of nuclear origin are worthy of study in themselves. The chemical effects of nuclear mass, although small, are subject to rather precise prediction and measurement. Nuclear rearrangement reactions are usually accompanied by chemical reactions, both within the altered atom and in its environment. Although the emphasis upon these various subjects will depend upon the lecturer's training and inclinations, they constitute the material which most clearly conforms to the title "Nuclear Chemistry."

The second broad classification of subject matter which must be considered is best described as "Applied Nuclear Chemistry." A large amount of material describing the application of nuclear techniques to the study of the problems of chemistry and allied sciences is available. However, the object here is to point out the particular advantages accruing to the study of more or less classical problems through the ability to detect and distinguish the nuclear varieties of an atomic type. Therefore, a limited number of examples are briefly considered, in the belief that detailed discussion and interpretation are properly left to more specialized works.

The widespread emphasis on preparative and analytical radiochemistry techniques and on the application of tracer techniques indicates that nuclear chemistry is, to a considerable extent, an applied science and, as such, calls for an extensive discussion of laboratory practice. In the belief that detailed discussion of such material is best left to books intended for direct laboratory guidance, this text will attempt to put major emphasis on principles and to explore as many facets of the subject as possible.

References to the original literature in the discussions of nuclear physics are infrequent since this material is readily available in more elaborate treatments of this subject. Several such sources are given in the supplementary reading lists of the early chapters. In dealing with more strictly chemical problems, however, the material discussed more closely approaches the actual frontiers of the science, and reference to the original literature is intended to be more complete. Even in this phase of the treatment, no attempt is made to trace a historical pattern. This is evidenced by the omission of a direct discussion of the work of the Curies, who might be regarded as the first nuclear chemists.

It is a pleasure to acknowledge the guidance and inspiration of numerous colleagues at the Clinton Laboratories, Oak Ridge, Tennessee, during 1944-46, and at Notre Dame since that time. Dr. T. Harrison Davies of the University of Chicago has been especially helpful with detailed criticism of the manscript.

R.R.W., Jr.

Notre Dame, Ind.
January 1950

CONTENTS

CHAPTER I

THE ATOMIC NUCLEUS

ATOMIC STRUCTURE

OUR PRESENT understanding of atomic structure began with the discovery and characterization of the electron by J. J. Thomson in 1897. This particle is common to all types of atoms and was first recognized in the "cathode rays" produced by electrical discharge in gases. It has a mass of 9.1066×10^{-28} gram and a negative charge of 4.8021×10^{-10} electrostatic unit. Since the mass of the lightest atom, hydrogen, is 1.67339×10^{-24} gram, it is apparent that the positive ion residue left after electron removal has a mass much greater than that of the electron, 1837 times as great in the case of hydrogen, and proportionately greater for heavier atoms.

The Nuclear Atom. The modern concept of the spatial distribution of mass and charge within the atom is due to Rutherford,[1] who proposed the nuclear theory of atomic structure. This theory describes the atom as consisting of a small, heavy *nucleus* carrying a positive charge, surrounded by the light, negative electrons at distances many times the nuclear diameter. Rutherford reached this conclusion from consideration of experiments on the scattering of positive ions by metal foils [2] as indicated in Fig. 1.1. A collimated beam of high-velocity positive ions (He^{++}) is allowed to fall on an extremely thin metal foil, and some form of ion detector is used

---

[1] Rutherford, *Phil. Mag.* **21**, 699 (1911).
[2] Geiger and Marsden, *Proc. Roy. Soc.* **82**, 995 (1909) ; *Phil. Mag.* **25**, 604 (1913).

to measure the intensity of scattering at various angles. Most of the positive ions pass through the foil with little or no deflection, but a few ions are scattered through various angles. The intensity of scattering decreases with the angle of scattering, but ions are detected at angles of nearly 180°.

Since most of the positive ions suffer little or no deflection, even though the foil must be several hundred atoms thick, the

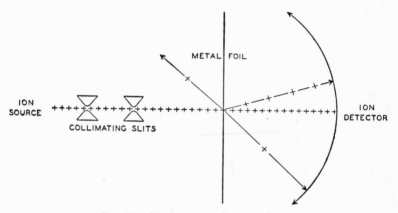

FIG. 1.1. Nuclear scattering experiment.

positive charge or scattering center must be highly concentrated, presumably in a central position in the atom. Further, since the probability of deflection is apparently small, the few large deflections observed cannot be attributed to multiple collisions, but must arise from close approach of the positive projectiles to some concentrated unit of mass and positive charge. Assuming a coulombic repulsion law between the energetic positive ion and the scattering center, a relationship describing the fraction f of ions scattered through an angle θ may be stated in the form

$$f(\theta) = \text{const.}\ (Ze)^2\ \csc^4\ \theta/2$$

where Ze is the charge on the scattering center and the constant depends on various properties of the bombarding ions and the experimental arrangement. In an encounter resulting in a large angle of scattering, the potential energy at the distance of closest approach d may be approximately equated to the kinetic energy of the bombarding ion, yielding

$$d = \frac{2ZZ'e^2}{mv^2} \qquad (1.1)$$

where

m = mass of the projectile
v = velocity of the projectile
$Z'e$ = charge on the projectile
Ze = charge on the nucleus

This relation and the relation expressing the number of particles scattered at various angles assume the scattering center to be infinitely massive in comparison to the projectile. For the scattering of light particles, such as protons or helium nuclei, by heavy nuclei the scattering equation agrees very well with observation and was, in fact, used by Rutherford to determine the nuclear charge of some atoms. The distance of closest approach may apparently be as small as 10^{-12} cm without intervention of nuclear forces. This is to be contrasted with atomic radii which are of the order of magnitude of 10^{-8} cm.

Electronic Structure. The periodic classification of the elements was originally proposed on the basis of essentially chemical properties, before any direct investigation of atomic structure was accomplished. Its full significance and usefulness, however, were only realized when it was closely tied to the details of electronic structure. The necessary information was derived from a large variety of methods, among them studies of the absorption and emission of radiation, ionization by electric fields and electron impact, and the magnetic properties of atoms and molecules. Most of these methods are concerned with transitions between various electronic energy states, and it is now possible to construct a fairly detailed picture of the energy states of most atoms and many molecules. Some of this information is incorporated into the more complete periodic tables which are familiar to all chemists.

It should be noted that a knowledge of the electronic energy states of an atom and its electrons is not necessarily translatable into a description of the spatial orientation of electrons. The simple picture of minute electrons revolving in circular and elliptical orbits at distances determined by their potential energy fails under detailed examination. It has remained for the methods of wave mechanics to provide a more satisfactory and fundamentally different conception of the electron in the field of a nucleus, where its potential energy is rather precisely known. The Uncertainty Principle of Heisenberg postulates that the simultaneous determination of the position and momentum of a particle is always subject to an uncertainty in the product of the two quantities which is approximately equal to the Planck constant h. Thus if the momentum, or energy, of an electron is rather precisely known, its position will be somewhat uncertain. The "position" of an extra-nuclear electron may be represented by a wave function, rather than a point or orbit, this function having maxima in various characteristic regions about the nucleus and falling off asymptotically toward zero in other regions. The wave theory of matter is not confined to the electron, but rather it is most significant in this case because of the small mass involved, in accordance with the equation of de Broglie [3]

$$\lambda = \frac{h}{mv} \tag{1.2}$$

which predicts an inverse relation between mass and wave

---

[3] De Broglie, Thesis, Paris, 1924; *Ann. de phys* (10) **3**, 22 (1925).

length. In many subsequent discussions it will be useful to keep in mind the wave properties of particles.

Atomic Number. The progression of elements in the periodic system is properly based on the number of extra-nuclear electrons in the neutral atom, which is in turn equal to the number of unit charges on the atomic nucleus. This property, known as the *atomic number,* may in many cases be deduced from chemical properties, but a more unequivocal method is furnished by the measurement of the frequency of the most energetic lines of the X-ray spectra of the elements. These radiations arise from electronic transitions to the most firmly bound electronic energy state, the *K*-shell, whose potential energy is in turn determined by the nuclear charge. The simple relation deduced by Moseley,[4]

$$\sqrt{\nu} = C_1(Z - C_2) \tag{1.3}$$

where

ν = frequency of the most energetic X-ray lines
Z = atomic number

permits the precise determination of the atomic number, the proper placement of any element in the periodic system, and a measurement of the important nuclear property of charge. Elements of atomic number 1 through 96 are now known.

NUCLEAR MASS

A glance at the atomic weights of the elements as recorded in the Appendix shows that there is no simple integral relation as is the case with atomic numbers and, in fact, the progression of atomic weights actually reverses in a few cases. In order to retain the attractive hypothesis that nuclear mass, like nuclear charge, will always be some integral multiple of a unit mass, we must introduce the concept of *isotopes,* atoms of the

---

[4] Moseley, *Phil. Mag.* **26**, 1024 (1913) ; **27**, 703 (1914).

same atomic number but different masses, and account for non-integral atomic weights through varying abundances of the isotopes of the elements. We may expect the masses of isotopes to differ by some integral multiple of a unit mass and may describe the masses of all nuclei by the *mass number,* the integral multiple of the unit mass.

The relative constancy of atomic weight values, regardless of source and treatment of the element, indicates that the nuclear mass is not a major determinant of chemical properties. However, chemical differences between isotopes can be detected and measured in favorable cases, as will be discussed in Chapter II. At least one element, lead, does show a comparatively large variation in atomic weight according to source. This variation may be attributed to a variable abundance of its isotopes, and it was one of the earliest experimental supports for the isotope hypothesis.

Mass Spectroscopy. The most direct method of determining the relative masses and abundances of isotopes is known as mass spectroscopy, since it resembles optical spectroscopy in that the components of the mixture are geometrically resolved into a "mass spectrum" by an experimental arrangement which accommodates material particles rather than radiations. The analysis depends upon the forces exerted on moving changed particles in electric and magnetic fields.

If an ion of charge e and mass m is accelerated through a potential difference V, its kinetic energy will be given by

$$Ve = 1/2mv^2 \qquad (1.4)$$

and its velocity by

$$v = \sqrt{\frac{2Ve}{m}} \qquad (1.5)$$

If such an ion is next projected into a homogeneous magnetic field of strength H, in a direction perpendicular to the lines of force, it will describe a path whose radius of curvature r, will be given by

$$r = \frac{v}{H} \cdot \frac{m}{e} \tag{1.6}$$

Substituting the ion velocity as given by equation 1.5, the fundamental equation for the mass spectrograph is found to be

$$r = \frac{1}{H} \sqrt{2V \cdot m/e} \tag{1.7}$$

which states that for a fixed accelerating potential and mag-

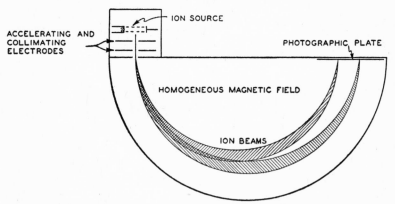

FIG. 1.2. Dempster mass spectrograph.

netic field strength the radius of curvature will be proportional to the square root of the mass-to-charge ratio of the ion.

The physical arrangement in a typical mass spectrograph, a type originated by Dempster,[5] is shown in Fig. 1.2. The substance of interest is vaporized in the source region and ionized by electron bombardment. Careful control of the electron beam will insure the formation of singly charged ions in large majority. The positive ions are accelerated and collimated by the increasingly negative electrodes and then projected into the region of homogeneous magnetic field. Here

[5] Dempster, *Phys. Rev.* 11, 316 (1918) ; 18, 415 (1921) ; 20, 631 (1922).

they describe semicircular paths, striking a photographic emulsion at points characteristic of their masses. The whole system is evacuated to a pressure such as to permit transit of the ions from source to detecter without collision. Some divergence of the ion beam at the point of entry into the magnetic field is permissible, since this will be greater at the 90° position and decrease to a small amount at the detector (180°). A typical mass spectrum obtained in such an instrument is shown in Fig. 1.3.

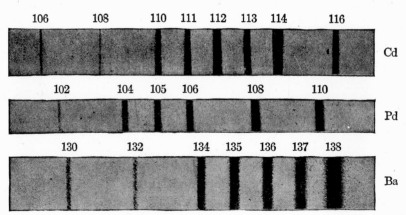

FIG. 1.3.   Mass spectra of cadmium, palladium and barium (Dempster).[6]

In the arrangement described above all singly charged ions, regardless of mass, enter the magnetic field with the same kinetic energy, except for negligibly small variations in original velocity with respect to the direction of acceleration. Their velocities, however, will depend on their masses, and the mass spectrum at the detector is a square root function as shown by equation 1.7. Instruments of this type, in which a simultaneous record of the location of several mass peaks is obtained, are most useful in the precise determination of atomic masses. For

---

[6] From S. Glasstone, *Textbook of Physical Chemistry*, D. Van Nostrand Co., Inc., 1946.

many applications of chemical interest, however, the relative abundance of different mass types is of primary interest. In this case it is more satisfactory to measure individually the ion current corresponding to a single mass type as is done in the Nier [7] mass spectrometer shown in Fig. 1.4. In this device the ions are formed by electron bombardment, accelerated and collimated by the indicated electrodes, and projected into a magnetic field shaped in the form of an equilateral triangle.

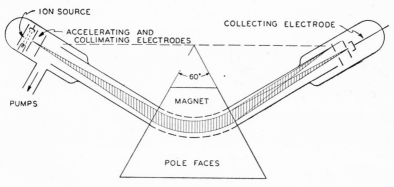

FIG. 1.4. Nier mass spectrometer.

The ions enter and leave the field normal to the faces of this triangle and finally fall on a collecting electrode which is attached to a sensitive electrometer circuit. Only one mass type reaches the detector at any time, and the mass spectrum is examined by alteration of either the accelerating potential or the magnetic field strength. The instrument responds to ions having a fixed radius of curvature, and equation 1.7 may be modified as follows

$$m = \frac{r^2 e}{2} \cdot \frac{H^2}{V} \tag{1.8}$$

to show the relationships between field strength, accelerating potential, and mass of the ions reaching the detector.

[7] Nier, *Rev. Sci. Inst.* **11**, 212 (1940).

It is difficult to measure the absolute value of the magnetic field strength in a mass spectrometer, and therefore the mass scale is usually calibrated with some convenient substance. Some discretion is necessary in the interpretation of the observed abundance ratios for various ionic types. For instance, a singly charged ion of mass 45 can be due to the type $C^{13}O^{16}O^{16+}$ or to $C^{12}O^{16}O^{17+}$. In natural carbon dioxide this confusion is not serious, since the O^{17} isotope is present to the extent of only 0.039% of all oxygen atoms, whereas C^{13} has an abundance of 1% and will therefore be the most important contributor to mass 45. In precise mass measurements such "doublets" are extremely useful, since, in general, the two ionic types will not have exactly the same mass. For instance a precise comparison of the masses of N^{14} and C^{13} is possible through the measurement of the very small separation of $N^{14}H_3^+$ and $C^{13}H_4^+$. This procedure considerably reduces the problem of mass-scale calibration and uniformity.

The mass spectrometer has recently found considerable use as an analytical instrument in the field of organic chemistry, since the ionic types detected will be characteristic of the source molecule. Especially in the case of complicated hydrocarbon molecules, where ordinary analysis may be difficult, the mass spectrum may be taken as an analytical characteristic, and rather small samples will suffice. In another application, the products of a reaction mixture may be fed directly into the source region. Free radicals as well as molecules may be ionized and characterized by the instrument. If the molecule or radical ions rapidly decompose, the corresponding mass charge may be detected by appropriate variation of the ion flight time in the instrument.

Atomic Mass Scale. It is convenient to state atomic and nuclear masses in a relative scale, and to choose some readily available and workable substance as the reference. Chemical considerations have led to the choice of the element oxygen as it occurs in nature ($O^{16} = 99.757\%$, $O^{17} = 0.039\%$, $O^{18} = 0.204\%$) as the standard for the *chemical atomic weight scale.* Comparison of other elements or their isotopes with this substance permits the determination of relative masses in a scale where oxygen is given the value 16.0000. Since the isotopic abundance in oxygen varies only slightly among various compounds and sources, this scale is satisfactory in most chemical calculations.

To avoid ambiguity and to recognize the possibility of small variations in the abundance of the oxygen isotopes, physicists have selected the oxygen isotope of mass number 16 as a standard substance, assigning it a value of 16.0000 atomic mass units (a.m.u.) in the *physical atomic weight scale.* Since the chemical standard contains small amounts of the two heavier isotopes of oxygen, chemical atomic weights will be slightly smaller than physical atomic weights. The conversion factor is given by

$$1.000272 \times \text{Chemical atomic weight} = \text{Physical atomic weight}$$

Thus the nuclear type O^{16} has a mass of 15.9956 on the chemical scale. Care must be taken to use appropriate and consistent units where precise calculation is desired, as in the case of mass discrepancies and nuclear energetics, where the physical scale is most commonly used.

Packing Fraction. The precise determination of atomic masses indicates that they are not exactly integral multiples of some unit mass. By definition O^{16} has a mass of 16.0000 amu, but lighter and heavier nuclei have masses slightly different from integral multiples of this number. This mass discrepancy changes in a fairly regular fashion in the sequence of nuclei and may be expressed as a packing fraction, defined as follows:

$$\text{Packing fraction} = \frac{\text{Measured atomic mass} - A}{A} \quad (1.9)$$

where A, the mass number, may be defined as the nearest whole number to the measured mass. Fig. 1.5 shows the variation of the packing fraction as a function of A. The significance of these mass discrepancies will be considered in a later section.

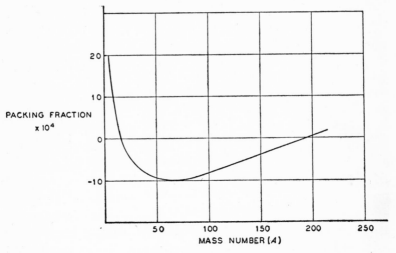

Fig. 1.5. Packing fraction.

NUCLEAR COMPOSITION

An inspection of the atomic masses given in the Nuclide Chart of the Appendix will show that they are all very nearly whole numbers. If the values were less precise we would be inclined to accept immediately the attractive hypothesis that the various nuclei are composed of integral numbers of some fundamental particle or particles. In spite of the small discrepancies this is still possible, since it is this mass discrepancy, through the Einstein mass-energy equivalence concept, which represents the binding energy of the nucleus. This aspect of nuclear mass-energy will be deferred to the next section while we first consider the question of nuclear composition.

Protons and Neutrons. Although the various nuclear masses appear to be very nearly integral multiples of the proton mass, this particle alone is not sufficient for our description of nuclei. The atomic number, or nuclear charge, has values from 1 to 92 in the natural elements, but the mass number changes from 1 through 238. At one time this difficulty was explained by assuming the nucleus consisted of a number of protons equal to the mass number, plus sufficient electrons to reduce the nuclear charge to the value required by the atomic number. For several reasons which we cannot enumerate here, this description is unsatisfactory.

The discovery by Chadwick, in 1934, of an uncharged particle of mass very nearly the same as that of the proton furnished a satisfactory answer to this problem of nuclear composition. With this particle, known as a neutron, and the proton, the composition of all nuclei can be described. The two particles are known collectively as nucleons. The number of protons is equal to the atomic number, whereas the number of neutrons is equal to the mass number less the atomic number. Atomic and mass numbers are frequently given as subscript and superscript to the chemical symbol to describe a particular variety of nuclei, thus: $_zX^A$. The term *nuclide* will be used to refer to a variety of atoms whose nuclei have the same atomic and mass numbers, and the term *isotopes* may now be defined as referring to atoms whose nuclei have the same atomic numbers but different mass numbers. Similarly, the term *isobars* denotes identical mass numbers but different atomic numbers.

The mass of the proton is readily measured by the mass spectrographic technique, and the value has been given previously. The mass of the neutron cannot be measured in any such direct fashion but must be obtained by determination of the masses and energies involved in some nuclear rearrangement reaction as will be shown later.

Stable Nuclei. The known stable nuclei are represented by solid circles in Fig. 1.6 in terms of their atomic and mass numbers. The open circles represent some semistable nuclei which occur in nature in weighable amounts by virtue of a decomposition rate so small that they have not disappeared in geologic time. All nuclei other than those indicated are presumed to be unstable.

Note that the region of stability lies at approximately $A = 2Z$ for the lighter elements, indicating that nuclei with approximately equal numbers of protons and neutrons are most likely to be stable. With the heavier nuclei, the stable proportion of neutrons increases somewhat, decreasing the slope of the curve. Beyond $Z = 83$ and $A = 209$, the only stable isotope of bismuth, all combinations are more or less unstable.

Several interesting regularities may be observed by reference to Fig. 1.6., especially if the consideration is restricted to nuclei with fairly large numbers of nucleons, say $A > 20$. (1) There are no stable nuclei of odd Z and even A in this region. Apparently any combination consisting of an odd number of protons and an odd number of neutrons is always unstable. (2) Elements of odd Z have a small number of isotopes, frequently only one, in comparison to the elements of even Z. Thus it would seem that even when the number of neutrons is even, an odd number of protons is likely to be unstable. (3) Considering cross sections of constant A rather than Z, it is seen that the isobaric series of odd A have only one stable member, with three exceptions (113, 115, 123), whereas isobaric series of even A may have two or three stable isobars,

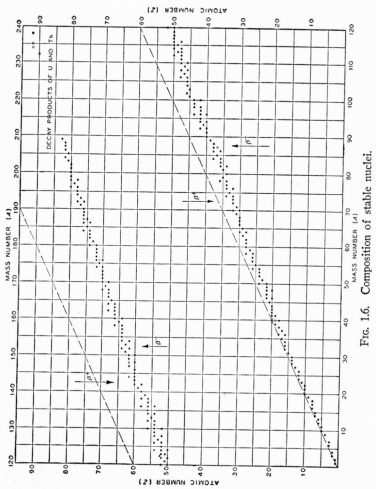

FIG. 1.6. Composition of stable nuclei.

although these are never adjacent.[8] These regularities can be incorporated into a semi quantitative theory of nuclear stability which is useful in predictions about unstudied nuclei. A good example of this method is available in the cases of elements 43 and 61, whose existence as stable nuclides has been disputed for some time. Note that all isotopes of these elements will contain an odd number of protons in their nuclei. Item (1) indicates that the isotopes of even A (odd neutrons) will be unstable. If the isotopes of odd A (even neutrons) are examined, it is found that the elements preceding and following 43 and 61 always have a stable isobar. Item (3) thus makes it seem extremely unlikely that a stable isotope of these two elements exists.

Changes in Composition. Changes in nuclear composition occur in two ways: first, by interaction of some particle or radiation with a nucleus and, second, by the spontaneous process of radioactive decay.

The first process is usually referred to as a bombardment reaction since it frequently involves the projection of energetic radiations or particles such as electrons, deuterons $(1p, 1n)$, helium nuclei $(2p, 2n)$, protons, or neutrons onto a target containing stable nuclei. These agents may undergo a variety of interactions with the target nuclei such as elastic collision, inelastic collision, particle capture, or particle capture followed by emission of some other particle. Depending on the particular process, the mass and/or the atomic number of the target nucleus may be changed, but generally only by a few units, since both captured and emitted particles are relatively simple units.

The radioactive decay process is the mechanism by means

---

[8] Recent data have indicated that the nucleus La^{138} is stable, in spite of its odd proton-odd neutron configuration. It also falls between the two stable isobars Ba^{138} and Ce^{138}.

of which an unstable combination of nucleons rearranges to approach stability. It proceeds at a rate which is independent of all ordinary experimental conditions, such as temperature, pressure, and chemical state. Again the nuclear changes involved in a single decay process are small in terms of atomic and mass numbers. Very energetic particles and radiations are emitted in the course of radioactive decay.

NUCLEAR ENERGETICS

Mass-energy Equivalence. One of the most significant features of the nuclear rearrangement reactions just mentioned is the magnitude of the energy changes associated with them. It is not uncommon to find that such processes absorb or release as much as 10^8 kg cal/mole, which is many orders of magnitude greater than the energy terms in chemical reactions. In the latter cases, the classical assumption of energy conservation is sufficiently precise, but with nuclear reactions the broader concept of mass-energy conservation must be used. The fundamental equation, due to Einstein,

$$E = mc^2 \tag{1.10}$$

where c is the velocity of light, connects the two quantities mass, m, and energy, E. A simple calculation shows that the energy equivalent of one gram of matter is 2.15×10^{10} kg cal, or that one atomic mass unit (physical scale) is equal to 932 million electron volts (mev).[9]

The consequences of the concept indicated by equation 1.10 are very important in the study of nuclear phenomena. Changes in kinetic or potential energy and the emission or absorption of radiant energy must be accompanied by appropriate mass changes. A particle moving with kinetic energy E will have

---

[9] Electron volt = energy acquired by an electronic charge falling through a potential difference of one volt. See the Appendix for conversion factors.

an apparent mass m somewhat greater than its rest mass m_o as given by the relation

$$m = m_0 + \frac{E}{c^2} \qquad (1.11)$$

The limiting velocity which a particle may approach is that of light, and the apparent mass may be given as a function of velocity by the relation

$$m = \frac{m_0}{\sqrt{1 - \beta^2}} \qquad (1.12)$$

where β is the ratio of the particle velocity to that of light. It is apparent that the relativity effect is appreciable only at large velocities, and that heavy particles such as positive ions will behave classically at much greater energies than will electrons. Radiant energy, with zero rest mass, will have a mass equivalent given by the second term of equation 1.11. The energy and momentum of a particle or radiation will be given by the expressions

$$E = mc^2 - m_0c^2 = m_0c^2 \left[\frac{1}{\sqrt{1 - \beta^2}} - 1 \right] \qquad (1.13)$$

and

$$p = mv = \frac{1}{c} \sqrt{E(E + 2m_0c^2)} \qquad (1.14)$$

Fig. 1.7 shows the behavior of β and m/m_o for electrons and protons of various energies.

In any process, whether nuclear or extra-nuclear, mass-energy will be conserved, and we may equate the mass-energy of the reactants to the mass-energy of the products. For instance, consider the addition of a proton to the stable nucleus $_6C^{13}$

$$_6C^{13} + _1H^1 \rightarrow _7N^{14} + Q,$$
$$13.0075 + 1.0081 = 14.0075 + ?$$

and let the symbol Q represent the energy change in the process. The masses given are the rest masses of the neutral atoms [10] and represent the mass-energy of the lowest energy states of these particles. The value of Q may be computed by subtracting the total rest mass of the products from the total rest mass of the reactants, and in this case the answer is -0.0081 amu. Therefore the process is exoergic by 7.55 mev.

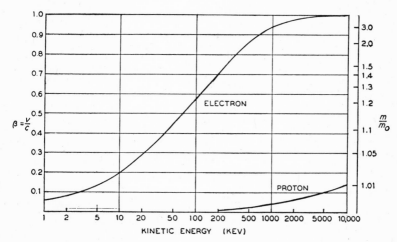

Fig. 1.7.   Velocity-mass-energy relationships for electrons and protons.

The manner in which this energy appears, whether as radiant energy or as kinetic energy of the product nucleus or some fragment of it, is not specified by this calculation.

The energy term in any nuclear process, in principle, may be calculated by consideration of the masses of reactants and products. Although fairly extensive mass data are available for the stable nuclides (see Appendix), such information is practically nonexistent for the hundreds of unstable nuclides,

---

[10] Atomic, rather than nuclear, masses are normally available and are therefore used in such calculations. The masses of the extra nuclear electrons cancel out in the case given.

and, in fact, energy measurements are commonly used to compute nuclear masses, as exemplified in the next section.

Neutron Mass. The precise mass of the neutron is a very important quantity, since this particle is involved in many nuclear reactions and is a constituent of all nuclei. The uncharged nature of the neutron precludes a mass determination by means of the mass spectrograph, and the problem must be approached indirectly, through the mass-energy conservation principle.

The nucleus of the less abundant stable isotope of hydrogen, deuterium, consists of one proton and one neutron. This nucleus, known as a deuteron, may be dissociated into a proton and a neutron by sufficiently energetic electromagnetic radiation. The precise determination of the energy threshold for this process permits the calculation of the mass of the neutron through the use of equation 1.10. The process may be represented by the equation

$$\gamma\, (\geqslant 2.18 \text{ mev}) + {}_1H^2 \rightarrow {}_1H^1 + {}_0n^1$$
$$0.0023 + 2.0147 = 1.0081 + ?$$

where the symbol γ represents the energetic radiation. The atomic masses of the two hydrogen isotopes as determined in the mass spectrograph, as well as the mass equivalent of the radiant energy, are given below the equation. If the products of this reaction have negligible kinetic energy, as is the case near the threshold, the mass of the neutron is found to be 1.0089 amu. Other similar reactions may be used for this calculation.

Nuclear Binding Energy. As a measure of the stability of any combination of nucleons we may compute the energy released in a hypothetical formation reaction from its constituent nucleons. This energy, the nuclear binding energy, may be obtained by comparing the measured mass of the nucleus with the total mass of the appropriate number of protons and neutrons. For instance, the measured atomic mass of the nuclide $_{29}Cu^{65}$ is 64.955 amu, whereas the mass of its constituents, 29 protons, 29 electrons and 36 neutrons, is 65.557 amu. The mass discrepancy is 0.602 amu, corresponding to a binding energy of 560 mev. The binding energy of the stable nuclides

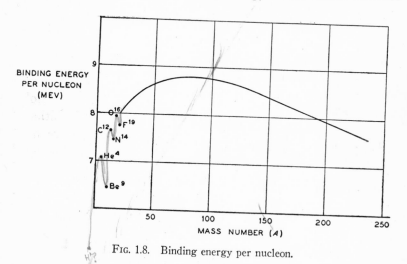

FIG. 1.8.   Binding energy per nucleon.

increases with increasing nuclear size, reaching a magnitude of approximately 1750 mev at $_{92}U^{238}$.

An idea of the magnitude of the interparticle forces within a nucleus and the effect of changing composition on this quantity may be gained from a consideration of the average binding energy per nucleon. This may be obtained by dividing the total binding energy, obtained as shown above, by the mass number A. The values of this quantity for the stable nuclei of $A > 20$ fall on a smooth curve as shown in Fig. 1.8. The maximum in this curve occurs at mass number approximately 70, and binding energy per nucleon of approximately 8.8 mev. Comparison of this quantity for a number of isotopes or isobars shows that the value is not a strong function of composition. Thus we may expect that even unstable nuclei which are not far removed from the stable neutron-proton ratios will have similar binding energies per nucleon.

The value of the binding energy per nucleon may be used to estimate the energy term in reactions such as proton or neutron capture. It is apparent that with all of the stable nuclei such processes will be exoergic by approximately 8 mev. Conversely, the emission of a proton or neutron from a nucleus will always be endoergic by a similar amount, pointing out the impossibility of observing such particles as decay products of the lower energy states of nuclei near the stable region of composition.

Nuclear Energy States. There is considerable experimental evidence that nuclei absorb and emit radiant energy in discreet units, or quanta. Nuclei can be raised to higher energy states or "excited" by energetic radiations or particles. From such excited states they most frequently and rapidly return to the lowest, or "ground" state, emitting radiations of characteristic wave lengths. With smaller probability the excited state may decay by particle emission, giving rise to a new nucleus, frequently in an excited state.

The interaction of a charged particle, such as a proton, with a nucleus may be represented as in Fig. 1.9, where the potential energy of the system is plotted as a function of the particle-nucleus separation. With decreasing separation the potential energy increases in conformity with the inverse square repulsion law observed in the scattering experiments described previously. Since this relation is valid even for extremely close approach, the nuclear forces which finally hold the particle with a binding energy of several mev must be of extremely short range, as indicated in the figure. Several hypothetical excited states of the product nucleus have been indicated by horizontal lines.

The figure as drawn indicates that a charged particle with little kinetic energy will have no chance of entering the nucleus because of the coulombic "barrier." However, no sharp threshold capture energy corresponding to the height of the barrier exists, owing to the quantum-mechanical tunnel effect.

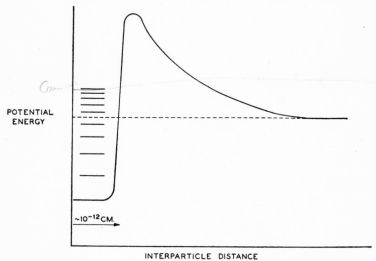

POTENTIAL
ENERGY

~10⁻¹²CM.

INTERPARTICLE DISTANCE

Fɪɢ. 1.9.   Energy surface for nucleus-charged particle interaction.

This is a consequence of the wave properties of the approaching particle, which, although nominally on the outside of the barrier, has a finite, but small probability of existence inside. This probability may be expected to increase with decreasing barrier width, that is, with increasing particle energy.

The potential energy curve for a neutron-nucleus system has no coulombic repulsion term and may be represented as a simple potential well, as shown in Fig. 1.10. Again several hypothetical excited states of the product nucleus are indicated. If the approaching neutron has an energy such that some excited state of the compound nucleus can be formed with little gain or loss of energy, the probability of interaction may be tremendously increased, and the effect is known as "resonance capture." At intermediate energies, the capture probability is inversely proportional to the neutron velocity.

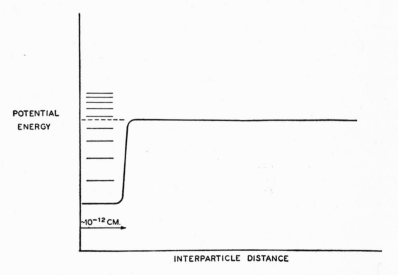

POTENTIAL ENERGY

~10^{-12} CM.

INTERPARTICLE DISTANCE

FIG. 1.10.   Energy surface for nucleus-neutron interaction.

The capture process is generally accompanied by loss of energy in the form of radiation to yield a lower or perhaps the ground state of the product nucleus. The magnitude of this energy term may be estimated from the binding energies indicated in Fig. 1.8, which refer only to ground states. Note that, in contrast to the case of the charged particle, neutrons of vanishingly small energy may be efficiently captured by nuclei.

Neutron ejection will require excitation of the nucleus to some excited state above the level representing the separated nucleus and neutron. Again the absence of the coulombic barrier makes neutron ejection a more likely process than charged particle ejection at low excitation energies.

UNSTABLE NUCLEI

This discussion of nuclear properties will be concluded with a brief extension of the description to the case of unstable nuclei. Their composition may be inferred from Fig. 1.6, which indicates that, for a nucleus of a given size (A), stability is possible only for a limited value of the neutron-proton ratio. Since nuclei other than those indicated in the figure spontaneously rearrange to one of the stable configurations, we must conclude that the process is exoergic and that all unstable combinations have a positive potential energy with respect to some other combination. However, the opposite prediction, that if a more stable arrangement is possible the change will occur, must be qualified in the same sense that the considerations of kinetics qualify the predictions of thermodynamics in chemical processes. An exoergic rearrangement process, due to the existence of some potential energy barrier, may proceed so slowly as to be undetectable.

Decay by Nucleon Emission. In all nuclei where the binding energy per nucleon has a finite value, the emission of a single proton or neutron will be endoergic, and therefore these particles are never observed as products of the spontaneous decay of the ground states of nuclei. However, if two or more nucleons were emitted as a unit, the binding energy of this combination might more than compensate for the energy required to remove them from the parent nucleus, and thus render the whole process exoergic. In other words, the total binding energy of the system may increase by division of the nucleus into two more stable groups.

In considering the various combinations of nucleons which might be emitted as decay products, we may use the binding energy per nucleon, as given in Fig. 1.8, as a rough guide. This function indicates that we shall be concerned chiefly with the heavy nuclei, where the binding energy per nucleon has decreased to the smallest values. Consider first the emission of a deuteron: 1p, 1n. The binding energy of this particle is 2.1 mev or 1.05 mev per nucleon. If a heavy nucleus, with binding energy per nucleon of about 7.5 mev, emits such a particle, the process will certainly be endoergic, since the new arrangement is, on the average, less stable. It is therefore apparent that we must look for the emission of a much more stable group of nucleons. The combination 2p, 2 n, known as an *alpha particle* is such a group, with a total binding energy of 28.2 mev or 7.05 mev per nucleon. Although this is not yet quite equal to the value for the heaviest stable nuclei, we must remember that a decrease of four units in the mass number of the parent nucleus will also result in increased binding energy. Consider the case

$$_{78}Pt^{194} \rightarrow {}_2\alpha^4 + {}_{76}Os^{190} + Q$$

194.040 amu 4.004 amu 190.038 amu 1.9 mev

in which alpha particle emission by the "stable" nucleus Pt^{194} is exoergic by 1.9 mev.[11] Several similar cases are known among the heavy elements.

It is not difficult to find even larger groups of nucleons where the binding energy per nucleon is still greater. For instance, the binding energy per nucleon in $_6C^{12}$ is 7.5 mev, and therefore emission of this group by a large nucleus would undoubtedly be exoergic. To go to the extreme case, we may consider the division of a nucleus of mass number 200 into two approximately equal groups of nucleons. In this reaction, the binding energy per nucleon would increase, *for each nucleon,* from 7.6 to 8.6 mev, an increase of 1 mev per nucleon, or a

---

[11] The masses of the two heavy nuclei are probably not known with the precision indicated, but it is quite certain that the difference between them is less than the mass of an alpha particle, and therefore the process is exoergic.

total energy of reaction of approximately 200 mev. This is the process known as *nuclear fission,* and inspection of Fig. 1.8 will show that it will be exoergic for all nuclei of mass number greater than 100.

Alpha Decay. Alpha particle emission is the only one of the processes mentioned above which occurs in many nuclei at appreciable rates. However, in spite of the fact that the process is exoergic for nuclei of mass number well below 200, the reaction is not observed until mass number 211 is reached, except for one rather light nuclide, Sm^{152}.

The limitation on the rate of this reaction and the emission of other charged particles is to be found in Fig. 1.9, the potential energy curve for nucleus-charged particle interaction. A nucleus unstable to alpha particle emission would be represented by a similar curve, except that the ground state would lie above the horizontal line representing the nucleus and particle at some distance from each other. Just as charged particles of low energy have a vanishingly small chance of entering the nucleus, so a low-energy alpha decay process will have a vanishingly small probability of occurrence. If the departing particle is to have a still higher charge, as in the case of $_6C^{12}$ mentioned previously, the coulombic barrier will be even more formidable and make such a reaction even less likely. Thus it is that the alpha particle represents a compromise between low charge and high binding energy for the departing particle and becomes the only important group of nucleons emitted in spontaneous decay reactions. In further confirmation of these explanations, the rate of alpha particle emission increases in a regular fashion with increasing decay energy.

Nuclear Fission. The nucleus U^{235} has been found to undergo spontaneous fission at a rate which is 10^{-8} times that at which this nucleus emits alpha particles. The rates of spontaneous fission for lighter nuclei are vanishingly small, in spite of the highly exoergic nature of the process. However, fission may be readily induced in several heavy nuclei by particle capture. The uncharged neutron is readily captured even at small velocities, and the exoergic capture process yields an excited product nucleus which can readily undergo fission. In a sense, it is the neutron capture energy (7-8 mev) which activates the fission process.

The Neutron-proton Rearrangement. We have indicated that proton or neutron emission by nuclei near the stable region will always be endoergic and, further, that emission of more complex decay products is almost exclusively confined to the heaviest nuclei. The process by which the hundreds of unstable nuclei of the lighter elements rearrange toward a stable neutron-proton ratio must therefore be a more subtle one. It is the process of beta decay, in which a nuclear proton becomes a neutron, or vice versa. The former process may be expected to occur when the neutron-proton ratio is less than the stable value, and the latter when the neutron-proton ratio is greater than the stable value. The outward manifestation of the $p \rightarrow n$ transformation is either the emission of a positive electron (positron) from the nucleus or the capture of a negative electron from the extra-nuclear orbits of the reacting nucleus. The $n \rightarrow p$ transformation is evidenced by the emission of a negative electron from the nucleus. The two processes may be written as follows

$$\begin{cases} {}_{z}X^{A} \rightarrow {}_{z-1}Y^{A} + \beta^{+} \\ {}_{z}X^{A} \rightarrow {}_{z-1}Y^{A} \text{ (orbital electron capture)} \end{cases}$$

and

$${}_{z}X^{A} \rightarrow {}_{z+1}Y^{A} + \beta^{-}$$

where the symbols β^{+} and β^{-} denote the electrons of nuclear origin. Their properties will be discussed in Chapter IV.

The beta decay processes are almost without exception the only mechanisms of spontaneous nuclear change available to nuclei of $A < 200$ in their lowest energy states, and they give rise to isobaric product nuclei. In predicting the mode of decay of an unstable nucleus, therefore, we may say that the observed decay reaction will be one which approaches the stable configuration and that, in general, the energy of decay will decrease as stability is approached. For instance, con-

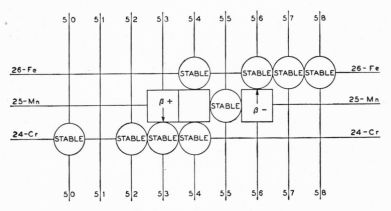

FIG. 1.11. Nuclides in the region of manganese.

sider the unstable isotopes of the element manganese with relation to their stable isobars as shown in Fig. 1.11. Mn^{53} has a lower neutron-proton ratio than its stable isobar, Cr^{53}, and may therefore be expected to decay by positron emission or orbital electron capture as follows:

$$_{25}Mn^{53} \rightarrow {}_{24}Cr^{53} + \beta^{+}$$

On the other hand, Mn^{56} has a higher neutron-proton ratio than its stable isobar, Fe^{56}, and may therefore be expected to decay by negative beta particle emission as follows:

$$_{25}Mn^{56} \rightarrow {}_{26}Fe^{56} + \beta^{-}$$

Mn^{54} lies between two stable isobars, and in principle either mode of decay is possible. In this particular case orbital electron capture is observed.

Gamma Decay. The rearrangements of nucleons mentioned previously may leave the product nucleus in an excited state analogous to those produced by direct excitation. Prompt transition to a lower state of the nucleus is very probable, and it is accompanied by the emission of quanta of electromagnetic radiation of appropriate energy. This radiation is known as gamma radiation to distinguish its nuclear origin. It may have energies up to several mev per quanta and very small absorption coefficients. Methods of detection and characterization will be discussed in later chapters.

SUPPLEMENTARY READING

Condon, "Fundamentals of Nuclear Physics," *Nucleonics*, Sept., 1947.

Cork, "Radioactivity and Nuclear Physics," D. Van Nostrand, New York, 1946.

Volkoff, "The Fundamentals of Nuclear Energy," *J. Chem. Ed.* **24**, 538 (1947).

Washburn, Riley, and Rock, "The Mass Spectrometer as an Analytical Tool," *Ind. Eng. Chem., Anal. Ed.* **15**, 541 (1945).

Williams, "Nuclear Energetics," *J. Chem. Ed.* **23**, 508 (1946).

"Symposium on Mass Spectroscopy," *J. App. Phys.* **13**, 526-569 (1942).

NUMERICAL EXERCISES

1. What minimum energy must a helium ion (He^{++}) have in order to approach within a distance of 10^{-12} cm of the nuclei $_6C^{12}$, $_{29}Cu^{63}$, $_{82}Pb^{206}$?

2. Calculate the De Broglie wave length of the proton and electron at a kinetic energy of 1 mev.

3. If the K-excitation potential for the element Fe is 7.10 kev, what element will have a K-excitation potential of 24.4 kev?

4. Calculate the velocity, apparent mass, and radius of curvature in a magnetic field of 1000 gauss of electrons of the following kinetic energies: 10^3 ev, 10^5 ev, 10^7 ev.

5. A beam of protons, having a kinetic energy of 100 kev, is passed into a region of homogeneous magnetic field, and the particles travel in a circular path with radius of curvature of 10 cm. What radius of curvature will (a) electrons and (b) sodium ions of the same energy have in this field?

6. In a mass spectrograph of the Dempster type, with an accelerating potential of 1000 volts and a magnetic field of 1000 gauss, the isotopes of neon ($A = 20$ and 22) are subjected to mass analysis. Consider the ions to be singly charged, and compute the linear separation at $180°$.

7. In a Nier-type mass spectrograph, normal carbon dioxide gives a strong peak (CO_2^+) at an accelerating voltage of 3000 and an electromagnet current of 1 ampere. (a) At the same current, what voltage will be required to detect CH_4^+? (b) At the original voltage, what current will be required to detect CH_4^+?

8. Compute the nuclear binding energy in kilocalories per mole, for the nucleus $_2He^4$. Compute the same quantity for 2 gram atomic weights of $_1H^2$.

9. The photo-neutron threshold for Be^9 lies at about 1.7 mev. The products of the reaction are two alpha particles in addition to the neutron. Use the known masses of helium and Be^9 to compute a neutron mass.

10. From data given in the Appendix calculate the following items:
   a. the packing fraction of Mg^{25}
   b. the total binding energy of Mg^{25}
   c. the energy term in the reaction $_{12}Mg^{25} + _0n^1 \rightarrow _2He^4 + _{10}Ne^{22} + Q$
   d. the photo-neutron threshold for Mg^{25}

Chapter II

PHYSICAL AND CHEMICAL MANIFESTATIONS OF NUCLEAR MASS

As INDICATED in the first chapter, many elements consist of a mixture of atoms of identical nuclear charge, but with nuclear masses differing by amounts corresponding almost exactly to the mass of one or more neutrons. Among such isotopes differences in properties will arise from the variation in nuclear mass which, although small in comparison to differences arising from variations in nuclear charge, are quite noticeable and important. The differences, of course, will be greatest where the masses of the isotopes show the greatest fractional difference, as in the lighter elements, and will be almost undetectable with the heavier elements. Thus we will find the most striking differences in the isotopes of hydrogen, known as protium ($_1H^1$), deuterium ($_1H^2$), and tritium ($_1H^3$). The latter isotope is unstable and has only recently been available in macroscopic quantities, but very pure deuterium has been available for some years.

PHYSICAL PROPERTIES OF ISOTOPIC NUCLIDES

Comparative values of the properties of isotopic molecules are readily estimated when the property is directly related to the atomic or molecular weight, as in the case of molecular velocities, collision numbers, viscosity, and similar properties of gases. For the hydrogen isotopes, the approximate relationships of the kinetic theory of gases indicate that the mean molecular velocities will be in the proportion

$$V_{H_2}:V_{D_2}:V_{T_2} = 1:\frac{1}{\sqrt{2}}:\frac{1}{\sqrt{3}}$$

while the viscosities will be in the proportion

$$\eta_{H_2}:\eta_{D_2}:\eta_{T_2} = 1:\sqrt{2}:\sqrt{3}$$

Atomic Spectra. A relatively simple and fundamental property of all atoms and molecules is represented by the characteristic wave lengths of light absorbed or emitted after excitation. The line spectra of hydrogen-like atoms are accurately described by the well-known equation

$$\bar{\nu} = \frac{M}{m+M} RZ^2 \left(\frac{1}{n_1^2} - \frac{1}{n_2^2}\right) \tag{2.1}$$

where $\bar{\nu}$ is the frequency of a spectral line in wave numbers, m and M are the masses of the electron and the "atomic core" respectively, Z is the charge on the "core," and n_1 and n_2 are positive integers which may be correlated with the principal quantum numbers of the single electron in its various energy states. The Rydberg constant R involves various fundamental constants such as the electronic charge and mass, the Planck constant, and the velocity of light. The value of this constant is 1.096×10^5 cm^{-1}. The term $M/m + M$ indicates the magnitude of the isotopic shift, which, even in the case of protium-deuterium, will be small. For the protium line at 4861 Å, the isotopic shift amounts to 1.32 Å, toward shorter wave lengths. A corresponding difference in the ionization potential of the isotopic hydrogen atoms is indicated by the limiting form of equation 2.1.

$$\bar{\nu} = \frac{M}{m+M} R \left(\frac{1}{1} - \frac{1}{\infty}\right) \tag{2.2}$$

Although the deuterium line is not readily detected in natural hydrogen, measurements on samples containing increased amounts of deuterium confirm such calculations, and, in fact, the existence of deuterium was first confirmed by this method.

Molecular Spectra. Isotopic shifts are also well known in molecular spectra and resulted in the discovery and identification of the less abundant isotopes of oxygen, carbon, and nitrogen. Since the molecular band spectra involve changes in the electronic, vibrational, and rotational energy of the molecules involved, they provide a rather detailed picture of molecular energy states. This information can be used, in turn, in the computation of thermodynamic properties, as will be indicated later.

Although the simple relation for electronic energy transitions given previously is not valid for molecular systems, it indicates that the effect of isotopic mass differences on electronic energy diminishes rapidly in the elements heavier than hydrogen and therefore cannot be an important contributor to the isotopic shifts observed in heavy molecules. The effect of isotopic substitution in the rotational contribution to the total energy change is also small. The rotational energy of a diatomic molecule may be given in approximate form as

$$E_r = \frac{h^2}{8\pi^2 r^2 \mu} J(J+1) \tag{2.3}$$

where J, the rotational quantum number, may be zero or an integer. r is the interatomic distance, and μ the reduced mass of the molecule, defined in terms of the individual atomic masses as follows:

$$\mu = \frac{m_1 m_2}{m_1 + m_2} \tag{2.4}$$

Selection rules require that the rotational quantum number

change shall be zero or ± 1, and therefore the rotational contribution to the total energy change may be given by

$$\Delta E_r = \frac{h^2}{4\pi^2 r^2 \mu} J \qquad (2.5)$$

where J is the higher rotational quantum number. It is apparent that isotopic replacement will alter the value of μ, perhaps almost by a factor of two as in the case HC1-DC1. However, the rotational energy changes which are observed in the band spectra, corresponding to J values of 10 or 20, are relatively small, as may be deduced from the fact that the lines corresponding to changes in J are very closely spaced. The isotopic shift, except in cases such as that mentioned previously, will amount to a small fraction of the rotational energy change, and hence is not ordinarily observed.

The principal isotope effect with heavy nuclides is found in the vibrational energy term. The vibrational energy of a diatomic molecule may be given to a first approximation by

$$E_v = (v + \tfrac{1}{2}) hc\omega \qquad (2.6)$$

where the vibrational quantum number v may be zero or an integer. ω is known as the fundamental vibration frequency and is related to the reduced mass by

$$2\pi\omega = (f/\mu)^{1/2} \qquad (2.7)$$

where f is the force constant for the vibration. This is assumed to be unchanged by isotopic replacement and, in this approximate form, by change in electronic or rotational state. There is no general restriction on the change in the vibrational quantum number in electronic-vibrational-rotational spectra, and the general expression for the contribution of a vibrational change will be

$$\Delta E_v = hc\omega \Delta v \qquad (2.8)$$

The effect of isotopic replacement in a given transition may be given in the form

$$\Delta E_v - \Delta E_v' = hc\omega\left(1 - \frac{\omega'}{\omega}\right)\Delta v = hc\omega\left(1 - \left(\frac{\mu}{\mu'}\right)^{1/2}\right)\Delta v \quad (2.9)$$

In terms of a frequency shift this becomes

$$\nu - \nu' = \omega\left(1 - \left(\frac{\mu}{\mu'}\right)^{1/2}\right)\Delta v \quad (2.10)$$

Choosing the HC1 molecule as a typical example,[1] we find that the fundamental vibration frequency of $HC1^{35}$ is about 3000 cm^{-1}. Therefore, substitution of $C1^{37}$ shifts the fundamental vibration a small amount, about 3 cm^{-1}, and substitution of D causes a large shift of about 900 cm^{-1}. These isotopic shifts will be relatively constant throughout the rotational members of a particular band and, because of the relatively great abundance of $C1^{37}$ in natural chlorine (25%), cause the rotational lines of ordinary HC1 to appear as doublets which are readily resolved. In the case of deuterium substitution, the greater shift causes the isotopic band to be distinctly separated from the normal band in the higher order vibrational transitions such as $\Delta v = 3$.

The isotopic shift in the fundamental vibration frequency has a consequence of special interest to chemists. Equation 2.6 indicates that even in the lowest vibration state, when $v = 0$, the molecule still has a certain amount of vibrational energy, known as the "zero point energy." At room temperature, most molecules will be in this lowest vibration state, whose energy is given by

$$E_v{}^0 = \frac{1}{2}hc\omega \quad (2.11)$$

In a dissociation reaction, energy must be supplied to separate the atoms to a distance where the interatomic forces are neg-

---

[1] Herzberg, *Molecular Spectra and Molecular Structure*, D. Van Nostrand Co., Inc., New York, 1939.

ligible. Isotopic replacement causes an appreciable shift in the energy of the initial state

$$E_v^0 - E_v^{0\prime} = \frac{1}{2} hc\omega \left[1 - \left(\frac{\mu}{\mu'}\right)^{\frac{1}{2}} \right]$$ (2.12)

but a much smaller change in the electronic energy of the

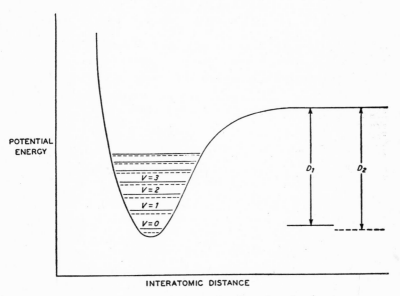

Fig. 2.1. Potential energy of a diatomic molecule.

separated atoms, as noted previously. Fig. 2.1 represents the potential energy of such a diatomic molecule as a function of the interatomic distance. Vibrational energy levels of two isotopic molecules are indicated, the dashed lines referring to the heavier isotope. The difference in dissociation energies $D_1 - D_2$ will be approximately given by equation 2.12. In the case of $HCl^{35} - DCl^{35}$, the fundamental vibration frequency given on p. 36 may be used to calculate that the dissociation energy of the deuteride is about 2 kcal/mole larger.

Other Properties. The more involved properties of matter in bulk are not readily calculated, and we must be satisfied to quote experimental measurements, using as our example the well-studied case of protium-deuterium, where the differences are relatively large. Table 2.1 contains representative data.

TABLE 2.1. PHYSICAL PROPERTIES OF THE COMPOUNDS OF HYDROGEN ISOTOPES[2]

Property	H_2	D_2
Vapor pressure at 18.65° K. (mm Hg)	450	130
Normal boiling point (° A)	20.38	23.50
Heat of fusion (cal/mole)	28	47
	H_2O	D_2O
Specific gravity at 20° C.	0.9982	1.1059
Freezing point (° C)	0	3.82
Boiling point (° C)	100	101.42
Temp. of max. density (° C)	4	11.6
Heat of vaporization (cal/mole)	9700	9960
Ionic mobilities (in H_2O and D_2O, resp.)	315.2(H^+)	213.7(D^+)
Solubility of NaCl (g per g)	0.359	0.305

[2] Farkas, *Orthohydrogen, Parahydrogen and Heavy Hydrogen,* University Press, Cambridge, Eng., 1935.

It is apparent that several of these properties are sufficiently different for the two isotopes to suggest methods of analysis and separation. Density determinations have been widely used for analysis of $H_2O - D_2O$ mixtures, since it is not difficult to determine density to a part in 10,000. This would represent a precision of about 0.1% in determining the abundance ratio. While this is not sufficient to detect the presence of deuterium in its natural abundance (0.02%), it permits ready analysis of enriched samples. The difference in boiling points of the two isotopes in both the molecular form and as oxides suggests a separation method based on fractional distillation, which has indeed been successfully used.

A comparison of hydrogen and heavier atoms with regard to isotopic properties is offered in Table 2.2. Note that the vapor pressure of the lighter molecule is always greater. It is apparent that the differences become smaller as the mass ratios of the isotopic molecules approach unity. This points out the increasing difficulty to be expected in isotopic separations with the heavier elements.

TABLE 2.2. RATIO OF VAPOR PRESSURES OF LIQUID ISOTOPIC COMPOUNDS AT THE BOILING POINT[3]

Compounds	p_1/p_2
N_2^{14}, N_2^{15}	1.0081
$N^{14}H_3$, $N^{15}H_3$	1.00246
NH_3, ND_3	1.110
H_2O^{16}, H_2O^{18}	1.0046
H_2O, D_2O	1.051

[3] Urey, see Supplementary Reading.

CHEMICAL PROPERTIES OF ISOTOPIC NUCLIDES

The discussion of the effects of isotopic substitution in the optical spectra given previously served to indicate the effects of nuclear mass on the energy states of atoms and molecules. Since the rate and equilibrium constants of chemical reactions can be expressed, in principle, in terms of such fundamental properties, it follows that isotopic substitution will alter rates and equilibria in a predictable fashion.

We shall begin this subject with a qualitative discussion of the effect of isotopic substitution on the equilibrium and rate of a generalized reaction involving hydrogen, which may be represented by

$$HX + YZ = HY + XZ \quad K = \frac{[HY][XZ]}{[HX][YZ]}$$

as compared to

$$DX + YZ = DY + XZ \quad K = \frac{[DY][XZ]}{[DX][YZ]}$$

The energy terms for these two reactions may be compared through consideration of the dissociation energies of the protium and deuterium compounds only, since YZ and XZ are common to the two systems. Recalling equation 2.12 and Fig. 2.1, we see that DX will have a greater dissociation energy than HX, and DY a greater dissociation energy than HY. Therefore, the effect of isotopic substitution on the over-all reaction will be given by $(D_{DX} - D_{HX}) - (D_{DY} - D_{HY})$, which is the difference of two rather small quantities. The net effect will depend on whether the change $(D_{DX} - D_{HX})$ or $(D_{DY} - D_{HY})$ is the greater, and this, in turn, will depend on the reduced masses and fundamental vibration of frequencies of the two molecular species involved (see equation 2.12). For example, if X represents a radical or atom heavier than Y or less firmly bonded than Y, we may expect the fundamental vibration frequency ω to be smaller in the X molecule (see equation 2.7), and therefore the effect of isotopic subtstitution in the X molecule to be smaller. This, in turn, indicates that the deuterium equilibrium will lie further to the right (more toward the Y form).

The isotope effect on reaction rates will be much greater than on equilibria, as may be seen from a similar qualitative consideration. Not only does the collision number decrease for the heavier molecule, but only the energy difference of the reactants appears if we assume that the energy of any "activated complex" is not strongly affected by isotopic substitution. Since the energy difference of the reactants is not partially cancelled by the energy difference of the products, as in the equilibrium case, we may expect considerable differences in activation energies (up to ~2 kcal for hydrides) and consequently smaller rates for the heavier molecule.

Isotopic Exchange Reactions. More direct comparison of isotopic molecules is obtained through consideration of exchange reactions. In the instance of the equilibria mentioned above, the corresponding isotopic exchange reaction would be obtained by subtraction (division of equilibrium constants).

$$HX + DY = HY + DX \quad K = \frac{[HY][DX]}{[HX][DY]}$$

If the two hydrogen isotopes had identical chemical properties, but were still distinguishable by some means, the value of this equilibrium constant would be unity. The isotope effect will be noted by a small variation from this "classical" value. The classical value is not always unity, as for example in the case of the exchange reaction

$$HCl^{35} + Cl^{35}Cl^{37} = HCl^{37} + Cl^{35}Cl^{35}$$

where the equilibrium constant is

$$K = \frac{[HCl^{37}][Cl^{35}Cl^{35}]}{[HCl^{35}][Cl^{35}Cl^{37}]}$$

Here a given Cl^{37} atom has about twice the chance of being in Cl_2 as in HCl, giving the equilibrium constant a classical value of $\frac{1}{2}$. Again we may expect the calculated and observed values to differ slightly from this figure.

Partition Functions. The methods of statistical mechanics are designed to describe the gross properties of a system containing a large number of individuals in terms of the fundamental characteristics of the individual units. They may be used to define a quantity known as the partition function or summation of states, denoted by the symbol Q. This function is related to the free energy of a system by

$$F = -RT \ln Q$$

and is written in terms of the translational, electronic, vibrational, and rotational energy states of the molecules involved.

$$Q = Q_t \times Q_e \times Q_v \times Q_r$$

All these forms of energy of a molecule are quantized, of course, but fortunately, in most cases of interest, only the vibrational energy state need be written in quantized form. This is because both translational and, for heavy molecules, rotational energy states are so closely spaced that many states are occupied at ordinary temperatures, and a classical expression is a good approximation. In addition, simple chemical reactions usually involve only the lowest electronic state of each constituent, and so this term may be completely neglected in the partition function. The form of the partition function for diatomic molecules written below, therefore, involves only the translational, rotational, and vibrational energies, the first two written in the form from classical mechanics, and the latter with consideration of quantized vibrational states, since these are only partially occupied at ordinary temperatures.

$$Q = \left(\frac{2\pi m k T}{h^3}\right)^{3/2} V \cdot \frac{8\pi^2 I k T}{\sigma h^2} \cdot \frac{e^{-u/2}}{(1 - e^{-u})} \qquad (2.13)$$

$$\underset{\text{translation}}{} \qquad \underset{\text{rotation}}{} \qquad \underset{\text{vibration}}{}$$

Where

h = Planck constant
k = the Boltzman constant
T = temperature ($°$ Abs.)
m = molecular mass
V = volume of system
$I = \mu r^2$ = moment of inertia
$u = hc\omega/kT$
c = velocity of light
ω = fundamental vibration frequency
σ = symmetry number ($= 2$ for diatomic molecules with identical atoms, $= 1$ for diatomic molecules with distinguishable atoms)

The Equilibrium Constant. From the relationship between

the free energy and the partition function it is apparent that the equilibrium constant for a chemical reaction may be written

$$aA + bB + \ldots = nN + mM + \ldots$$

$$K = \frac{Q_N{}^n \cdot Q_M{}^m \cdot \ldots}{Q_A{}^a \cdot Q_B{}^b \cdot \ldots} \tag{2.14}$$

and for a simple isotopic exchange reaction

$$aA_1 + bB_2 = aA_2 + bB_1$$

may be given as

$$K = \left(\frac{Q_{A_2}}{Q_{A_1}}\right)^a \bigg/ \left(\frac{Q_{B_2}}{Q_{B_1}}\right)^b \tag{2.15}$$

Only the ratios of partition functions for the two isotopic molecular forms are involved, and this ratio, for a given compound, reduces to

$$\frac{Q_2}{Q_1} = \left(\frac{M_2}{M_1}\right)^{3/2} \frac{\sigma_1}{\sigma_2} \frac{I_2}{I_1} \frac{(1 - e^{-u_1})e^{-u_2/2}}{(1 - e^{-u_2})e^{-u_1/2}} \tag{2.16}$$

where the subscripts refer to the isotopic molecules. This relationship contains quantities which, at least in principle, are determinable from spectroscopic measurements on the isotopic molecules. For rarer isotopic species, the values of I and u may be computed from those for the more abundant isotopes by the methods indicated in an earlier section.

The relatively simple relationship given above is an approximate one, since it assumes that the vibrations of the diatomic molecule are perfectly harmonic and neglects vibration-rotation interactions. In addition, molecules in which the hydrogen-deuterium exchange is considered have such small moments of inertia that the classical expression for rotational motion must be replaced by the more complicated quantum expression for the rotational partition function. This will also be true for the heavier molecules at low temperatures, where only a few rotational levels are occupied. Needless to say, the expression will require still further alteration when polyatomic molecules are considered.

Table 2.3 gives some of the ratios of partition functions and equilibrium constants calculated by Urey.[3] The values of the equilibrium constants for all possible exchanges between the substances listed are given at 273.1°K. In general, the distinction between isotopes is smaller at higher temperatures. A number greater than unity means that the heavier isotope will concentrate in the compound at the left. For instance, reference to the table indicates that the isotopic exchange equilibrium

$$DCl + HI = DI + HCl$$

TABLE 2.3. ISOTOPIC EXCHANGE EQUILIBRIUM CONSTANTS FOR GASEOUS SUBSTANCES AT 273.1° K

A. Hydrogen

	$\left(\dfrac{D_2O}{H_2O}\right)^{1/2}$	$\dfrac{DCl}{HCl}$	$\dfrac{DBr}{HBr}$	$\left(\dfrac{D_2}{H_2}\right)^{1/2}$	$\dfrac{DI}{HI}$	$\dfrac{LiD}{LiH}$	$\dfrac{NaD}{NaH}$	$\dfrac{KD}{KH}$
$\dfrac{Q_2}{Q_1}$	16.467	6.3726	5.1278	4.2803	4.0172	1.8604	1.608	1.5047
$\left(\dfrac{D_2O}{H_2O}\right)^{1/2}$	1.000	2.584	3.211	3.847	4.099	8.851	9.739	10.944
$\dfrac{DCl}{HCl}$		1.000	1.243	1.489	1.586	3.425	3.769	4.235
$\dfrac{DBr}{HBr}$			1.000	1.198	1.276	2.756	3.033	3.408
$\left(\dfrac{D_2}{H_2}\right)^{1/2}$				1.000	1.065	2.301	2.532	2.845
$\dfrac{DI}{HI}$					1.000	2.159	2.376	2.670
$\dfrac{LiD}{LiH}$						1.000	1.100	1.236
$\dfrac{NaD}{NaH}$							1.000	1.124

B. Oxygen

	$\left(\dfrac{CO_2^{18}}{CO_2^{16}}\right)^{1/2}$	$\left(\dfrac{CO_3^{=18}}{CO_3^{=16}}\right)^{1/3}$	$\left(\dfrac{SO_4^{=18}}{SO_4^{=16}}\right)^{1/4}$	$\left(\dfrac{SO_2^{18}}{SO_2^{16}}\right)^{1/2}$	$\left(\dfrac{O_2^{18}}{O_2^{16}}\right)^{1/2}$	$\dfrac{H_2O^{18}}{H_2O^{16}}$	$\left(\dfrac{ClO_2^{18}}{ClO_2^{16}}\right)^{1/2}$
$\dfrac{Q_2}{Q_1}$	1.1331	1.1090	1.1073	1.1017	1.0923	1.0741	1.0717
$\left(\dfrac{CO_2^{18}}{CO_2^{16}}\right)^{1/2}$	1.000	1.022	1.023	1.029	1.037	1.055	1.057
$\left(\dfrac{CO_3^{=18}}{CO_3^{=16}}\right)^{1/3}$		1.000	1.002	1.007	1.015	1.033	1.035
$\left(\dfrac{SO_4^{=18}}{SO_4^{=16}}\right)^{1/4}$			1.000	1.005	1.014	1.031	1.033
$\left(\dfrac{SO_2^{18}}{SO_2^{16}}\right)^{1/2}$				1.000	1.007	1.026	1.028
$\left(\dfrac{O_2^{18}}{O_2^{16}}\right)^{1/2}$					1.000	1.017	1.019
$\dfrac{H_2O^{18}}{H_2O^{16}}$						1.000	1.002

C. Chlorine

	$\dfrac{Cl^{37}O_4^-}{Cl^{35}O_4^-}$	$\dfrac{Cl^{37}O_3^-}{Cl^{35}O_3^-}$	$\dfrac{Cl^{37}O_2}{Cl^{35}O_2}$	$\left(\dfrac{Cl_2^{37}}{Cl_2^{35}}\right)^{1/2}$	$\dfrac{HCl^{37}}{HCl^{35}}$
$\dfrac{Q_2}{Q_1}$	1.0972	1.0551	1.0360	1.0086	1.0050
$\dfrac{Cl^{37}O_4^-}{Cl^{35}O_4^-}$	1.000	1.040	1.059	1.088	1.092
$\dfrac{Cl^{37}O_3^-}{Cl^{35}O_3^-}$		1.000	1.018	1.046	1.050
$\dfrac{Cl^{37}O_2}{Cl^{35}O_2}$			1.000	1.027	1.031
$\left(\dfrac{Cl_2^{37}}{Cl_2^{35}}\right)^{1/2}$				1.000	1.004

will have an equilibrium constant of 1.586 at 273.1° C, and that deuterium will concentrate in the form of the iodide. The ratio D/H in the iodide will be 1.586 times as great as the ratio D/H in the chloride when equilibrium is attained.

Separation Factor. For a consideration of chemical processes, we are usually interested in the over-all ratio of isotopes in one chemical form compared with this ratio in another form. The separation factor α will be identical with the equilibrium constant in a case of exchange such as given above and in

$$C^{13}O_3^= + C^{12}O_2 = C^{12}O_3^= + C^{13}O_2$$

$$K = \frac{[C^{12}O_3^=][C^{13}O_2]}{[C^{13}O_3^=][C^{12}O_2]} = \alpha \tag{2.17}$$

where only one exchanging atom is present in each molecule. However, when two or more exchanging atoms are present in the molecules, intermediate forms must be considered as in the case

$$\tfrac{1}{2}O_2^{18} + H_2O^{16} = \tfrac{1}{2}O_2^{16} + H_2O^{18}$$

where the formation of $O^{16}O^{18}$ may be represented by

$$O_2^{18} + O_2^{16} = 2O^{16}O^{18}$$

If the partition function for $O^{16}O^{18}$ is the geometric mean of those for O_2^{16} and O_2^{18}, then the equilibrium constant for this expression reduces to the ratios of symmetry numbers, or 4.

The separation factor for the water-oxygen exchange is given by

$$\alpha = \frac{2[O_2^{18}] + [O^{16}O^{18}]}{2[O_2^{16}] + [O^{16}O^{18}]} \Big/ \frac{[H_2O^{18}]}{[H_2O^{16}]} \tag{2.18}$$

By use of the relation

$$\frac{[O^{16}O^{18}]^2}{[O_2^{18}][O_2^{16}]} = 4$$

equation 2.18 may be reduced to

$$\alpha = \frac{[O_2^{18}]^{1/2}}{[O_2^{16}]^{1/2}} \Big/ \frac{[H_2O^{18}]}{[H_2O^{16}]} \tag{2.19}$$

The separation factor for more complicated molecules will be given by a similar form, as in the case

$$CO_2{}^{18} + CO_3{}^{16=} = CO_2{}^{16} + CO_3{}^{18=} \quad \text{(all possible exchanges)}$$

where

$$\alpha = \frac{[CO_3{}^{18=}]^{1/3}}{[CO_3{}^{16=}]^{1/3}} \Big/ \frac{[CO_2{}^{18}]^{1/2}}{[CO_2{}^{16}]^{1/2}} \tag{2.20}$$

The assumption that the partition function for the mixed form will be equal to the geometric mean of the partition functions of the two pure forms is noticeably in error only in some of the hydrogen-deuterium exchanges. This will result in a small dependence of the separation factor on the isotope concentration.

The data of Table 2.3 are arranged to permit ready estimation of separation factors in various exchange reactions. Applications to the separation of isotopes by chemical exchange will be noted later.

Atomic Weights. The existence of exchange equilibria having separation factors notably different from unity for many commonly used elements casts some doubt on the significance of the atomic weight values reported. The high precisions quoted are not justified in some cases and arise simply because various investigators have drawn their samples from similar sources and subjected them to nearly identical treatments. Dole [4] has investigated the relative weights of oxygen samples drawn from several sources, using a density method of analysis. Great care was exercised to insure that all other factors involved in the preparation of samples remained constant, and noticeable variations in density of water prepared with various samples of oxygen were observed as indicated in Table 2.4.

Although the rather large density variation in marble can be explained on the basis of isotopic exchange equilibria between

---

[4] Dole, *J. Chem. Phys.* **4**, 268 (1936) ; Dole and Slobod, *J. Am. Chem. Soc.* **62**, 471 (1940).

water and carbonate existing at the time of deposition, the density differences between water and air oxygen have so far eluded quantitative explanation. This difference corresponds to an atomic weight difference of about 0.0001 units and introduces this uncertainty into atomic weight determinations based on oxygen.

TABLE 2.4. DENSITY VARIATIONS IN WATER PREPARED FROM VARIOUS OXYGEN SOURCES[4]

Oxygen Source	Density Difference (parts per million)
Atmosphere	
Lake Michigan	6.0
Ocean	7.6
Grenville Marble	13.9–15.2

Reaction Rates. The calculation of absolute reaction rates from fundamental properties involves many of the same operations which were indicated in connection with the calculation of equilibrium constants. In this case, however, the properties of an "activated complex," or reaction intermediate, must be estimated, and the appropriate partition functions used to compute the rate of formation of the activated state in terms of the free energy change of the activation process. The estimation of the properties of the transient intermediate is a complicated process and has been possible only with the simplest types of molecules. We will not attempt to follow this treatment but will only present some experimental data on the isotope effect on reaction rates.

The comparative reaction rates of hydrogen and deuterium have been studied in a number of cases. Rates of D-reactions are consistently less than the corresponding H-rates, by factors approaching 10. The activation energies of the D-reactions are also always greater than those of the H-reactions, although rarely by as much as the difference in zero-point energies.

Table 2.5 gives typical results on the comparison of reaction rates.

TABLE 2.5. RELATIVE REACTION RATES FOR HYDROGEN
AND DEUTERIUM

Reaction	Ratio of Rate Constants	Difference in Activation Energies
$\dfrac{Na + HCl^5}{Na + DCl}$	1.2 (238° C)	
$\dfrac{Cl + H_2^6}{Cl + D_2}$	13.5 (0° C)	1.6 kcal
$\dfrac{Br + H_2^7}{Br + D_2}$	5.7 (276° C)	2.0 kcal
$\dfrac{I_2 + H_2^8}{I_2 + D_2}$	1.69 (427° C)	0.75 kcal
$\dfrac{C_2H_4 + H_2^9}{C_2H_4 + D_2}$	2.5 (~500° C)	0.95 kcal

[5] Bawn and Evans, *Trans. Far. Soc.* **31**, 1392 (1935).
[6] Rollefson, *J. Chem. Phys.* **2**, 144 (1934).
[7] Bach, Bonhoeffer, and Moelwyn-Hughes, *Z. physikal. Chem.* **B27**, 71 (1934).
[8] Geib and Lendle, *Z. physikal. Chem.* **B32**, 463 (1936).
[9] Wheeler and Pease, *J. Am. Chem. Soc.* **58**, 1665 (1936).

Most rate studies have been limited to hydrogen, but recently an interesting example of the effect of carbon isotope substitution has been reported.[10] A symmetrical dicarboxylic acid, malonic acid, was prepared with radioactive C^{14} tracer incorporated in *one* carboxyl group. This acid was decomposed to form a monocarboxylic acid and carbon dioxide. The increased specific activity (proportional to the ratio of C^{14} to C^{12}) of the former product and the decreased specific activity of the latter, compared to the original dicarboxylic acid, indicate that the $C^{12} - C^{12}$ bond ruptures about 1.12 times as fast as the $C^{12} - C^{14}$ bond in malonic acid. In bromo-malonic acid

[10] Yankwich and Calvin, *J. Chem. Phys.* **17**, 109 (1949).

the ratio of rates is about 1.4. These separation factors are, of course, much greater than could be expected in an equilibrium process.

CONCENTRATION OF ISOTOPIC NUCLIDES

In spite of the extreme similarity of the properties of isotopic nuclides, especially those of the heavier elements, various physical and chemical methods have been successfully employed to produce materials containing a very high proportion of some particular isotope. Not only have these isotopically enriched products been useful as "stable tracers" but also their availability has permitted studies of reactions otherwise undetectable.

Mass Spectrograph. The mass spectrograph, described in Chapter I, represents a method of separating isotopes, but on a submicrochemical scale. The numbers of ions required to darken a photographic plate or actuate an ion detector are far below weighable amounts. Nevertheless, as early as 1937, W. R. Smythe [11] separated by this method sufficient quantities of the potassium isotopes ($A = 39, 40, 41$) to show that the middle isotope is responsible for the weak radioactivity of the natural element.

During World War II, the mass spectrographic method was intensely developed as a means of separating the isotopes of uranium (U^{235} and U^{238}) for use in nuclear weapons (see Chapter V). Serious difficulties were encountered in operating at the desired levels, chief among which were the following: (1) the problem of producing large quantities of gaseous ions; (2) the loss of a large number of these ions because of the necessity for collimating the beam; (3) the effect of space charge (mutual repulsion of the ions in the beam) which scatters the beam and interferes with separation. These difficulties

---

[11] Smythe, *Phys. Rev.* **51**, 178 (1937).

were overcome, and the electromagnetic separation method was a successful method of producing uranium enriched in U^{235}. Since the war these units have been used to produce macroscopic amounts of the separated stable isotopes of many other elements, a considerable service to physical and chemical research.

Physical Fractionation. While the electromagnetic method of isotope separation handles the individual atoms and can therefore be expected to give a cleaner separation, several other methods depending on small differences in the gross properties of isotopic materials are more adaptable to large-scale separation. These methods may be classed as statistical or fractionation methods, since they depend on many-fold multiplication of a small, single-stage separation factor.

Graham's law of effusion states that the rate of effusion of a gas through a small orifice is inversely proportional to the square root of its molecular weight, and suggests a method of isotope fractionation which was used as early as 1913 by F. W. Aston, and later improved by others. In one instance neon gas was allowed to diffuse repeatedly through porous clay pipes in an arrangement such as represented in Fig. 2.2. Starting with the normal gas at the left, diffusion through T_1 gave a portion richer in the light component. This is passed on to the next stage by the pump P_1. Here a portion diffuses through T_3 and on to the next stage, while the remainder returns to T_2, since it is now depleted in the light component. This process is repeated through many stages, and the heavy component concentrates at the left, whereas the light component concentrates at the right. Hertz [12] reported that he was able to change the ratio of the neon isotopes by a factor of about 10 using an apparatus containing 24 pumps and 48 diffusion tubes.

---

12 Hertz, *Z. Physik* **79**, 108 (1932).

The ideal separation factor a_0 for each stage will be given by

$$a_0 = \sqrt{\frac{M_2}{M_1}} = \sqrt{\frac{d_2}{d_1}} \tag{2.21}$$

which is raised to a power equal to the number of stages used. M and d represent the molecular weights and densities of the

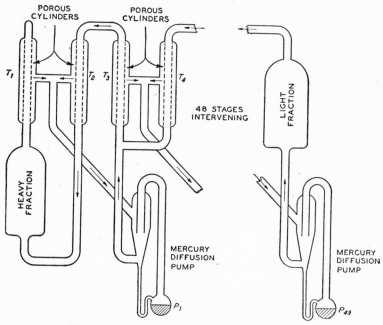

Fig. 2.2. Fractionation of isotopes by gas effusion.

isotopic gases. The observed separation factor is somewhat less than the ideal value for several reasons: (1) The ideal effusion law assumes effusion against zero pressure, a practical impossibility. This results in some back-diffusion, with separation in the opposite direction from the main flow. (2) The two species never actually effuse independently of one another; collisions occur in the holes and the effusion rates approach each other. This results in disappearance of the separation effect with large holes. (3) Even in the smallest holes, a certain amount of non-separating viscous flow occurs. These considerations indicate that some compromise in design must be accepted when appreciable amounts of material are to be handled as in the production of U^{235}. While small holes and low pressures give greater separations, they reduce the amount of material which can be handled.

Although the gaseous diffusion method was the most important fractionating method of isotope separation employed in the separation of U^{235} on a large scale, several other methods received considerable attention. Among these the method of thermal diffusion as developed by Clusius and Dickel [13] is notable because of the relative simplicity of the apparatus used.

Gaseous mixtures, when placed between surfaces at different temperatures, show a separation effect according to molecular mass, the heavier molecules concentrating at the cold wall. Chapman [14] has deduced a relation expressing this effect in the form

$$\Delta X_2 = \frac{17}{3} \frac{M_2 - M_1}{M_2 + M_1} \cdot \frac{X_1 X_2}{9.15 - 8.25 X_1 X_2} \ln \frac{T'}{T} \quad (2.22)$$

where ΔX_2 is the difference in concentration of one component between the two temperature regions T and T' when two gases of molecular weights M_1 and M_2 are present at mole fractions X_1 and X_2. This equation has been deduced for molecules behaving as elastic spheres, i.e., the repulsive forces fall off very rapidly with increasing separation. The separation effect is much smaller with "soft" molecules, disappearing entirely when the repulsion falls off as the inverse fifth power of distance. Separations nearly as great as predicted by the theory

---

[13] Clusius and Dickel, *Naturwiss.* **26**, 546 (1938) ; **27**, 148, 487 (1939).
[14] Chapman, *Phil. Mag.* **38**, 182 (1919).

are found with the rare gases, but become less with polyatomic molecules.

The single-stage separation predicted by equation 2.22 is quite small in comparison to the molecular effusion effects, but many-stage operation is readily accomplished in an arrange-

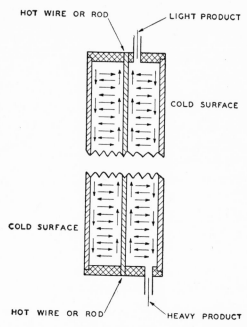

FIG. 2.3.   Fractionation of isotopes by thermal diffusion.

ment devised by Clusius and Dickel [15] and indicated in Fig. 2.3.

The apparatus consists of a long, narrow, cooled cylinder with a heated central rod or wire. Thermal siphoning causes the gas near the hot wire to rise, and that near the wall to descend. Each molecule makes many trips back and forth between the wire and the wall, and eventually a concentration

---

[15] Clusius and Dickel, *Naturwiss.* **26**, 546 (1938).

gradient is established between the top and bottom of the column.

Separation of the chlorine isotopes is an especially favorable case for the operation of this method since the isotopic abundances are not greatly different ($Cl^{35} = 75.4\%$, $Cl^{37} = 24.6\%$). Inspection of equation 2.22 indicates that the maximum value of X_2 will be observed when $X_1 = X_2 = 0.5$. With a single tube 3 meters long and 1 cm. in diameter, Clusius and Dickel were able to change the isotope ratio in HCl to 60/40. With five tubes of total length 36 meters they obtained the two chlorine isotopes more than 99% pure.

Other fractionation methods which have been more or less successfully applied include centrifugation, evaporation, and various chemical methods which will be discussed later. Centrifugation is worthy of special mention, since the separation effect, given in the equation

$$\frac{R_0}{R} = C^{(V^2/2RT)(M_2-M_1)} \tag{2.23}$$

where

R, R_0 = isotope ratios at periphery and center
V = peripheral velocity
M_1, M_2 = molecular weights of the isotope compounds

is dependent on the difference in molecular weights rather than their ratio. This indicates that the centrifugation method would be especially adaptable to isotope separation with heavy elements, where the mass ratio approaches unity, but the mass difference is still of the same magnitude as with the lighter elements.

The fundamental properties of the fractionation methods lead to large material hold-up, long start-up time, and rapidly decreasing yields as complete separation is approached. In addition, only two fractions can be produced, precluding the separation of isotopes of intermediate weight and small natural abundance. The electromagnetic method avoids the particular disadvantages mentioned above and is especially useful where small quantities of very pure isotopes are desired, but is not so adaptable to quantity production.

Chemical Fractionation. Several successful attempts have been made to make use of the equilibrium separation factors in chemical exchange reactions to effect a concentration of stable isotopes. The method has been useful chiefly with the elements carbon, nitrogen, and sulfur, using the exchange equilibria indicated in Table 2.6. The small values of the separation factors observed in these cases indicate the necessity for a fractionation process in which the two forms are equilibrated many times. This, in turn, shows that the system chosen must approach exchange equilibrium rapidly and that the substances must be readily mixed and separated.

TABLE 2.6. ISOTOPIC EXCHANGE EQUILIBRIA[16]

	Separation Factor	
Equilibrium	*Calculated*	*Observed*
$N^{15}H_3(g) + N^{14}H_4^+(aq.) = N^{14}H_3(g)$ $+ N^{15}H_4^+(aq.)$	1.033	1.023
$HC^{12}N(g) + C^{13}N^-(aq.) = HC^{13}N(g)$ $+ C^{12}N^-(aq.)$	1.026	1.013
$S^{34}O_2(g) + HS^{32}O_3^-(aq.) = S^{32}O_2(g)$ $+ HS^{34}O_3^-(aq.)$	.....	1.012

[16] Urey, *J. App. Phys.* **12**, 270 (1941).

Choosing as our example the fractionation of the carbon isotopes,[17] we see from Table 2.6 that the heavy isotope (normal abundance $\sim 1\%$) concentrates in the gas phase. A counter-current scrubbing system is used, with hydrogen cyanide gas bubbling up the column and sodium cyanide solution flowing

[17] Hutchison, Stewart and Urey, *J. Chem. Phys.* **8**, 532 (1940).

down. At the bottom of the column, acid is added to generate the gas, and at the top the hydrogen cyanide is absorbed in sodium hydroxide solution to effect a reflux action. In a column of 12 meters length and 2.2 cm diameter, an over-all

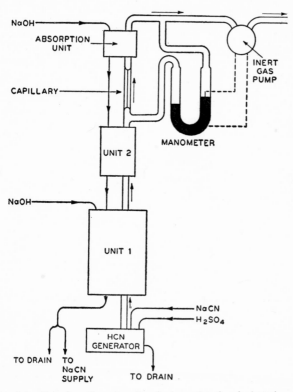

Fig. 2.4.   Fractionation of carbon isotopes by chemical exchange.

separation factor of about 5 was achieved. A second unit, operating on a small fraction of the output of the first, as indicated in Fig. 2.4, gave a further separation factor of about 6. Concentrations as high as 22% C^{13} have been produced at a rate of 0.1 gram of C^{13} per day.

Electrolysis. The largest single-step separation factor in isotope enrichment processes is observed in the electrolysis of water. Protium is evolved at a rate from three to eight times as great as is deuterium, and therefore continued electrolysis produces water which is continually richer in the heavier isotope.

The electrolyte commonly used for this process is 0.5 N sodium hydroxide, and the electrolysis is conducted in several stages as indicated in Table 2.7. After each stage the concentrated electrolyte left is neutralized, distilled, and again brought to the desired concentration with sodium hydroxide. In the later stages the considerable deuterium content of the electrolytic gas is recovered by returning this product to the preceding stage. Also, since the ratio of vapor pressures of H_2O and D_2O (see Table 2.2) indicates a considerably smaller separation factor in evaporation, the electrolytic cells are cooled to prevent loss in this fashion.

TABLE 2.7. CONCENTRATION OF DEUTERIUM
BY ELECTROLYSIS[18]

Stage	Liters of Solution Electrolyzed	Density d_4^{20}	Deuterium Content of Residue
1	2300	0.998	0.1%
2	340	0.999	0.5
3	52	1.001	2.5
4	10	1.007	8.0
5	2	1.031	30.0
6	0.42	1.098	93.0
7	0.08	1.104	99.0

[18] Taylor, Eyring and Frost, *J. Chem. Phys.* **1**, 823 (1933).

The separation factor observed depends to a considerable extent upon the electrode used, and much conflicting data and theory are available on this point. One widely held view is that the higher separation factors, around 5-7, are observed with electrodes having a high hydrogen overvoltage, and that the low separation factors, around 3, are observed with low overvoltage electrodes. Also, a negative temperature coefficient is usually observed in the former cases, whereas little or no temperature coefficient is observed in the latter.

SUPPLEMENTARY READING

Aston, *Mass Spectra and Isotopes,* 2nd ed., Edward Arnold & Co., London, 1942.

"Availability of Stable Isotopes," *Nucleonics,* Jan., 1948.

Squires, "The Fractionation of Isotopes," *J. Chem. Ed.* **23,** 538 (1946).

Urey, "Thermodynamic Properties of Isotopic Molecules," *J. Chem. Soc.* **1947,** 562 (1947).

NUMERICAL EXERCISES

1. An important line in the atomic hydrogen spectrum occurs at $\lambda 6562.79$ Å. What will be the wave length of the corresponding deuterium line?

2. The fundamental vibration frequency of the molecule H^1I^{127} is 2309.5 cm^{-1}. Compute the fundamental vibration frequency of H^2I^{127}. The dissociation energy of H^1I^{127} is 70 cal/mole. Compute the dissociation energy of the isotopic molecule.

3. Assuming that the oxygen isotopic equilibrium between water and carbonate is responsible for the density difference between Lake Michigan water and Grenville Marble water reported in Table 2.4, calculate the separation factor and compare with Table 2.3.

4. The vapor density of a mixture of H_2 and D_2 is found to be 0.1 g/l at a temperature of 25° C and a pressure of 700 mm. What is the mole per cent of D_2 in this mixture?

5. Using the ideal separation factor given by Graham's Law, calculate the number of stages of diffusion required to change the abundance of U^{235} to 50%, using gaseous UF_6.

6. In the concentration of C^{13} by counter-current exchange between HCN and CN^- the single-stage separation factor is 1.013. Calculate the abundance ratio of the carbon isotopes which can be attained in a column of 1000 theoretical plates.

CHAPTER III

DEVICES FOR PREPARATION AND DETECTION OF UNSTABLE NUCLIDES

BEGINNING with this chapter, our discussions will be chiefly concerned with the unstable nuclides or, more properly, with the phenomena accompanying their production and subsequent decay to stability. In preparation for the study of the chemical aspects of such nuclear changes, we must discuss many of the physical details of these processes, commencing in the present chapter with descriptions of some of the more important types of apparatus used in this work.

DETECTION OF NUCLEAR RADIATIONS

As mentioned in Chapter I, the spontaneous rearrangement of nucleons known as radioactive decay is accompanied by the emission of very energetic radiations and particles. Energies up to several million electron volts per quantum or particle are common. Since the ionization potentials of atoms and molecules are much smaller, we find that the absorption of nuclear radiations is marked by extensive ion formation, and experiment establishes the approximate relation that one ion pair (positive ion and electron) is formed for each 32 electron volts of energy expended. Therefore, a one-million volt particle may be expected to form approximately 3×10^4 ion pairs in the course of its absorption. The concentration of ions will depend on the penetrating ability of the particular type of radiation or particle, i.e., the length of path in which it expends its energy.

The Wilson cloud chamber gives a particularly graphic response to the passage of ionizing particles. In this apparatus the sensitive medium is a gas supersaturated with respect to some readily condensible vapor such as alcohol. This condition is brought about by a sudden and essentially adiabatic expansion of the saturated gas. The resulting temperature drop brings about the supersaturation, and the ions formed by the radiation act as condensation nuclei, resulting in the formation of visible liquid droplets along the path of the ionizing particle. The critical conditions for the formation of a vapor track are short-lived, and therefore the device is relatively inefficient as a detector. Fig. 3.1 shows the tracks produced by energetic positive ions (alpha particles) and electrons (beta particles). Note the extreme contrast in ion density along the paths of the two types of particles. This corresponds to the contrast in penetrating abilities. Energetic electrons will penetrate approximately one hundred times as much matter as alphas of the same energy, but the total ionization produced is about the same. Electromagnetic radiations are principally absorbed by interaction with the electronic systems of the matter through which they pass, producing energetic secondary electrons. These particles are responsible for the major part of the ionization produced by gamma and x-radiations. The penetrating ability of such radiations is still greater than either alphas or betas, and therefore the concentration of ions produced is still smaller.

The path of an energetic positive ion is also rendered visible in certain types of photographic emulsions. The formation of ions activates silver halide grains which are later developed (reduced) to render the track visible. The general darkening of such an emulsion may also be used as a measure of the total amount of radiation intercepted.

Ionization Chambers. Most of the devices used for quantitative detection of nuclear radiations depend on electrostatic

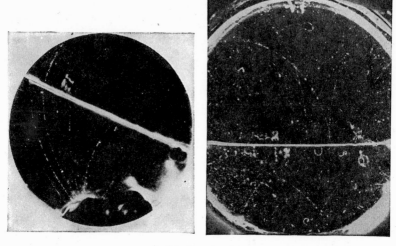

A. Electron tracks.

B. Alpha tracks.

FIG. 3.1. Ionization tracks in a Wilson cloud chamber.

collection of ions formed in a gaseous medium. In the absence of an electric field, the positive ions and electrons formed by the energetic particles or radiations will eventually recombine. However, when an electric field is impressed on the system, the positive ions drift toward the cathode while negative ions or electrons drift in the opposite direction. Recombination will still compete with the electric field for removal of the ions, and the fraction of initial ions which eventually reaches the elec-

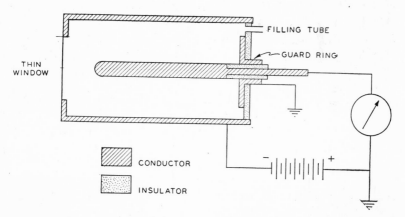

FIG. 3.2.   Ionization chamber.

trodes will depend on the electric field strength and upon the gas pressure. Other factors, such as the initial distribution of ions and the nature of the gas may also be important.

A typical arrangement for such an ionization chamber is indicated in Fig. 3.2. A central electrode in the shape of a cylindrical rod is placed in the center of a metallic "can" which serves as the other electrode. Special care is taken to insulate the two electrodes from each other, and a grounded "guard-ring" is frequently used to shield the central electrode. The chamber may be filled with dry air or with some pure gas at various pressures. A very thin "window" or direct access into the chamber may oe provided to permit detection of particles of small penetrating power.

The collection of ions and electrons on the electrodes of the chamber is equivalent to the passage of current and, in principle, may be measured by a circuit arrangement such as the simple form indicated in Fig. 3.2. The magnitude of the current flow for various collecting potentials at several radiation intensities is indicated in Fig. 3.3. The flat portion of the

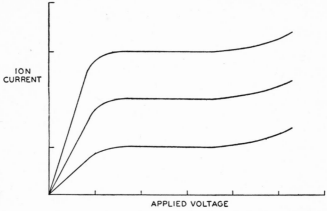

ION CURRENT

APPLIED VOLTAGE

Fig. 3.3. Current-voltage characteristic of an ionization chamber.

curves is known as the "saturation current," and under these conditions the magnitude of the response is directly proportional to the radiation intensity over a wide range of intensities. The voltage at which the saturation current is reached depends on the nature and pressure of the filling gas, increasing with increasing gas pressures. For maximum sensitivity and stability, chambers are normally operated at saturation.

Current-measuring Devices. With appropriate electrical circuits, the ionization chamber becomes a very sensitive detector of nuclear radiations. From the foregoing description, it is apparent that the response will be proportional to the number of ions formed by the ionizing radiation, rather than to the number of particles or quanta entering the chamber. To take an example, a single alpha particle can be expected to produce a maximum of about 10^5 ion pairs (electron and positive ion) within the sensitive volume of an ionization chamber. The passage of one such particle per second therefore corresponds to the very small current of approximately 3×10^{-14} amperes.

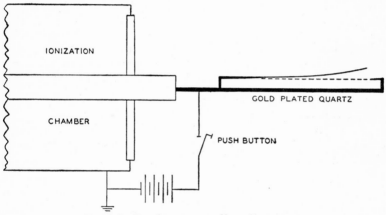

FIG. 3.4.   Lauritsen quartz-fiber electroscope.

The measurement of currents of such small magnitude requires special equipment of extreme sensitivity.

The integrated radiation intensity or current flow between the electrodes of the ionization chamber is frequently measured by a *Lauritsen electroscope*. This device consists of a flexible quartz fiber fixed at one end and extending parallel to a stiff quartz rod. This system is gold-plated to make it conducting and attached to the central electrode of the ionization chamber as shown in Fig. 3.4. A potential difference of about 100 volts is momentarily applied across the electrodes and then disconnected. In this charged condition, the flexible quartz fiber is repelled by the fixed rod to a position indicated by the dotted line.

As ions are formed and collected within the chamber, the charge on the central electrode and on the quartz system decreases and the flexible fiber returns to its original position. The motion of the fiber is observed through a microscope, and radiation intensity is measured by determining the time required for the fiber to move through a predetermined distance.

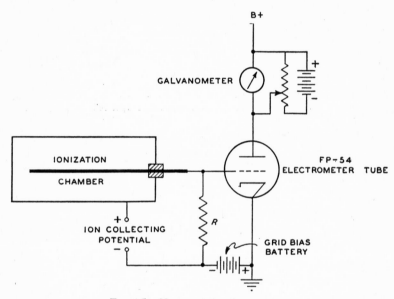

FIG. 3.5.   Vacuum-tube electrometer.

A small irreducible "background" rate of discharge in the absence of radiating samples limits the sensitivity of all devices of this type. This is due to leakage through the insulation and to natural sources of ionizing radiations such as cosmic rays.

For continuous recording of the ion current, the potential difference between the electrodes is maintained at a fixed value by a battery, and the current flow is measured as a potential drop across the resistance R shown in Fig. 3.5. Changes in this potential cause corresponding changes in the plate current in the vacuum tube, which amplifies the effect to a readily measureable magnitude. In order to detect ion currents as small as 10^{-14} amperes the resistance R must be as high as 10^{12} ohms and both the chamber and vacuum tube must be specially constructed to maintain this high value.

Counting Chambers. In many branches of nuclear science, it is very convenient to have a device which responds to the

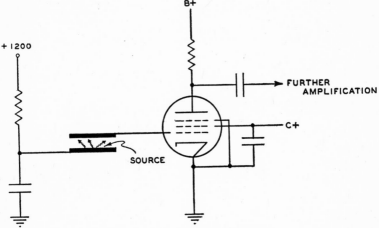

Fig. 3.6.   Alpha particle counter.

number of nuclear events occurring rather than to the number of ions produced. A single alpha particle frequently produces a detectable number of ions in an ionization chamber, and by suitable alteration of the response characteristics of the associated circuits, this current pulse may be amplified and recorded. A parallel plate ionization chamber has been used in this fashion with a circuit such as indicated in Fig. 3.6. The sample is placed on the lower plate of the counting chamber, which is maintained about 1200 volts positive with respect to the upper plate. Ions formed by an alpha particle in the sensitive region give rise to a short positive pulse of about 10^{-4} volts on the grid of the tube, and a corresponding amplified negative pulse at the plate. Suitable circuits further amplify and record these alpha counts.

With a weightless sample, this arrangement will count about 50% of the alpha particles emitted by the sample. Beta particles will not produce enough ions in the sensitive region to cause a measurable pulse. In some arrangements, the lower plate may be replaced by a perforated screen or a thin foil to permit entry of alpha particles from an external source. Any such device will register a certain number of pulses with no sample present. These may be due to "natural" contamination of construction materials, particularly brass, with alpha-active elements, or to the extremely small, natural radon content of air.

AMPLIFYING COUNTERS

The devices so far discussed have depended entirely on the ions formed by the energetic particle. In a reasonably large chamber, therefore, the pulse size will depend on the energy of the alpha particle, but will be of a size so small as to make any discrimination difficult. In the case of beta particles and electrons, a chamber of reasonable dimensions cannot collect enough ions from a single event to actuate a counting circuit. These considerations point out the desirability of a device which will produce an electrical impulse considerably larger than that to be derived from the primary ionization, and the response should preferably be proportional to the number of primary ions.

Gas Amplification. The desired amplification of the primary ionization event may be obtained in an electrode arrangement consisting of a cylindrical cathode with an anode made of a fine wire lying at the axis of the cylinder. Fig. 3.7 shows the relative sizes of the electrical pulses obtained from a typical alpha particle and a high-speed electron in passing through this chamber. At low voltages, the device acts as a simple ionization chamber and collects the ions formed by the energetic particle as described in Fig. 3.3. The difference in amounts of

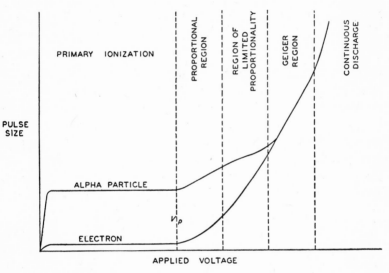

FIG. 3.7. Pulse height vs. voltage in a Geiger counter.

charge collected is due simply to the fact that, in a limited volume, an alpha particle forms several hundred times as many ions as does an equally energetic electron.

As the critical voltage V_p is exceeded, the amount of charge reaching the electrodes increases above that corresponding to the primary ionization. This phenomenon is known as "gas amplification" and is due to acceleration of electrons between collisions to energies sufficient to cause further ionization. The process is cumulative, since each new electron formed by an ionizing collision itself may be accelerated and cause further ionization, resulting in an "electron avalanche" toward the central wire. Gas amplification factors as high as 10^8 are frequently observed at voltages well above V_p.

The magnitude of the gas amplification factor and the value of the applied voltage at which it becomes appreciably greater than unity are governed by a number of experimental variables. Since the electric field strength in the electrode system decreases logarithmically with the distance from the axis, the region of electron multiplication will be close to the central wire anode. We may expect the critical potential V_p to decrease with decreasing wire diameter and the gas amplification factor to increase with increasing voltage as is shown in Fig. 3.7. A decrease in gas pressure may be expected to permit an electron avalanche at a lower voltage, since the electrons can be accelerated to higher energies between collisions. The collision cross section and ionization potential of the gas used in the chamber also influence V_p. and the gas amplification factor. Typical experimental conditions might be as follows: Cylinder —1 in. in diameter, 3 in. long; Wire —0.01 in. in diameter; Gas filling—argon, 100 mm pressure; V_p—500-800 volts.

Over a limited voltage region the gas amplification factor is independent of the number of primary ions formed, and therefore the charge reaching the electrodes will be proportional to the number of primary ions formed by the particle or radiation (see Fig. 3.7). Operation of a counter in this *proportional region* gives the considerable advantage of gas amplification, yet still allows discrimination between events producing different numbers of primary ions. Compared to the ionization chamber counting arrangement indicated in Fig. 3.5, the electronic circuits are considerably simplified by virtue of the larger initial pulse, and an appropriate arrangement will count alpha particles in the presence of a considerable beta flux. In a chamber large enough to absorb alpha particles completely (a few centimeters of air at STP) the device can be used to distinguish between alpha particles of different energies by virtue of the fact that the number of primary ion pairs produced is proportional to the energy of the particle.

A voltage *region of limited proportionality* is also shown in Fig. 3.7, where the gas amplification factor is not a function only of voltage. Here particles producing different numbers of primary ions in the counter may be distinguishable, but the simple proportionality of the lower voltage region no longer holds.

As the voltage applied to the wire and cylinder is still further increased, the amount of charge reaching the electrodes becomes independent of the initial number of ions, and a single electron within the chamber will produce the same effect as several thousand ion pairs formed by an alpha particle. Here the number of electrons traveling toward the central wire has reached the maximum value for a given voltage, and larger numbers of primary ions do not increase the ultimate ionization, although the pulse size will increase somewhat with increasing voltage. In this condition the device is known as a *Geiger counter* and performs the very useful function of yielding a rather large current pulse (10^{-9} coulombs) for each ionizing event within the chamber.

At still higher voltages a spontaneous discharge between the electrodes will occur, yielding large, repeated current pulses.

The Geiger Counter. This very useful device takes several forms, some of which are shown in Fig. 3.8. The cathode is a conducting cylinder of length a few times its diameter. It may form the outer wall of the tube or itself be enclosed in a glass or metal envelope. The central anode wire may be suspended from both ends or one, but in the latter case the open end is usually covered with a glass bead to avoid point discharges. The whole system is normally enclosed in a gas-tight

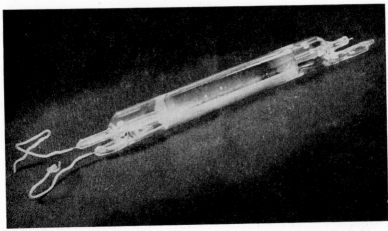

a. Glass wall Geiger tube. (Courtesy University of Notre Dame.)

b. Mica window Geiger tube. (Courtesy University of Notre Dame.)

FIG. 3.8. Geiger tubes and accessories.

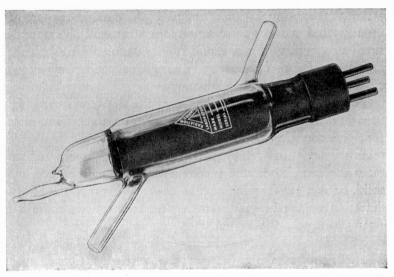

c. Liquid sample counter. (Courtesy Radiation Counter Laboratories, Inc., Chicago 8, Ill.)

d. Simple counting arrangement, including glass wall counter in holder, electronic circuit for high voltage supply and count recording, timing clock. (Courtesy University of Notre Dame.)

Fig. 3.8. Geiger tubes and accessories.

jacket to permit operation at reduced pressures. The tubes are usually filled with argon to a pressure of around 10 cm, and a small proportion of some polyatomic vapor such as alcohol may be added to obtain the "internal quenching" effect discussed below.

The sample whose radiations are to be detected is most frequently placed.outside the Geiger tube, and a very thin metal foil, glass or mica "window" in the tube may be necessary to permit entry of particles of small penetration power. In some cases the sample may be placed within the tube, either as a solid, or as a gas forming part of the counting mixture. In the detection of the very penetrating electromagnetic radiations (gamma rays), the response is due to secondary electrons ejected from the walls and surroundings of the Geiger tube. The efficiency of the counter toward such radiations may be increased by use of an internal grid made of a substance of high atomic number and low photoelectric work function, such as bismuth.

The essential features of the electrical circuit used with a Geiger counter are shown in Fig. 3.9. The occurrence of an ionizing event in the sensitive volume and the ensuing electron avalanche renders the Geiger tube temporarily conducting. A small current momentarily flows through the resistance R_c and the Geiger tube to ground, causing the potential of the anode to decrease from its normal highly positive value. This negative voltage pulse is transmitted through the capacitor C_g to the grid of the amplifying tube. The capacitance C_c represents the irreducible distributed capacitance of the Geiger tube, and the rate of recovery of the anode potential to its normal value after an electron avalanche is described by the time constant $R_c C_c$.

The Geiger counter is normally provided with a variable high-voltage supply and a pulse amplifying and recording circuit which responds only to pulses above a certain minimum voltage. If an active sample is placed near the tube and the number of pulses per unit time observed as a function of the applied high voltage, curves such as those shown in Fig. 3.10 will be obtained. The voltage at which the device first begins to register pulses is known as the threshold. Below this point, proportional action may be taking place, but the gas amplifi-

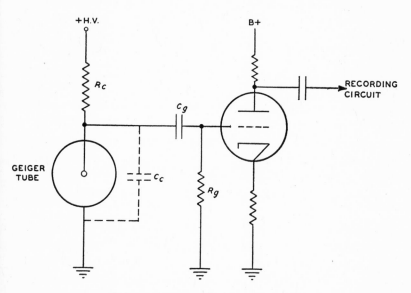

FIG. 3.9.   Fundamental counter circuit.

cation is not sufficient to produce an actuating pulse. In the first region of rapidly rising count rate it is apparent that only a portion of the ionizing events in the tube is registering, and a detailed examination of the pulses shows that they are of variable height. As the knee of the curve is passed, the pulses become more uniform in height and are almost always large enough to trip the circuit. Further increase in the voltage increases the pulse height still more, but does not greatly change the count rate until the region of spontaneous discharge is reached. Here a single pulse may serve to initiate a continuous discharge or rather a series of pulses, and the count rate again rises steeply. The region where the count rate is not strongly dependent on the applied voltage is referred to as the *plateau,* and the Geiger tubes are normally operated in this region for maximum stability and reproducibility. Unsatisfactory geometrical arrangements in the tubes or an unsatisfactory

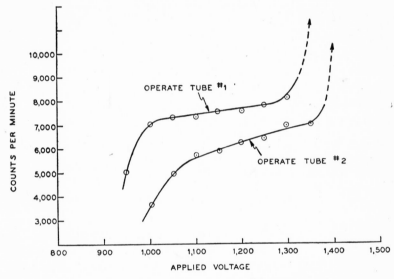

Fig. 3.10. Plateau characteristic of Geiger counter.

filling may cause this plateau to be shorter or steeper, or to disappear entirely. Such characteristics are tolerated only in unusual circumstances.

A small count rate is always observed in a Geiger counter, even in the absence of an active sample. This "background" is due to ionizing events from cosmic radiation and to radioactive contaminants in the constructional materials. Its exact value will depend on the volume of the counter and on the amount of matter surrounding the counter. A counter of 20 cc volume, shielded with several inches of lead, may show a background count rate of 10-20 counts per minute.

Many other practical considerations in the construction and operation of Geiger counters are avoided here, and the reader is referred to one of the more specialized works listed at the end of this chapter.

Recovery of the Geiger Counter. In a Geiger tube filled with argon at a pressure of a few centimeters, the electron avalanche toward the central wire anode is accomplished very quickly because of the high mobility of these particles, but the positive ions, most of which are formed near the wire, move less rapidly toward the cylindrical cathode. For the moment we will avoid the problems encountered in their neutralization, and assume that this event concludes the response of the counter. In a typical Geiger tube the electrons will be collected in less than 10^{-6} sec, while the positive ions may require as long as 10^{-3} sec to reach the cathode. The presence of a positive ion "sheath" near the central wire for many microseconds radically alters the electric field in this region and makes the system incapable of responding to another ionizing event with an electron avalanche. The rate of migration of the positive ion sheath toward the outer cylinder may be observed by noting the rate of "recovery" of the wire potential to its normal value.

The solid line in Fig. 3.11 represents an oscilloscope trace of the wire potential as a function of time, showing the recovery of the Geiger counter to the condition in which a second electron avalanche can occur. The dashed lines indicate the type of pulse seen when a second event occurs at various times after the first. The "dead time" t_d is defined as the time in which a second event will not produce a recognizable pulse, and the "recovery time" t_r is defined as the period required for the wire potential to return to its normal high value, so that a second ionizing event will produce a pulse equally as large as the first.

The dead time represents the time required for the positive ion sheath to migrate from the region of formation, near the neutral wire, to some critical distance between the electrodes

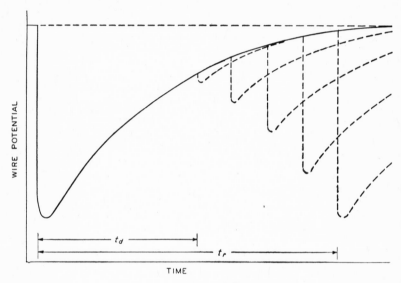

FIG. 3.11. Recovery of Geiger tube.

which returns the electric field strength near the anode to a value sufficiently high to permit a second electron avalanche of recognizable magnitude. The dead time will be a function of the applied voltage, the gas pressure, and the mobility of the positive ions in a fashion analogous to the critical voltage V_p and gas amplification factor previously discussed. In a typical Geiger counter the dead time will have a value of several hundred microseconds, which places a practical limitation on the rate at which ionizing events can be registered.

The Quenching Problem. We have so far assumed that the fate of the positive ions upon reaching the cathode is simple neutralization, with no complicating consequences. In a Geiger tube filled only with argon this is far from true. Upon reaching the vicinity of the cathode, a rare gas ion may draw more than one electron from the metallic surface, a process known as field emission, or the radiation emitted in the neutralization process may eject an electron from some metal surface in the tube, the well-known photoelectric effect. In either event there is ample opportunity for starting another electron avalanche, which may be repeated each time positive ions reach the cathode. Thus each ionizing event within the tube could give rise to an almost unlimited series of electron avalanches and electrical pulses in the amplifying circuit, and the counter would not be able to register a second nuclear event until this sequence had been halted.

This "continuous" discharge can be prevented by removing some condition necessary to the formation of the electron avalanche; for instance, lowering the high voltage on the central anode until the positive ions are discharged. A large value of R_c, perhaps 10^9 ohms, will produce the necessary potential decrease, but since the value of C_c cannot be much less than 10^{-11} farad, the time constant for recovery to operating potential becomes 10^{-2} sec. This is much too long for rapid registration of nuclear events, and therefore this method, known as "resistance quenching," is rarely used.

Electronic circuits are available which accomplish the desired potential decrease, but which recover to the operating potential more rapidly than the arrangement described above. One of these, due to Neher and Harper, is indicated in Fig. 3.12. The grid of the triode is normally held negative by the battery B, but an avalanche in the Geiger tube drives the grid positive. The resistance of the triode is now low, and the resulting current flow lowers the potential on the central anode.

The recovery time is governed by R_gC_c, the time constant of the grid circuit, and may be made about 10^{-4} sec. The fundamental time limit of this or any other quenching circuit is the time required for removal of the positive ions. In the Neher-Harper circuit, the triode effectively short-circuits the Geiger tube during this period, making the voltage-dropping resistance

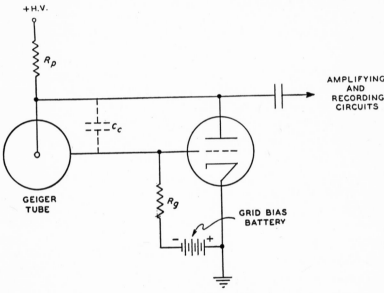

FIG. 3.12. Neher-Harper quenching circuit.

R_p more effective. In addition, the recovery resistance R_g is not the same unit, as in the previous circuit.

A Geiger tube filled with a monatomic or diatomic gas shows the "continuous" discharge characteristics previously described, but a polyatomic (>3 atoms) gas does not show this phenomenon. Only a single electron avalanche occurs, and apparently some mechanism operates to suppress the photons and secondary electrons which would continue the discharge. Polyatomic gases with sufficiently high vapor pressures, such as methane, ethane, and butane, can be used as counter fillings, although they require rather high voltages for Geiger or proportional action. More commonly a small quantity of polyatomic gas is added to a monatomic or diatomic gas. A common filling for Geiger tubes is 2 cm alcohol and 8 cm argon. Even in this small proportion the polyatomic gas will serve to quench the secondary discharges.

The quenching ability of polyatomic molecules arises from a group of related properties which are commonly found in such molecules. First, their excited states tend to predissociate, that is, convert to a repulsive electronic configuration. The probability of dissociation as compared to radiation is greatly increased over simpler molecules. Therefore the neutralization of polyatomic ions to form excited molecules will result in decomposition rather than radiation. In addition, the decomposition takes place so rapidly that field emission of electrons from the cathode is prevented. In this way two important sources of electrons for new avalanches are removed.

In the travel of the positive ion sheath toward the cathode, neutralization of argon ions will occur, resulting in ultraviolet radiation. Fortunately, this is readily absorbed by the polyatomic gas. The argon ions themselves never reach the cathode, since the ionization potential of argon is considerably greater than that of polyatomic molecules. Many collisions will occur, and charge transfer is very probable, the excess energy being emitted as radiation which is again absorbed by the polyatomic gas.

The net result of all these effects is that a small proportion of the polyatomic gas can prevent secondary electron emission and absorb all the photons which might give rise to photoelectrons. Of course, this action is accompanied by decomposition of the quenching agent, and the decomposition products may not be capable of similar action, so that the internal quenching effect may disappear in time. A tube using ethyl alcohol may have an effective internal quenching life of around 10^9 counts The more complicated molecules such as amyl acetate can undergo more steps of decomposition while still remaining effective than can methane. On the other hand, large molecules give ions of smaller mobility, thus lengthening the minimum recovery time. Counters are sometimes operated with methane at atmospheric pressure, using a slow flow of gas to remove decomposition products and maintain quenching action.

Other Counters. Recently, two new types of counters have been developed which offer certain advantages, among which is the use of a solid rather than a gas as the detecting medium. Such a device will be more efficient, on a volume basis, in detecting radiations such as gamma rays with their extremely small absorption coefficients. It has been reported [1] that certain crystals, such as diamond, will give rise to a detectable current pulse on absorption of an ionizing radiation when in a strong electric field. In practice, the crystal is placed between two electrodes and a large potential applied. The creation of an energetic free electron in the solid is immediately followed by the flow of a brief and detectable current in the solid. The magnitude of the charge reaching the anode indicates that many electrons have moved in the solid, apparently in a cascade set off by the initial electron.

The second type of counter [2] consists of a crystal of a substance such as naphthalene, which readily fluoresces on electron impact, and which is transparent to its own fluorescent radiation. The flash of light (visible wave lengths) which appears on absorption of an ionizing radiation is detected and amplified by a photoelectron multiplier tube placed very close to the

[1] Hofstadter, *Nucleonics,* April, May, 1949.
[2] Coltman and Marshall, *Nucleonics,* Nov., 1947.

naphthalene crystal. Again the use of a solid as the primary detector considerably increases the efficiency of the device for the more penetrating radiations. A rather high rate of thermal electron emission in the electron multiplier tube is observed at room temperature. This is equivalent to a very high background and consequently decreases the sensitivity of the arrangement. The difficulty can be partially overcome by refrigerating the device to decrease the rate of thermal electron emission.

EFFICIENCY AND RELIABILITY OF DETECTING DEVICES

Ionization Chambers. An ionization chamber arranged to measure the number of ions produced per unit time responds to ionizing particles and radiations in proportion to their ability to produce ions within the volume of the chamber. The very small penetrating power of typical alpha particles permits the complete absorption of these particles within the volume of a chamber of limited size, whereas the more penetrating beta radiations may expend only part of their energy within the chamber. The very penetrating gamma radiations will expend only a very small fraction of their energy within the chamber and produce a correspondingly small number of ions. Therefore, for an equal flux of particles or quanta of the same energy, the response of an ionization chamber of limited size will be greatest for alpha particles, less for beta particles, and still less for gamma radiations. Indeed, much of the response to gamma radiations is due to the effect of the energetic secondary electrons formed in the absorption of the radiation in the walls and surroundings of the chamber. The response to beta particles and gamma radiations may be increased by increasing the gas pressures within the chamber to afford a more effective absorbing body.

The ultimate sensitivity of an integrating ionization chamber, aside from the limitations of the electronic circuits, is determined by the "natural" rate of ion formation in the chamber. Cosmic events and radioactive contaminants in the constructional materials combine to produce "background" effect which is dependent on almost every constructional variable of the system. A typical value for a brass chamber of 100 cc volume, filled with dry air at atmospheric pressure, might be 10^{-15} ampere, the equivalent of two alpha particles per minute. The maximum ion current which can be measured is many orders of magnitude greater, being largely limited by the increasing ion recombination effects which occur at very high ion densities.

Geiger Counters. The Geiger counter is an extremely sensitive device, since the creation of a single ion pair within its sensitive volume is sufficient to produce a recognizable current pulse. The probability that such a response will be produced by an alpha or beta particle, or a gamma quantum, in passing through the chamber depends on the absorption characteristics of these agents. In the first two cases, the absorption properties are such that the probability of producing at least one ion pair in the gas of a typical Geiger counter is practically unity, and the counter may be expected to respond to every alpha or beta particle passing through the chamber. In such a case, the count rate observed will be proportional to the cross-sectional area which the sensitive volume of the counter presents to the particle flux.

The absorption coefficients of gamma radiations, on the other hand, are so small that only a small fraction of the quanta passing through the counter chamber may be expected to produce an ion pair in the gas. In this case the response may be expected to be proportional to the volume of the counter rather than to its cross-sectional area. This is not strictly true in practice, since most of the events are due to energetic secondary electrons ejected from the walls and surroundings of the Geiger counter, which represents a much more effective absorbing medium than the gas of the chamber. The net effect is an efficiency of about 1% for 1 mev gamma quanta and this value is energy-dependent. The efficiency may be increased to around 10% by the use of special grids to yield more secondary electrons.

The sensitive volume of a Geiger counter is not necessarily defined by its geometrical volume. The field intensity near the central wire may be sufficient to start an avalanche even when the ionizing event occurs a short distance outside the confines of the cylindrical cathode. On the other hand, there is some evidence that a small region near the cathode and inside the cylinder may be insensitive because the primary electron may be driven into the cathode and thus fail to cause an avalanche. Some alteration of the field intensity distribution may be imposed by charged conductors near the tube.

External Effects. Many uses of an ionization chamber or Geiger counter involve a determination of the activity of a localized, external sample near the detecting device. In addition to the simple inverse square law which describes the change of flux with distance from the sample, we must again consider the absorption characteristics of the particles and radiations emitted by the sample. The air between the sample and detector, the walls of the detector, and the mass of the sample itself may appreciably affect the relation of the observed response to the disintegration rate of the sample. Quantitative treatment of these absorption effects will be discussed in the next chapter.

Many of the difficulties involved in the computation of efficiency factors in the counter and its surroundings may be avoided by the use of standard samples of known disintegration rate, or by restriction to relative activity measurements under comparable conditions.

Statistical Fluctuations. The decay of a group of radio-active nuclei occurs in a random fashion which may be described by the laws of probability. The half-life of a radioactive nuclide represents the most probable time required for half of the nuclei to decay, and, when a large number of individual nuclei are considered, this probability function has a very sharp maximum. However, if a relatively small number of nuclear events are considered, as in counting a weak sample for a limited period of time, a considerable variation among successive measurements will be observed. The methods of probability theory may be used to show that the standard deviation σ of a given measurement, defined by the relation

$$\sigma = \sqrt{\frac{\Sigma d^2}{n}}$$

where d is the deviation of an individual measurement from the average, and n is the number of individual measurements, may be given in the approximate form

$$\sigma = \sqrt{N} \tag{3.1}$$

where N is the number of individual events observed in a given measurement.

The simple relation given above may be used to estimate the reliability of an activity measurement in most cases of interest, and it is particularly applicable to the case of "counters" where the number of ionizing events is registered. For instance, the background count rate value, and that of any observation of activity with which it must be compared, should be stated in the form

$$R = \frac{N \pm \sqrt{N}}{t}$$

counts per unit time where N is the total number of events registered, and t is the duration of the observation period. It can be seen that the standard deviation of a value based on 100 observed events amounts to ±10%, whereas that based on 10,000 events amounts to ±1%. Any supposed difference in counting rates should be examined in the light of this statistical reliability.

The random nature of nuclear events must also be considered in the estimation of the "dead time" losses in Geiger counters. Even though the average spacing of counts may be several times t_d, a particle may occasionally enter the tube during the insensitive period and thus be unrecorded. If particles are entering the sensitive volume of the tube at a rate R and the dead time is t_d, let r be the observed counting rate. The counter will be insensitive for a fraction $1 - rt_d$ of the time. The average number of particles entering during the insensitive time is rRt_d, and therefore the counting loss is

$$(R - r) = rRt_d$$

and

$$R = r/1 - rt_d \qquad (3.2)$$

These relations refer to the simplified case where t_d is not lengthened by an event occurring in the insensitive period and where losses do not exceed approximately 10%.

Since the dead time depends on so many experimental variables, it is usually necessary to determine the counting loss for each type of tube or circuit. To avoid the labor of extensive calibration it is usually sufficient to determine the counting rate of two samples individually and then together. The approximate form

$$t_d = \frac{r_1 + r_2 - r_{12}}{2r_1 r_2} \qquad (3.3)$$

may be used, and typical values of t_d lie in the region of 3×10^{-6} sec, which corresponds to a loss of 500 counts per minute at a rate of 10,000 counts per minute.

PRODUCTION OF UNSTABLE NUCLIDES

Of the several hundred known unstable nuclides, all bu
about forty must be prepared by artificially induced nuclea
rearrangement processes. The agents which are used to induce
such changes fall into three general classes: first, the true
radiations, called gamma or X-radiations according to origin
second, the charged particles, such as electrons, protons, deu
terons, and helium ions (alpha particles) ; and, in a class by
itself, the neutron. Until the recent development of the self
sustaining nuclear reactor known as a "pile," the primary
agent in all artificial nuclear reactions was some one of the
charged particles, accelerated to great energies by electric and
magnetic fields. These particles may be used directly on stable
nuclei to produce various reactions, including the production o
neutrons, or may interact with the electronic structure of a
target substance to yield energetic X-radiations. Limited "nat
ural" sources of energetic particles and radiations are available
in the radioactive nuclides which decay by alpha, beta, and
gamma emission.

To obtain appreciable yields in most nuclear reactions, the
charged particles must be accelerated to energies in excess o
one million electron volts per particle. This is a consequence
not only of the endoergic character of some of the reactions
but also of the coulombic repulsion between the positive par
ticles and the target nucleus. The methods of attaining the
necessary energies fall into two classes: Acceleration of the
charged particles through a single, large, potential difference
and repeated passage of the charged particles through some
smaller potential difference. Our discussion will be confined to
a description of the most widely used devices of these two
types.

High-voltage Devices. The establishment and maintenance
of a potential difference in excess of a million volts presen

many experimental difficulties. A single-stage transformer and rectifier unit is limited to a few hundred kilovolts, owing to the difficulty of insulating the windings of the transformer.

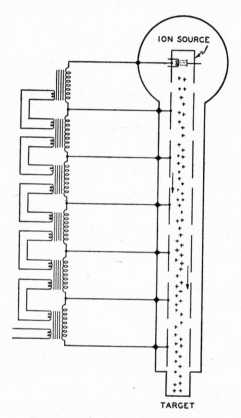

FIG. 3.13.   Transformers in cascade.

This may be avoided by operating a series of transformers in a cascade arrangement as shown in Fig. 3.13, thus reducing the insulation problem. In another type of voltage-multiplying device, a group of capacitors is charged in parallel and then switched so that they discharge in series, where the total potential difference is equal to some multiple of that supplied by the charging circuit. The spark gaps shown in Fig. 3.14 act as the switches, becoming low resistance arcs when the capacitors reach a certain potential. This device as well as the transformer cascade indicated above yield only bursts of energetic ions.

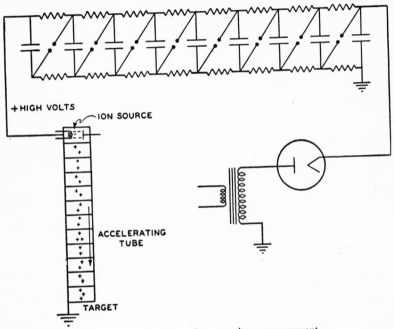

FIG. 3.14.   Parallel-series capacitor arrangement.

The most successful device for producing and maintaining potential differences in the million volt range was developed by R. J. Van de Graaf.[3] The potential difference is generated by the transfer of charge on a moving belt of insulating material as shown in Fig. 3.15. Electrons are sprayed onto the belt from discharge points at a relatively low potential. This

───────────────

[3] Van de Graaf, *Phys. Rev.* **38**, 1919 (1931).

charge is carried up to the high-potential electrode where it is removed by another set of discharge points connected to a

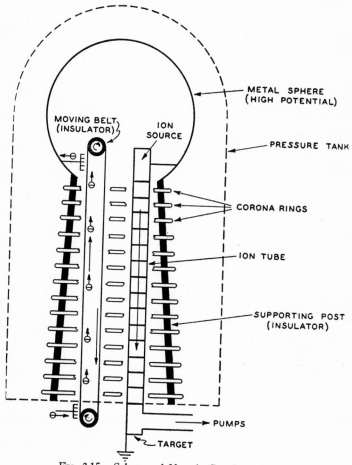

FIG. 3.15. Scheme of Van de Graaf generator.

large, hollow metal sphere. The charge distributes itself over the surface of this sphere because of mutual repulsion. Ions or electrons are generated in the sphere and are accelerated through an evacuated tube running from the sphere to ground. The large potential difference between the sphere and ground may be uniformly distributed along the accelerating tube by a series of metal rings with corona discharge points which give a small leakage current. This arrangement acts as a series of

FIG. 3.15a. The Notre Dame Van de Graaf generator. (Courtesy Nuclear Physics Laboratories, University of Notre Dame.)

high resistances connected between corresponding points on the ion tube.

The maximum potential difference which may be maintained is largely governed by the insulating ability of the gas near the high-voltage sphere. Dry air will withstand an electric field strength E of about 30,000 volts per centimeter, and the field strength at the surface of a sphere of radius r, charged to a potential V, is given by the relation

$$E = V/r \qquad (3.4)$$

which indicates that a sphere of one meter radius may be charged to a potential of 3,000,000 volts. This limit may be increased by surrounding the sphere with a gas of higher electric strength, commonly nitrogen at several atmospheres pressure, with small amounts of freon (CCl_2F_2) added. Still better would be complete evacuation of the space around the sphere, but this is mechanically unfeasible.

The Van de Graaf generator may be used to accelerate either electrons or positive ions, depending on the polarity given the high-voltage sphere. As an electron accelerator, it is also used to produce energetic X-rays, through electron targets. Electron currents in excess of 100 microamperes with energies of several million volts are readily produced.

Multiple Acceleration. Still higher particle energies are obtained in devices which avoid the high potential problem by repeated acceleration of the ions through relatively small potential differences. In the linear accelerator, the positive ions or electrons travel in a straight line, passing through a series of electrodes as indicated in Fig. 3.16. An alternating potential of several hundred kilovolts is applied to the electrodes through the circuit shown. In the acceleration of positive ions, a group will be accelerated into the first electrode when it is negative. If the lengths of the electrodes and the frequency of the oscillations are correctly related, the ion group will reach the second gap on the opposite half of the potential wave and again be accelerated. The electrodes are successively longer, so that the ion group arrives at each gap at the correct moment in the potential cycle to be again accelerated.

In the low-velocity region, the spacing of the accelerating gaps as a function of particle energy may be deduced from the classical expression for kinetic energy

$$E = \tfrac{1}{2}mv^2$$

and the relation

$$v/d = 2f \qquad (3.5)$$

where d is the electrode length and f is the full-wave frequency of the oscillating potential. As the particle velocity ap-

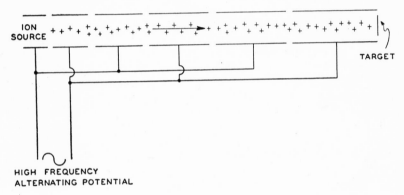

Fig. 3.16. Linear accelerator.

proaches its limiting value, the velocity of light, the relativistic expression for velocity as a function of energy must be used. In the limiting case where the particle moves with a velocity very close to that of light the electrode distance approaches a constant value of $3 \times 10^{10}/2f$, which indicates that oscillation frequencies of many megacycles must be used to achieve reasonable electrode sizes.

Because of its small rest mass, the electron enters the region of relativistic behavior at rather small energies. At 10 kev energy its velocity is about 1/10 that of light. Heavier particles, such as protons, follow the classical relationship quite well up to energies of several mev (see Fig. 1.7 for graphical representation of this information).

The cyclotron, developed by E. O. Lawrence,[4] has been one of the most successful devices for producing energetic particles for nuclear reactions. Again the principle is that of re-

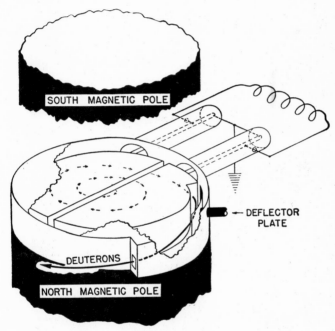

A. Schematic view, showing action of the cyclotron.

Fig. 3.17. Cyclotron.

peated acceleration through a moderate potential difference, but in this modification the ions travel in a circular path, passing between the same two electrodes many times as shown in Fig. 3.17. This is accomplished by introduction of a strong magnetic field in which the plane of motion of the ions will

---

[4] Lawrence and Edlefson, *Science* 72, 376 (1930).

B. Cyclotron magnet.   C. Tank assembly. (Mass. Inst. of Tech.)

Fig. 3.17. Cyclotron.

be perpendicular to the lines of force, with a radius of curvature given by equation 1.6, modified to the form

$$\frac{2\pi r}{v} = \frac{2\pi m}{He} = t \qquad (3.6)$$

which indicates that the time t required for a particle of a given e/m to complete one circuit remains constant as its velocity and energy increase, owing to an increase in the radius of curvature. A group of ions formed at the central source is accelerated into one of the D-shaped electrodes and travels in a semicircular path, arriving at the gap in one half-cycle of the oscillating potential. Here it is again accelerated and, describing a larger semicircle inside the second electrode, reaches the gap again in phase with the accelerating potential. The magnetic field strength H and the oscillation frequency f must be related as follows:

$$H \cdot \frac{1}{2\pi} \frac{e}{m} = f \qquad (3.7)$$

In this resonant condition, the cyclotron accelerates ions in groups or bursts. The ions may be directed out of the chamber by a deflecting electrode such as indicated in the figure.

It is seen from equation 3.7 that a change in the apparent mass of the ions as the velocity of light is approached will alter the resonance conditions and limit the energy attainable. This difficulty may be avoided by altering the frequency of the potential oscillation, so that the resonance condition may be maintained at higher energies. Such frequency modulation cuts down the ion currents, since a single group of ions must travel the complete route before the frequency returns to the resonant value for low-velocity ions.

The maximum energy of the ions produced by a cyclotron may be described in terms of the diameter of the maximum circular path and the magnetic field strength. Since the latter is limited in practice by the magnet construction to about

20,000 gauss, the approximate maximum energy is proportional to the square of the diameter of the pole pieces, which limit the region of homogeneous field. Thus, if a 60-inch cyclotron produces a deuteron beam of 20 mev, a 180-inch cyclotron, such as recently constructed at the University of California, may be expected to yield 200 mev deuterons.

Supplementary Reading

Borkowski, "Instruments for Measuring Radioactivity," *Anal. Chem.* 21, 348 (1949).

Brown, "Theory and Operation of Geiger Counters," I, II and III. *Nucleonics,* June, Aug., and Sept., 1948.

Ghelardi and Brown, "Electronic Instruments for Use with Geiger-Muller Tubes," *Nucleonics,* Sept. 1947.

Kohman, "Measurement Techniques of Applied Radiochemistry," *Anal. Chem.* 21, 352 (1949).

Korff, *Electron and Nuclear Counters,* D. Van Nostrand Co., Inc., New York, 1946.

Kurie, "Present-Day Design and Technique of the Cyclotron," *J. App. Phys.* 9, 691 (1938).

Salisbury, "Accelerators for Heavy Particles," *Nucleonics,* Nov., 1947.

Wells, "Production of High Energy Particles," *J. App. Phys.* 9, 677 (1938).

Numerical Exercises

1. Calculate the current in amperes which corresponds to a flux of 10^3 5-mev alpha particles per second completely absorbed in an ionization chamber. Assume that 32 ev are required for formation of each ion pair and that all ions and electrons are collected.

2. If the response time in an alpha counting chamber is 10^{-6} sec, and a resistance of 10^7 ohms is used, what is the magnitude of the voltage pulse on the grid after collection of all ions from a 5-mev alpha?

3. From the following data, calculate the dead time of a Gieger tube. Indicate the reliability of the result.

Sample 1 ....22,490 counts in 2 min
Sample 2 ....18,220 counts in 2 min
Sample 1 + 2 ....38,470 counts in 2 min

4. From the following data and the dead time computed above calculate the number of ionizing events per minute due to the presence of the samples listed. Indicate the reliability of each answer.

No sample (background) .... 200 counts in 5 min
Sample 1 .... 250 counts in 5 min
Sample 2 .... 2500 counts in 5 min
Sample 3 ....25,000 counts in 5 min

5. If the first electrode in a linear accelerator is 1 cm long, how long should the second and third electrodes be? Assume that the same energy change occurs at each gap, and that the speed of light is not approached.

6. If the accelerating potential in problem 5 is 200 kv, and the ions are protons, what should the full-wave frequency of oscillation be?

7. Applying the above conditions to a cyclotron, what magnetic field strength would be required? What energy could be achieved with 50-in. pole pieces?

CHAPTER IV

NUCLEAR DECAY REACTIONS

THIS CHAPTER will be devoted to a more careful consideration of the experimental characteristics of the radioactive
decay processes, and in particular to the properties of the particles and radiations evolved, in order to prepare for a discussion of the chemical phenomena associated with these reactions and later consideration of radioactive tracers as an analytical method in the study of chemical reactions.

TYPES OF DECAY

We have indicated in Chapter I that three general types
of nuclear decay are observed and that three corresponding
types of particles or radiations are emitted. The distinction
between these three types is illustrated by experiments first
performed with the natural radioelements shortly after the
discovery of radioactivity by Becquerel in 1896. As shown
in Fig. 4.1, a sample of active material is placed at the
bottom of a narrow hole in a lead block, to produce a narrow
pencil of radiation. A photographic emulsion or other ion
detector is placed above the block to record the impact of the
radiations. If a magnetic field is imposed with the lines of
force perpendicular to the path of the radiations, three components are noted. One is curved readily in such a direction
as to indicate a negative charge, another less readily in the
opposite direction, and one component is not deflected at all.
The three types are commonly called alpha, beta, and gamma
radiations as indicated in the figure and represent the most
frequently encountered types of nuclear radiation.

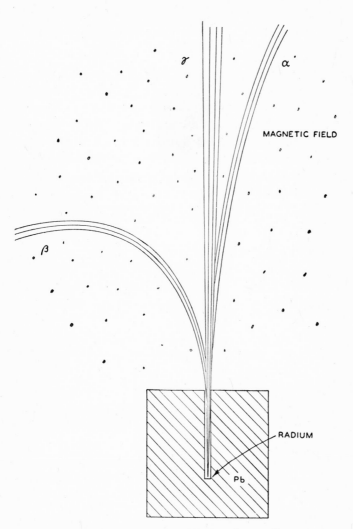

Fɪɢ. 4.1. Resolution of radiations from radium.

Alpha Decay. By the combined use of electric and magnetic deflection experiments the charge-to-mass ratio of the positively charged component, the alpha radiations, may be established as 1.45×10^{14} esu per gram, corresponding to that of the doubly charged helium ion $(2p, 2n)$. This value is also characteristic of other particles, such as the deuteron $(1p, 1n)$ but the matter has been settled by independent charge determination and by collection and spectroscopic identification of helium in the presence of this radiation. From the nature of the alpha particle, we may infer that its release corresponds to the nuclear rearrangement which may be generalized as

$$_zX^A \rightarrow {}_2\alpha^4 + {}_{z-2}Y^{A-4}$$

Having established the charge-to-mass ratio of the alpha particle, its curvature in a magnetic or electric field may be taken as a measure of its momentum and energy. Discrete values of the energy ranging from 1 to 10 mev are observed, the precise values depending on the particular unstable nuclide. These observations are in agreement with the concept of quantized energy states of nuclei, and the several energies sometimes observed in the decay of a single nuclide must arise from the existence of several energy states of reacting or product nucleus.

Beta Decay. The charge-to-mass ratio of the negative component of the radiations (beta radiations) indicated in Fig. 4.1 is found to be 5.28×10^{17} esu per gram, the well-known electronic value. In these experiments the relativistic variation of mass with energy must be considered, since the energies encountered range up to several mev, and the small mass of this particle makes the correction appreciable at energies above a few kev.

In contrast to the alpha particles which are emitted with discrete energies, beta radiations, even from a single nuclide, have a continuous energy and momentum distribution of a form shown by the solid line in Fig. 4.2. The shape of the distribution curve is approximately the same for all beta radiations, but the maximum beta energy observed is a characteristic of the particular nuclide. This behavior would seem to be a contradiction of the concept of quantized nuclear energy states and considerable attention has been given this problem.

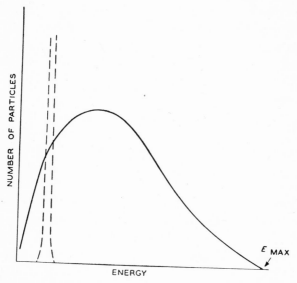

FIG. 4.2. Energy distribution in beta radiation and monoenergetic electrons.

Several experiments have been performed to measure simultaneously the momentum of the product nucleus and the beta particle. One finds that, in the consideration of only these two particles, momentum is not conserved in the beta decay process. Qualitatively, it appears that the product nucleus does not always recoil in a direction exactly opposite to the direction of beta emission. This and other properties of the beta decay process have led to the postulation of a particle called the *neutrino,* to be emitted simultaneously with the beta, and to have no charge and rest mass a small fraction of the electronic value. These properties would make this particle practically undetectable. The nuclear energy change is presumed to be the same for all the various beta energies observed; the neutrino carries off the energy difference. A beta particle of the maximum energy is accompanied by a neutrino of vanishing energy and vice versa. The emission of a negative beta particle indicates the nuclear change

$$_z X^A \rightarrow {}_{-1}\beta^0 + {}_{z+1}Y^A$$

Positron Decay. The emission of positive beta particles is frequently observed among the artificial unstable nuclides whose neutron-proton ratio is less than the stable value. The positron radiations show a similar momentum distribution to that seen in the case of negative beta particles, and an antineutrino is postulated on the same basis. The creation of a positron requires a nuclear energy change of at least 1.02 mev, or twice the energy equivalent of the mass of an electron. The kinetic energy of the positron and antineutrino is less than the nuclear energy change by this amount. This decay reaction may be written in the form

$$_z X^A \rightarrow {}_{+1}\beta^0 + {}_{z-1}Y^A$$

Orbital Electron Capture. The nuclear transition $p \rightarrow n$ may also be accomplished by the capture of an extra-nuclear electron, usually of the K or L shell. No large threshold energy for this decay reaction exists, and therefore it becomes the only mechanism available when the energy necessary for positron emission is not available. It is most frequently noted with unstable nuclides having stable isobars. The outward manifestation of the decay process is the emission of characteristic X-radiations in the filling of the electronic vacancy in the extra-nuclear structure.

Isomeric Transition. The undeflected component of nuclear radiations indicated in Fig. 4.1 consists of electromagnetic radiations of extremely short wave length. Such gamma radiations arise from transitions between various energy states of nuclei and have discrete energies corresponding to these transitions. Although the majority of excited nuclear energy states are extremely short-lived and decay to the ground state practically instantaneously, a number of cases are known where this transition rate is sufficiently slow to permit isolation and more or less independent study of such an excited nuclide. Although strictly applicable to all excited nuclei, regardless of decay rate, the term "nuclear isomer" is usually used to refer to those which decay slowly. Similarly, the term "isomeric transition" commonly refers to the measureably slow transitions between nuclear energy states. This decay process involves no change in atomic or mass number and may be written as

$$_{z}X^{A*} \rightarrow {_{z}X^{A}} + \gamma$$

where the asterisk indicates an excited nuclide.

Internal Conversion. In addition to gamma emission a transition between nuclear energy states may be accomplished by the mechanism of internal conversion. An extra-nuclear electron, usually of the K or L shell, may interact with the nucleus and receive the transition energy. Such an electron will be ejected from the atom with a kinetic energy equal to that of the nuclear transition less the electronic ionization energy. Internal conversion electrons will therefore have discrete energies, in contrast to beta radiations, as shown by the broken line of Fig. 4.2. The vacancy left in the electronic structure of the product atom will be filled by electronic transitions from outer shells, accompanied by the emission of characteristic X-radiations.

Neutron Decay. A few nuclides are observed to emit neutrons in their decay toward stability. This process cannot be the result of spontaneous decay of the ground state of an unstable nucleus, since the emission of a neutron would be highly exoergic except at extremely great neutron-proton ratios. It therefore must represent an alternate decay mechanism for some excited nuclear state, formed by beta particle emission from the preceding isobar. In confirmation of this description, the neutron decay rate is extremely great, and the neutron appears to be emitted coincidentally with the beta decay which forms the necessary excited state.

ABSORPTION OF NUCLEAR RADIATIONS

The penetration power of nuclear radiations is a function of the energy as well as the type of radiation. It is a relatively simple and important method of characterization of an unstable nuclide and is an important consideration in many chemical aspects of nuclear science.

Experimentally, the property is measured by interposing various amounts of matter between the radioactive sample and some detecting device. The substance used may be air, frequently used in the case of alpha radiations, or some solid, such as aluminum or lead, which are commonly used with beta and gamma radiations, respectively. It must be remembered that the walls of the detector and the matter of the sample itself may partially absorb the radiations. All other variables, and particularly the relative position of the sample and detector, remain fixed. After appropriate corrections for the background response of the detector, and for any dead time losses if a counter is used, the intensity of the radiation as a function of the total amount of matter between sample and detector decreases in a fashion characteristic of the energy and type of radiation.

Alpha Particles. Examination of Fig. 3.1 indicates that alpha particles have a quite definite "range," that is, alpha particles from a given nuclide will all be stopped in traversing a fixed amount of matter. In Fig. 4.3, the number of alpha particles detected as a function of distance in air at atmospheric pressure is shown (solid line). The small "straggling"

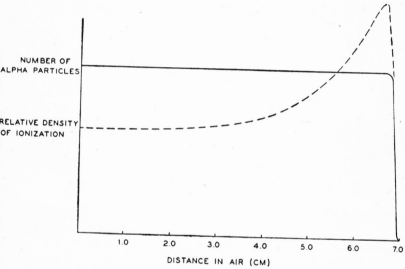

NUMBER OF ALPHA PARTICLES

RELATIVE DENSITY OF IONIZATION

1.0 2.0 3.0 4.0 5.0 6.0 7.0

DISTANCE IN AIR (CM)

Fig. 4.3. Path length and density of ionization by alpha particles from $RaC^1(_{84}Po^{214})$.

observed causes the individual path lengths to fall about the most probable value in a Gaussian error distribution. Thus the true "range" of a given group of alpha particles may be more precisely defined as the most probable range, rather than the maximum range. However, the straggling effect is small and affects only the most precise calculations. The range of alpha particles varies with their energy as shown in Fig. 4.4.

An alpha particle loses its energy by interactions with the extra-nuclear electrons of the atoms it passes. On the average it creates approximately one ion pair for each 32 ev energy loss. Since this energy is considerably greater than the average ionization potential of the electrons removed, a fraction of this energy loss must appear as excitation rather than ionization. The relative density of ionization (and presumably also of excitation) along the path of an alpha particle is shown in

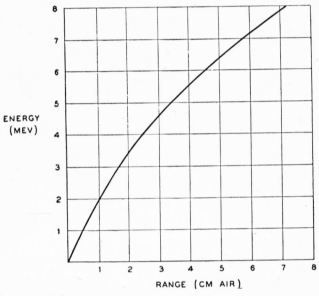

Fig. 4.4.   Range-energy relationship for alpha particles.

Fig. 4.3 (dotted line). The increased ion density as the particle loses energy and moves more slowly is clearly shown. Both excitation and ionization represent electronic interactions, and therefore it might be expected that the stopping power of an absorber would be proportional to the density of electrons present, which in turn would be proportional to

$$\frac{d}{A} \times Z$$

where d is density, A is the atomic weight, and Z is the atomic number of the absorber. Experimental test shows that a function such as

$$\frac{d}{A} \times Z^{\frac{2}{3}} \qquad (4.1)$$

gives a better description of stopping power as a function of absorber characteristics, since the tightly bound inner electrons of the heavier elements do not contribute their share to the ionization and excitation processes.

Beta Particles. Even if beta particles were monoenergetic in a given decay, a fixed range for all particles could not be expected, since their small mass permits ready deflection by the electrons with which they collide. With the additional complication of a continuous energy distribution, the absorption curve for beta radiation takes a shape which represents a nearly expotential absorption of the radiation. Fig. 4.5 is a typical absorption curve for a simple beta decay reaction, where logarithm of observed activity is plotted against amount of absorber (Al) interposed between simple and detector. This latter variable is expressed in terms of milligrams per square centimeter, a unit computed by multiplying the density of the absorber in milligrams per cubic centimeter, by the thickness of the absorber, in centimeters. Careful consideration of the data in the region where the activity of the sample blends into the background permits estimation of the "range" of the beta radiation. However, it must be remembered that this is the maximum range of the most energetic particles, and that most particles are stopped at a fraction of this value. In fact, a useful generalization states that about half of the beta particles will be absorbed by an amount of absorber corresponding to one-tenth the maximum range.

The shape of the absorption curve will depend to an appreciable extent upon the particular experimental arrangement used, but the characteristic range for a given beta radiation will remain constant. Since the energy distribution of beta

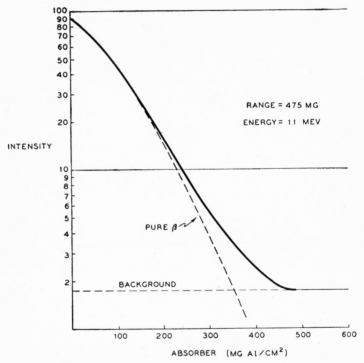

FIG. 4.5. Beta absorption curve for RaE($_{83}$Bi^{210}).

radiations of various maximum energies is of approximately the same form, we may expect that the various beta absorption curves will be of approximately the same shape, when observed under the same experimental conditions. This permits estimation of the range of an unknown beta radiation without direct determination of the whole absorption curve.

The range of beta radiations is an almost linear function of the maximum energy as shown in Fig. 4.6. Use of this curve permits estimation of the beta decay energy from the absorption characteristics of the radiation.

Positrons. The absorption curve for positrons is of the same form as that observed for negative beta particles, and the same range-energy correlation may be used. However, the final act in the absorption of a positron consists of an annihi-

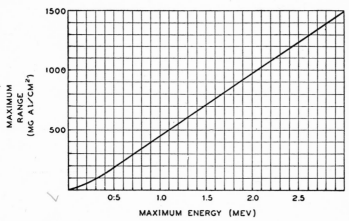

FIG. 4.6.   Range-energy relation for beta radiations.

lation reaction with a negative electron. In this process the two particles disappear, and the energy equivalent of their mass (1.02 mev) appears as two gamma quanta of equal energy. This annihilation radiation is always present in matter absorbing positrons.

Conversion Electrons. The absorption curve for conversion electrons, which have a discreet energy rather than the distribution characteristic of beta radiations, is found to be linear with added absorber, except at extreme values, as shown in Fig. 4.7. The extrapolation of the linear portion to the absorber axis is usually taken to indicate the range of such particles and may be translated to energy by use of Fig. 4.6.

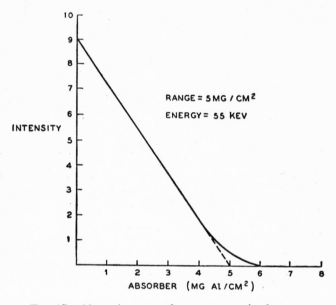

FIG. 4.7. Absorption curve for monoenergetic electrons.

Gamma Radiations. The absorption of monoenergetic gamma radiations is described by Beer's law

$$\frac{I}{I_0} = e^{-\mu T} \tag{4.2}$$

where I and I_0 represent the final and initial intensities of radiation after traversing a thickness of matter T. μ is the linear absorption cofficient of the medium and is a function of the nature of the absorber and the energy of the radiation. Statement of the absorption law in logarithmic form

$$\ln I = \ln I_0 - \mu T \tag{4.3}$$

indicates that a semilogarithmic graph will show a linear behavior, as in Fig. 4.8. The absorption cofficient is frequently expressed in the form of the half-thickness, defined by the relation

$$T_{1/2} = \frac{\ln 2}{\mu} = \frac{0.693}{\mu} \tag{4.4}$$

which is seen to be independent of intensity.

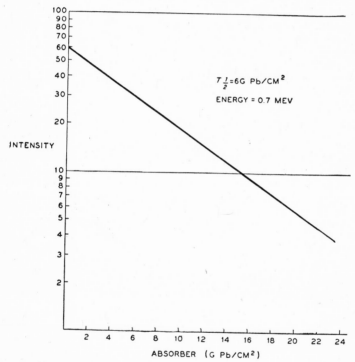

FIG. 4.8.   Absorption of monoenergetic gamma radiation.

Gamma radiation (and X-radiation) is absorbed by three types of interaction with matter, the relative contribution of the three processes depending on the nature of the absorbing matter and the energy of the radiation. *Photoelectron emis-*

sion is the most important process at energies less than 0.5 mev. This process consists of the complete transfer of the gamma energy to some extra-nuclear electron in the absorber. This electron acquires a kinetic energy equal to the gamma energy, less the electronic ionization potential. The efficiency of this process changes rather sharply at energies correspond-

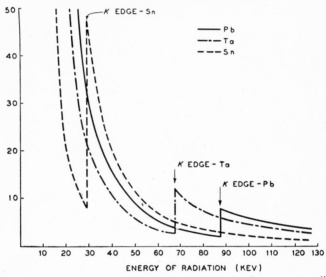

Fig. 4.9. Absorption coefficients of various elements for low-energy radiations.

ing to the ionization potential of the various extra-nuclear electronic energy states of the absorbing atoms. The most firmly bound electrons are those of the K-shell, which have an ionization potential of 87.6 kev in the case of lead. Fig. 4.9 shows the behavior of the absorption coefficient of several elements in this energy region. Similar but successively less pronounced breaks occur at lower energies, corresponding to the L, M, . . . electrons. The energy of the K-edge, as it is called, increases with atomic number in a fashion described by the Moseley relation (see equation 1.3 and Appendix), and the magnitude of the change is such that it may be used to establish quite precisely the energy of gamma or X-radiations in the energy range 1-100 kev. This technique, known as a *critical absorption* measurement, consists in the measurement of the absorption coefficient of a particular radiation with absorbers of various elements, until the sharp change is found. For instance radiations of 79 kev would be strongly absorbed by Pt, in which the *K*-edge is 78.1 but much less strongly absorbed by Au which has a *K*-edge of 80.5 kev.

At energies above 0.5 mev, the *Compton effect* becomes more important than the photoelectric effect. This process is essentially an elastic collision of the gamma quantum with an electron in the absorber. The gamma is scattered with decreased energy and the electron given a corresponding energy. The principles of conservation of energy and momentum permit calculation of the energy transfer as a function of the angle of scattering. At gamma energies above 1.02 mev, the process of *pair production* sets in and becomes increasingly important at higher energies. In the field of a nucleus, the gamma ray forms a positive and negative electron in the reverse of the positron annihilation reaction. The energy threshold for this process is set by the energy-mass of the two electrons formed.

The total absorption coefficient is the sum of the absorption cofficients corresponding to the three individual processes, which are shown for lead in Fig. 4.10. The minimum in the absorption coefficient will correspond to a maximum in the half-thickness curve, which is shown in Fig. 4.11. Values of half-thickness for aluminum are also given in this figure.

DECAY SCHEMES

A decay scheme is a description of the types and energies of the decay products emitted by a given nuclide. The decay scheme usually includes all the decay reactions involved in the

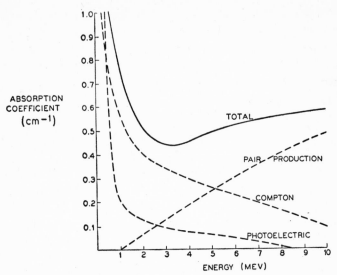

FIG. 4.10. Absorption coefficients for gamma radiations in lead.

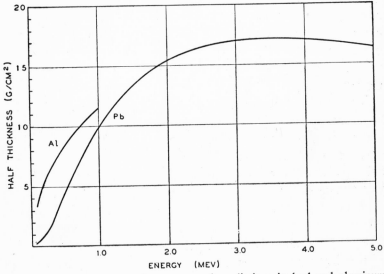

FIG. 4.11. Half-thickness of monoenergetic radiations in lead and aluminum.

transition from one relatively long-lived state to another. This may include several intermediate states of very short half-life ($<10^{-6}$ sec) which appear to decay coincidentally with the primary reaction. The initial nucleus may show only a single type of decay reaction and only one energy of decay, or it may show two or more alternate decay reactions of different energy or type.

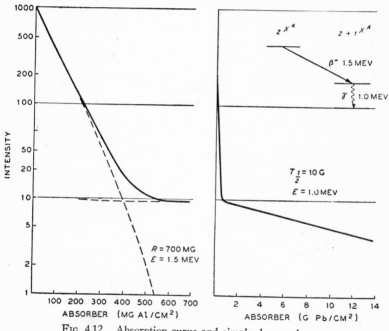

FIG. 4.12. Absorption curve and simple decay scheme.

Simple Decay. All types of decay reactions may leave the product nucleus in an excited state, which usually decays very rapidly by gamma emission to a lower and more stable state. When the half-life of the excited product nucleus is immeasurably short, the gamma radiation is said to be emitted coincidentally with the primary reaction. Fig. 4.12 shows the type of absorption curves to be expected if a simple beta decay is followed by the emission of a gamma quantum. A conventional method of summarizing this decay scheme is also shown. This example and those which follow are based on the use of a Geiger counter as the detector, and the low counting efficiency of this device for gamma radiations results in a very large

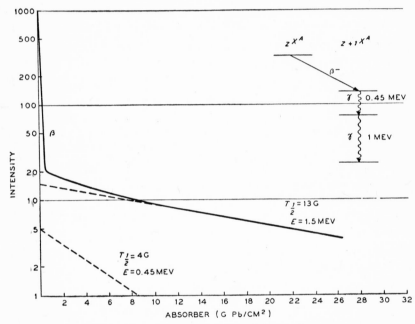

FIG. 4.13. Absorption curve and decay scheme.

ratio of beta to gamma intercepts. If we assume in this case that each beta particle is followed by one gamma quantum, it is apparent that the counting efficiency of the gamma quanta is approximately 1/100 that of the beta particles.

A simple beta decay process may also be followed by the emission of more than one quantum of gamma radiation, as illustrated in Fig. 4.13. The gamma absorption curve can frequently be analyzed into two linear components as shown, and the half-thickness of each indicates its energy. Again assuming that both gamma quanta are emitted after each beta decay, it appears that the counting efficiencies are approximately 0.5% for 0.45 mev and 1.5% for 1.5 mev.

For further illustration, let us assume that the 0.45 mev transition in the product nucleus of Fig. 4.13 proceeds partially by the mechanism of internal conversion. In such a case, the intensity of this component in the gamma absorption curve would be diminished, and weak monoenergetic electron components would be added to the beta absorption curve. If $Z + 1$ = 80 (Hg), then K-conversion yields 0.367 mev electrons, and L-conversion yields 0.435 mev electrons. If the extent of conversion is small, these might well be indistinguishable from the primary beta radiations, but magnetic analysis would clearly show their monoenergetic character (see Fig. 4.2).

Inspection of the data given in the Appendix will disclose many examples of the types mentioned and also many cases where alpha emission and positron emission are accompanied by gamma radiation. Some confusion is possible in the latter case, since the 0.5 mev annihilation radiation always accompanies the absorption of positrons.

Branching Decay. Many nuclides emit beta particles in two distinct energy groups. These represent two alternate decay reactions for the nuclide resulting in two different energy states of the produce nuclide. The higher of these two states usually decays promptly to the lower state, which in turn may decay still further to a ground state of the product nucleus.

Fig. 4.14 represents a case of branching beta decay. The observed beta absorption curve is the sum of the contributions of the two individual betas and may be resolved as indicated. The ratio of intercepts at zero absorber gives directly the relative numbers of the two betas, known as the branching ratio. If the initial and final states are the same, energy conservation requires that the overall decay energy shall be the same for each route. This condition is fulfilled only if the maximum beta energy, rather than the average or most probable value, is used. Therefore, it is the maximum beta energy which corresponds to the energy of the nuclear transition.

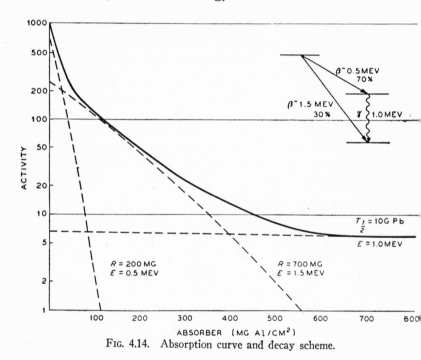

FIG. 4.14. Absorption curve and decay scheme.

In some cases a given energy state of an unstable nuclide may decay by two distinctly different mechanisms. An excited nuclear isomer of reasonable half-life may decay by isomeric transition or particle emission. The ground state of an unstable nuclide may decay by two different types of particle emission. For example, the nuclide K^{40} emits both positrons and negative beta particles. Since it lies between two stable isobars, both of these alternate decay reactions produce a stable configuration. The nuclide $_{83}Bi^{214}$ (RaC) emits both alpha and beta particles, branching to $_{84}Po^{214}$ (RaC′) and $_{81}Tl^{210}$ (RaC″).

Activity Determinations. In addition to the problems of efficiency, geometry, etc., discussed in the preceding chapter, the problem of relating a count rate (or other response) to the disintegration rate in an active sample requires careful consideration of the nature of the decay process. If the nuclide under observation emits only a single type of alpha particle, the determination is quite reliable, since this particular radiation has a quite definite range and is not readily scattered.

The absorption curve for beta particles indicates that even small amounts of matter between the active nuclide and the detector may absorb an appreciable fraction of the beta particles. Usually an absorption curve for the particular radiation is required, in order that the count rate at zero absorber may be estimated. This extrapolation must take into account the absorption by the air, by the counter wall, and by the sample itself, if it is of appreciable weight. The magnitude of such corrections will be strongly dependent upon the experimental arrangement and upon the energy of the radiation.

If the decay scheme includes an internally converted transition coincident with the beta emission, the number of electrons plus beta particles will amount to more than one per disintegration. In this and other cases of complex and branching decay schemes, the determination of the disintegration rate may be very difficult.

The rather poorly known and small counting efficiencies of gamma and X-radiations preclude the accurate determination of disintegration rates from counting data on these radiations.

The nuclides connected by a radioactive decay process such as alpha or beta particle emission are said to be genetically related, and the terms "parent" and "daughter" are used in reference to succeeding members of the decay chain. If a nuclide many units removed from stability is considered, it is apparent that the decay chain will consist of several unstable nuclides, each with its own characteristic decay rate and decay scheme.

Beta Decay Chains. Reference to an isotope chart shows that several unstable nuclides produced by neutron capture,

$$_{54}Xe^{143} \xrightarrow[1.3 \text{ sec}]{\beta^-} {}_{55}Cs^{143} \xrightarrow[\text{short}]{\beta^-} {}_{56}Ba^{143} \xrightarrow[< 30 \text{ sec}]{\beta^-} {}_{57}La^{143} \xrightarrow[20 \text{ min}]{\beta^-} {}_{58}Ce^{143}$$

$$\xrightarrow[36 \text{ hr}]{\beta^-} {}_{59}Pr^{143} \xrightarrow[13.5 \text{ days}]{\beta^-} {}_{60}Nd^{143} \text{ (stable)}$$

FIG. 4.15.

such as Se^{83}, are two units removed from their stable isobars. Therefore they constitute the first member of a two-member beta decay chain. In the case mentioned the parent decays by beta emission with a 25-minute half-life, forming Br^{83}, while this daughter decays by beta emission with a 2.4-hour half-life, yielding stable Kr^{83}.

As pointed out in Chapter V, the fission of a heavy nucleus into two approximately equal fragments gives rise to highly unstable nuclei, since they will have an abnormally high neutron-proton ratio. This gives rise to beta decay, and as many as five or six steps may be necessary to reach a stable isobar. In general, the decay energies decrease and the half-lives increase as stability is approached. Fig. 4.15 represents such a chain. Since each member of the chain has a different atomic number, it is possible in principle to isolate the individual members by chemical methods which will be discussed in a later chapter. However, unless the individual has some rather distinctive chemical property, as is the case with the rare gas member of the chain given above, such separations are feasible only with the members having half-lives of about a minute or greater.

Alpha-beta Decay Chains. The two semistable elements at the end of the periodic system, uranium and thorium, together constitute the starting points for three alpha-beta decay chains as outlined in Fig. 4.16. Since the various decay reactions can change the mass number only by zero (isomeric transition and beta decay) or four units (alpha decay) the various chains may be characterized by their mass numbers as $4n$, $4n + 1$, $4n + 2$, and $4n + 3$. Again it is apparent that chemical procedures may be used to isolate various members of the chains, in particular element 86, which is a rare gas (radon).

A rather confusing nomenclature based on some of the longer-lived members was originally adopted for nuclides in this region. Both these genetic names and the usual chemical symbols are indicated in the figure.

Only three of the possible chains occur in nature, the $4n + 1$ chain having only recently been observed by artificial production of some of its members, in particular U^{233} (half-life = 1.6×10^5 years) and Np^{237} (half-life = 2.25×10^6 years). Although these are the longest-lived members of the $4n + 1$ chain, their half-lives are only about 1/1000 as long as those of Th^{232}, U^{235}, and U^{238}, the progenitors of the natural series.

Isomeric Transition. Nuclear isomers represent a rather unique case of genetic relationship, in that both parent and

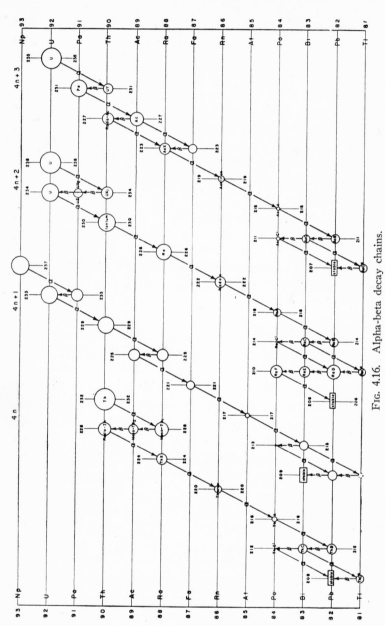

Fig. 4.16. Alpha-beta decay chains.

Legend: The radii of the circles are proportional to the logarithms of the half-lines of the various nuclides.

daughter have the same atomic number and mass number. This means that the usual chemical and physical methods will not separate them and consequently it may be difficult to disentangle their individual decay schemes.

The two isomeric states may be formed by a bombardment reaction or by a branching decay as in the case of Pa^{234} (see Fig. 4.16). Each state will show its own characteristic decay scheme. The upper state may decay by both isomeric transition and beta decay. It may or may not yield the same product nucleus as the decay of the lower state.

RATE EQUATIONS

The radioactive decay process is unimolecular and first order, that is, the rate of decay is proportional to the number of unstable nuclei present at any time as expressed by the differential equation

$$-\frac{dN}{dt} = \lambda N = A \qquad (4.5)$$

where N represents the number of unstable nuclei, and λ is the decay constant, a characteristic of the particular nuclide. This rate constant is independent of temperature, pressure, and chemical state within the practical limits of laboratory facilities.[1] The activity A is defined as the rate of disintegration and is usually observed through the detection of the nuclear radiations emitted in the decay process.

The variation of N or A with time is given by the integrated form of equation which may be expressed in exponential or logarithmic form thus:

$$\frac{N}{N^0} = \frac{A}{A^0} = e^{-\lambda t} \qquad (4.6)$$

$$\ln A = \ln A^0 - \lambda t$$

---

[1] It has been anticipated that the rates of decay processes involving the extra-nuclear electronic structure, i.e., orbital electron capture and internal conversion, might depend on the chemical state. This effect has been sought for, with doubtful results. See Segré and Weigand, *Phys. Rev.* **75**, 39 (1949).

where the superscript 0 denotes the number of unstable atoms or activity at the beginning of the time interval t. Linear and semilogarithmic graphs of activity versus time are given in Fig. 4.17.

The decay rate of a particular unstable nuclide is most frequently stated as a half-life, $t_{1/2}$, which is the time required

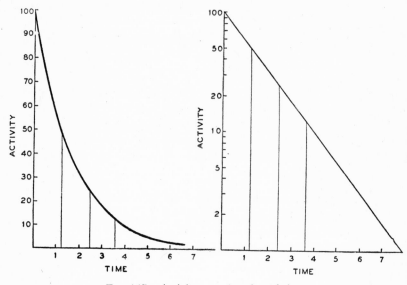

Fig. 4.17. Activity as a function of time.

for the activity to decrease by a factor of 2. Its relation to the decay constant is given by the equation

$$\ln \frac{A^0}{2} = \ln A^0 - \lambda t_{1/2}$$

$$t_{1/2} = \frac{0.693}{\lambda} \tag{4.7}$$

which shows that the half-life is independent of the number of unstable atoms and the activity. The half-life may be determined by inspection of the activity versus time graph in cases where the value is neither too great nor too small for experimental observation. With very long-lived nuclides, the decay constant may be evaluated by measurement of the activity of a measured sample of unstable atoms, as indicated by equation 4.5.

Independent Decay. When a mixture of two unstable nustable nuclides which are not genetically related undergo radioactive decay, the rate of disappearance of each may be described by independent differential equations such as

$$\frac{dN_a}{dt} = -\lambda_a N_a \qquad\qquad \frac{dN_b}{dt} = -\lambda_b N_b \quad (4.8)$$

where λ, N, and t are used as in equation 4.5, and the subscripts a and b refer to the two different nuclides. The total activity at any time will be the sum of the individual activities, given by the following equation:

$$A_{\text{tot.}} = A_a{}^0 e^{-\lambda_a t} + A_b{}^0 e^{-\lambda_b t} \qquad (4.9)$$

where $A^0{}_a$ and $A^0{}_b$ are the individual activities when $t = 0$. An efficiency factor E may also be included in computing the response R of the detecting device, to allow for differences in the two radiations.

$$R = E_a A_a{}^0 e^{-\lambda_a t} + E_b A_b{}^0 e^{-\lambda_b t} \qquad (4.10)$$

This relation is illustrated in Fig. 4.18 for a case where $\lambda_a = 10\lambda_b$. Note that after a decay period many times the half-life of the shorter-lived nuclide, the total response is practically equal to that characteristic of the longer-lived nuclide. This permits graphical analysis of the data and estimation of the shorter half-life as indicated.

Decay of Chains. If the decay of an unstable nuclide gives rise to an unstable product nuclide, the activity of the latter may be expected to contribute to the total activity in a manner characteristic of its nuclear properties of half-life and decay reaction. The decay of the parent may be described by the simple first-order relation

$$\frac{dN_1}{dt} = -\lambda_1 N_1 \tag{4.11}$$

but the rate of change of number of daughter atoms is given

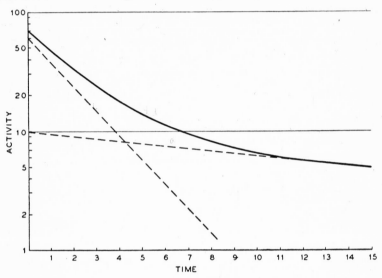

FIG. 4.18. Independent decay ($\lambda_a = 10\,\lambda_b$).

by two terms, one for formation from the

$$\frac{dN_2}{dt} = \lambda_1 N_1 - \lambda_2 N_2 \tag{4.12}$$

parent, and one for its own decay. The subscripts 1 and 2 refer to parent and daughter respectively. Using the previously derived relation for the dependence of N_1 on t, equation 4.12 may be integrated to yield

$$N_2 = \frac{\lambda_1 N_1{}^0}{\lambda_2 - \lambda_1}\,(e^{-\lambda_1 t} - e^{-\lambda_2 t}) + N_2{}^0 e^{-\lambda_2 t} \tag{4.13}$$

for the number of daughter atoms as a function of time. N^0_1 and N^0_2 are the numbers of parent and daughter atoms at zero time. The response of a detecting device will depend upon the total activity of parent and daughter, where each activity is multiplied by the appropriate efficiency term. The general expressions for parent and daughter activity are

$$A_1 = A_1^0 e^{-\lambda_1 t}$$

$$A_2 = \frac{\lambda_2}{\lambda_2 - \lambda_1} A_1^0 (e^{-\lambda_1 t} - e^{-\lambda_2 t}) + A_2^0 e^{-\lambda_2 t} \qquad (4.14)$$

When the decay constant of the parent is very small, so that decay of the parent is not observable during the period of the

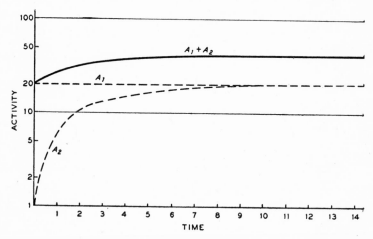

FIG. 4.19.   Growth curve λ_1 very small.

experiment, a condition known as *secular equilibrium* may be approached. Equation 4.14 is modified to the form

$$A_2 = A_1^0 (1 - e^{-\lambda_2 t}) \qquad (4.15)$$

with the added condition that $N^0_2 = 0$. Fig. 4.19 shows the time dependence of parent, daughter, and total activity in this case. The time axis is given in multiples of the daughter half-life. The observed response will depend on the relative detection efficiencies of the parent and daughter radiations. Secular equilibrium is defined as the state where $A_2 = A_1$, and the relative numbers of parent and daughter atoms will be given by

$$\frac{N_2}{N_1} = \frac{\lambda_1}{\lambda_2} = \frac{t_{1/2(2)}}{t_{1/2(1)}} \tag{4.16}$$

When the decay constant of the parent is smaller than that of the daughter, but still large enough to produce observable

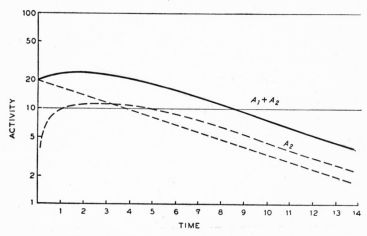

Fig. 4.20. Growth and decay curve—$\lambda_1 = \frac{1}{4}\lambda_2$.

decay during the course of the experiment, the steady state is referred to as a *transient equilibrium*. Fig. 4.20 shows the time dependence of parent, daughter, and total activity for the case where $N^0{}_2 = 0$ as given by equation 4.14. Again the time axis is given in terms of the daughter half-life and the relation $\lambda_1 = 1/4\lambda_2$ has been chosen. Note that for a short period of time the growth will be approximately given by equation 4.15, and that after a long time the daughter appears to decay with the half-life of the parent. The solution of equation 4.14 after several daughter half-lives (when $e^{-\lambda_2 t} \to 0$)

$$A_2 = \frac{\lambda_2}{\lambda_2 - \lambda_1} A_1 \qquad (4.17)$$

gives the relative activities of parent and daughter.

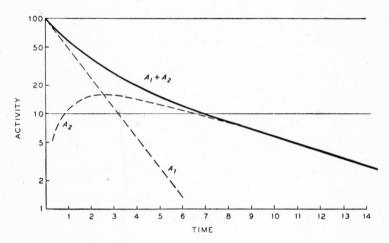

Fig. 4.21. Growth and decay curve—$\lambda_1 = 4\lambda_2$.

When the decay constant of the parent is greater than that of the daughter, no "equilibrium" is achieved where the two activities are related in some simple fashion. The activity-time relationship for a typical case is given in Fig. 4.21, taking $N^0_2 = 0$.

UNITS AND STANDARDS

Curie. The curie unit (c) has been commonly used in stating the activity of all types of radioactive materials, although it is properly defined as the quantity of radon in secular equilibrium with one gram of radium. This amount of radon has a disintegration rate variously reported as 3.40 to 3.72×10^{10} disintegrations per second. Because of this uncertainty, the arbitrary value 3.7×10^{10} has been recommended for general use. Extension of the curie unit to other members of the radium family is also proper. The use of the number 3.7×10^{10} as a unit disintegration rate for substances other than the radium family is quite common, although improper.

Rutherford. The rutherford (rd) has been proposed as a general disintegration rate unit and is defined as 10^6 disintegrations per second. Its size is more in keeping with the amounts of radioactive materials commonly used in laboratory work, and the uncertainty in the numerical value of the curie is avoided.

Standards. Considerable effort has been expended to measure the absolute disintegration rate of a few well-known beta emitters, among which are 5-year Co^{60} and 5-day Bi^{210} (RaE) (in equilibrium with 22-year Pb^{210} (RaD)), in order that these substances may be used as absolute beta standards. The first nuclide mentioned is produced through neutron capture by stable Co^{59}, and the determination of the absolute disintegration rate requires a very careful evaluation of all of the various factors contributing to counting efficiency such as geometry, absorption, etc. The nuclide Bi^{210} is a member of the radium family, and its disintegration rate, when in equilibrium with the earlier members of the chain, may be determined from the radon content of the source material. Standards of these types may be purchased from the U. S. Bureau of Standards.

A short-lived standard may be prepared by isolation of 24.5-day Th^{234} (UX_1) from a weighed sample of uranium.

Chemical aspects of such procedures are discussed in Chapter VI.

SUPPLEMENTARY READING

Evans, "Radioactivity Units and Standards," *Nucleonics,* Oct., 1947.
Fluharty, "Interaction of Isotopic Radiation with Matter, I and II," *Nucleonics*, May and July, 1948.
Glendenin, "Determination of the Energy of Beta Particles and Photons by Absorption," *Nucleonics,* Jan., 1948.
Hine, "Beta and Gamma Ray Spectroscopy," *Nucleonics*, Dec., 1948.
Seaborg, "The Neptunium ($4n + 1$) Radioactive Family," *Chem. Eng. News.* **26**, 1902 (1948).

NUMERICAL EXERCISES

1. From the data given below construct an absorption curve for the beta radiation in question and estimate the maximum energy. The data have been corrected for dead time loss, but not for background, which is 20 cpm in this case.

Absorber (mg Al/cm^2)	*Cpm*
15	3460
22	3360
38	3180
51	3040
69	2720
88	2380
153	1500
230	760
295	418
366	190
455	75
566	27

2. From the data given below, construct a beta absorption curve for the radiation in question. Analyze for the two components and estimate the maximum energy of each. A gamma component is present, as evidenced by a very penetrating component in small yield.

Absorber (mg Al/cm^2)	*Cpm*
15	15,565
22	13,072
35	10,452
55	8,014
71	6,729
87	5,981
127	4,257
231	2,618
370	1,495
443	1,053
559	729
630	571
871	361
1087	327
1299	332
1694	326
2115	324

3. The data given below represent the independent decay of two nuclides. Construct the decay curve and determine the half-life of each nuclide. The data have been corrected for dead time loss and background.

Time	*Cpm*	*Time*	*Cpm*
1 day	7,960	34	664
2	6,100	36	659
3	4,965	37	643
5	3,300	38	642
6	2,815	40	630
7	2,440	41	613
9	1,890	43	606
10	1,550	45	577
13	1,130	47	579
14	1,066	49	556
16	930		
19	870		
20	818		
22	780		
24	750		
26	725		
29	719		
31	699		

4. Construct the approximate type of absorption curve to be expected of a nuclide with the following decay scheme

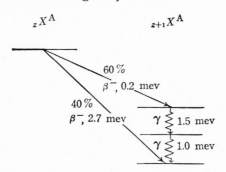

$_zX^A$ $_{z+1}X^A$

60 %
β^-, 0.2 mev

40 %
β^-, 2.7 mev $\gamma \lessgtr$ 1.5 mev

$\gamma \lessgtr$ 1.0 mev

5. A radioactive substance shows an activity of 1000 and 900 dpm when observed at the same time on two succeeding days. What is the apparent half-life of the activity and the specific activity of the pure nuclide?

6. RaE, a beta-emitter of 22-year half-life, is frequently used as a comparison standard. Assuming a counting precision of $\pm 2\%$, what is the maximum time over which the decay of the standard can be neglected?

7. A one-gram sample of radium is enclosed in an extremely thin-walled vessel, so that the alpha particles emitted by the radium and its decay products escape into an evacuated space of 100-cc. volume. In one year, what pressure (at 25° C.) will be built up?

8. A gram of radium is enclosed in a tight container with a free volume of 1 cc. What pressure of radon gas will be developed at 25° C, when secular equilibrium is reached?

9. What is the specific activity of radium in secular equilibrium with its decay products? What is the rate of energy dissipation (α and β only) of one gram of radium and its decay products?

10. A sample of Ba^{140} is isolated, but counting is delayed 10 hr and a rate of 2000 cpm is observed. Assuming equal counting efficiencies for Ba^{140} and its daughter La^{140}, correct the observed count to separation time.

If the rate of 2000 cpm had been observed 5 days after isolation, what would the corrected rate be?

11. Compute the disintegration rate of Te^{131} and its daughter, I^{131}, 10 hr and 100 hr after isolation of a sample of Te^{131} containing 10^5 dpm.

12. Compute the specific activity of potassium due to the natural abundance of K^{40}.

13. Compute the half-life of C^{14} from the following data: A sample of carbon, containing one atom per cent C^{14} is diluted by a factor of 10^4, then one milligram of the diluted carbon is found to have an activity of 10^4 disintegrations per minute.

14. If a sample of rock contains 1 mg of He for each 50 mg of thorium, what is the minimum age of this deposit? (See Chapter IX.)

15. A sample of uranium ore containing 15 grams of uranium also contains 5 grams of lead, which has an atomic weight of 206.083. What proportion of this lead originates from decay processes? What is the apparent age of this deposit? How much helium would you expect the sample to contain? (See Chapter IX.)

CHAPTER V

NUCLEAR BOMBARDMENT REACTIONS

Energetic particles and radiations are absorbed chiefly by interactions with the extra-nuclear structure of the absorbing material in processes of the types described in the preceding chapter. Although nuclear interactions constitute an absorption process which is negligible in terms of the total absorption, the unique and profound changes produced permit the recognition of such events in very small numbers. The production of an unstable nuclide, a frequent consequence of nuclear interaction, permits the use of the extremely sensitive detection methods for nuclear radiations, and the alteration of a few thousand nuclei may produce a detectable amount of radioactivity. This is in spite of the fact that no weighable fraction of the activating agent or absorbing atoms is involved.

The energy term in nuclear reactions may be estimated by the methods indicated in Chapter I. As mentioned there, mass data for unstable nuclides are rarely available, and therefore the energy term must be estimated from information on the stable nuclides. The reader is advised to review the principles of nucleus-particle interactions given there before proceeding to the discussion of experimental facts given below.

NUCLEAR CROSS SECTION

The rate of a nuclear bombardment reaction, in terms of the number of nuclei altered per unit time, will be proportional to the number of target nuclei and to the flux of energetic particles or radiations to which they are subjected. The proportionality constant has the dimensions of area and is known as the cross section. This property is a characteristic of the particular reaction considered and varies with energy as indicated previously.

Thin Target. The nuclear interactions easiest to detect are those leading to an active nuclide, since a few thousand such nuclei may be quantitatively observed. If an infinitely thin sample containing n target atoms is subjected to bombardment by a beam of uniform particle flux ϕ, the rate of change of active nuclei dN/dt will be given by

$$\frac{dN}{dt} = \sigma_a n\phi - \lambda N \qquad (5.1)$$

where σ_a is the activation cross section, and the second term accounts for decay of the unstable nuclide. Taking $N = 0$ at zero time, the integrated form of this equation is

$$N = \frac{\sigma_a n\phi}{\lambda} (1 - e^{-\lambda t})$$

$$A = \sigma_a n\phi (1 - e^{-\lambda t}) \qquad (5.2)$$

which is formally the same as equation 4.13 describing the growth of a short-lived daughter from a long-lived parent. In analogy to that case, bombardment for many half-lives of the active nuclide will induce a "saturation" activity given by

$$A = \sigma_a n\phi \qquad (5.3)$$

which states that the rate of decay is equal to the rate of formation. In a bombardment of one half-life, $e^{-\lambda t} = \frac{1}{2}$ and the activity has reached one-half the saturation value.

Thick Target. If the target is sufficiently thick to remove an appreciable fraction of the particles in the beam, this may be described by the differential equation

$$\frac{d\phi}{dx} = -\sigma n_x \phi \qquad (5.4)$$

where x is the thickness of target traversed, and n_x is the number of nuclei per unit volume. The cross section σ includes all processes which may remove particles from the beam, although, if the target is extensive, scattering is not included. The integrated form of this equation

$$\frac{\phi}{\phi_0} = e^{-\sigma n_x x} \qquad (5.5)$$

has the same form as Lambert's law for the absorption of light.

Since the energy of the incident particles may be considerably altered by collisions with the target atoms, and σ is a function of energy, this type of bombardment is not very useful in the measurement of activation cross sections except in the case of low-energy neutron bombardment where the average energy of the beam is not greatly different from the thermal energy of the target atoms.

For most purposes the target nuclei are limited to the stable or semi-stable nuclides occurring in nature. The probability for a given type of nuclear reaction varies widely, even among the isotopes of a single element, and values of the activation cross sections usually lie within a few orders of magnitude of 10^{-24} cm^2. This value is taken as the unit of cross section and is called a "barn."

TYPES OF REACTIONS

The first step in a nuclear bombardment reaction is the formation of an excited nucleus, either by energy transfer from the particle or radiation, or by particle capture. In the first case the excited nucleus has the same gross composition as the target nuclei, and in the second case the composition is that of a "compound nucleus" composed of the captured particle plus the target nucleus. The excited nuclei formed in this fashion are very short-lived, decaying by radiation or particle emission. A simple transition to a lower state of the compound nucleus is the most probable process, but the excitation energy is sometimes great enough to permit emission of a proton, neutron, or alpha particle.

The capture and subsequent particle or radiation emission are usually written in a single reaction as follows:

$$_0n^1 + {}_7N^{14} \rightarrow {}_6C^{14} + {}_1H^1$$

This is commonly abbreviated to

$$N^{14}(n,p)C^{14}$$

The various types of reactions will be grouped according to the type of particle or radiation which induces the reaction.

Radiations. The interaction of electromagnetic radiation with nuclei may be considered as an inelastic collision, in which part or all of the energy is transferred to the nucleus, elevating it to a higher energy state. This excited state usually decays rapidly to the ground state, but occasionally some intermediate state may be long-lived enough for experimental observation. Thus isomeric activities may be induced in stable nuclides, such as in the case

$$In^{115}(\gamma,\gamma)In^{115*}, \; I.T., \; 4.1 \; hr$$

When sufficient energy is imparted to the nucleus, a neutron (photoneutron) may be ejected; for example,

$$Br^{79}(\gamma,n)Br^{78}, \; \beta^+, \; 6.4 \; min$$

Unstable nuclides formed in this fashion usually decay by positron emission or K-capture, owing to the decreased neutron-protron ratio.

Although the threshold for photoneutron emission is about 8 mev for most elements, it is considerably lower for some of the light elements. The two reactions listed below serve as neutron sources, using radiations from a Van de Graaf generator or radioactive materials.

$$D^2(\gamma,n) - \text{Threshold, } 2.2 \text{ mev}$$

$$Be^9(\gamma,n) - \text{Threshold, } 1.7 \text{ mev}$$

Electrons. Electron-nucleus interactions are few and very inefficient. Inelastic scattering with In^{115} has been observed, and neutrons may be ejected from Be^9.

Protons. As with all charged particle reactions, proton reactions become more efficient with decreasing atomic number and with increasing particle energy, owing to the coulombic repulsion effect.

Proton capture has been observed with several light elements and is exoergic by several mev. Unstable nuclides produced by this reaction will frequently decay by positron emission or K-capture, because of the decrease in the neutron-proton ratio, as in the case

$$O^{16}(p,\gamma)F^{17}, \beta^+, 70 \text{ sec}$$

Proton capture may be followed by particle emission, most probably a neutron, because of its lack of charge. The decrease in the neutron-proton ratio indicates likelihood of positron or K-capture decay in unstable nuclides formed in this fashion, such as

$$C^{13}(p,n)N^{13}, \beta^+, 10 \text{ min}$$

Reactions of the type

$$N^{14}(p,\alpha)C^{11}, \beta^+, 20 \text{ min}$$

have been observed with light nuclei.

Deuterons. The deuteron has been very extensively used as a nuclear projectile. In the first place, since it has a mass twice that of the proton, it can be accelerated to greater energies in a cyclotron before the relativistic effect appreciably alters the resonance conditions (see equation 3.7). Secondly, in one

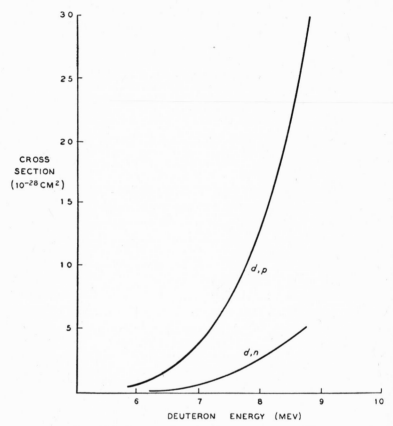

FIG. 5.1.[1] Cross sections for $d, p,$ and d, n on Bi[209].

very important type of reaction the coulombic repulsion effect is partially avoided. In this reaction, exemplified by

$$Na^{23}(d,p)Na^{24}, \beta^-, 14.8 \text{ hr}$$

[1] See Irvine (Ch. 14), Supplementary Reading.

the deuteron apparently does not actually enter the nucleus, but is "polarized" by the field of the nucleus and only the neutron enters. Unstable nuclei formed by this process may be expected to undergo beta decay because of the increased neutron-proton ratio.

With a somewhat higher energy barrier, the deuteron may be captured and cause emission of one or more nucleons. A

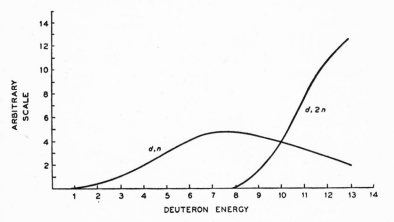

FIG. 5.2.[2] Excitation curves for deuterons on Fe^{56}.

neutron or, at higher energies, two neutrons may be ejected, as in the cases

$$Fe^{54}(d,n)Co^{55}, \beta+, 18.2 \text{ hr}$$

$$Cu^{63}(d,2n)Zn^{63}, \beta+, 38 \text{ min}$$

The decrease in the neutron-proton ratio leads to positron or K-capture decay in unstable nuclides formed in this fashion. A less probable process is the ejection of an alpha particle exemplified by

$$Fe^{54}(d,\alpha)Mn^{52}, \beta+, 21 \text{ min}$$

----

[2] Tatel and Cork, *Phys. Rev.* **71**, 159 (1947).

A few cases are known where deuteron capture produces a tritium ($_1H^3$) nucleus. Bombardment of B^{10} and Be^9 yields this product. In the latter case, neutrons are also produced in useful yields and the reaction may be used for neutron production. However, the D-D reaction

$$_1H^2 + {}_1H^2 \rightarrow {}_0n^1 + {}_2He^3$$

is fairly efficient at energies of a few hundred kilovolts, and has been frequently used for neutron production.

Alpha Particles. The coulombic repulsion effect is, of course, even greater with alpha particles than with protons or deuterons. This is partially compensated by the greater energy which this doubly charged particle attains in electrostatic acceleration devices. Therefore, at very high energies, where the coulombic barrier is relatively unimportant, alpha particles represent the most efficient particle for nuclear excitation.

The most common consequence of alpha particle capture is the ejection of one or more neutrons, depending on the energy of the incident particle. Such reactions are typified by

$$P^{31}(\alpha,n)Cl^{34}, \ \beta+, \ 33 \ min$$

Proton ejection is a much less probable alternate to neutron ejection, but has been observed with a few light nuclei as in the case

$$Zn^{67}(\alpha,p)Ga^{70}, \ \beta-, \ 19 \ min$$

Some very catastrophic nuclear reactions induced by alpha particles in the 100 mev energy region have recently been described by Seaborg.[3] The very energetic alpha may induce ejection of several neutrons and protons, forming a nuclide several units removed from the target substance. For instance the 37-min Cl^{38} is found among the products of the bombard-

---

[3] Seaborg, *Chem. Eng. News* **25**, 2319 (1947) ; *Phys. Rev.* **74**, 1189 (1948).

ment of arsenic with 400 mev alpha particles. The reaction might be written

$$_{33}As^{75}(\alpha, 18p, 23n)Cl^{38}$$

The products of such bombardments are quite varied, and nuclides of atomic number down to 20 have been identified in the bombardment of heavy elements such as bismuth and lead.

Neutrons. Several usable neutron-producing reactions have been mentioned above. In addition the nuclear fission reaction (see p. 150) has lately increased by many orders of magnitude the available flux of neutrons.

Since there is no coulombic barrier for the interaction of a neutron with a nucleus, some types of neutron reactions may occur readily with neutrons of vanishingly small energy. In fact, the neutron capture cross section is inversely proportional to the neutron velocity in the low-energy region. At certain energies, strong resonance absorption may considerably increase the cross section (see Fig. 5.3).

The neutron-producing reactions previously mentioned all give rise to neutrons of considerable kinetic energy, either because of the exoergic nature of the reactions or because of the kinetic energy of the reactants. These fast neutrons can be "moderated" to thermal energies by elastic collisions with atomic nuclei. Simple dynamical considerations indicate that protons will be the most efficient moderating medium. Slow or thermal neutrons will have approximately a Maxwellian distribution of velocities and are usually more readily captured by stable nuclei than are fast neutrons.

The radiative capture of a thermal neutron is exoergic by 8-10 mev with most stable nuclei, since it is the reverse of the γ, n reaction. This reaction can be used to produce unstable nuclides of almost every element, with the capture cross sections indicated in the nuclide chart of the Appendix. Unstable nuclides produced in this fashion usually show beta decay, as in the case

$$I^{127}(n, \gamma) I^{128}, \beta^-, 25 \text{ min}$$

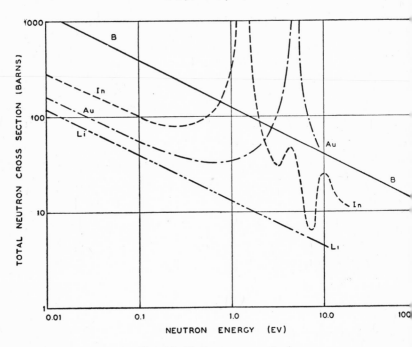

FIG. 5.3. Neutron cross section[4].

Inelastic neutron-nucleus collision gives rise to observable isomeric states in several cases, such as

$$Sr^{87}(n, n) Sr^{87*}, I.T., 2.7 \text{ hr}$$

Energetic neutrons may impart enough energy to a nucleus to cause neutron ejection, in analogy to the γ, n reaction, and

4 Goldsmith, Ibser and Feld, Appendix C, *The Science and Engineering of Nuclear Power*, Addison-Wesley, Cambridge, Mass., 1947.

as with that reaction, an energy threshold of about 8 mev is expected in most cases. The decreased neutron-proton ratio in nuclides produced in this way indicates that positron or K-capture decay is most probable, as in the case

$$Co^{59}(n, 2n)Co^{58}, \beta+, 72 \text{ days}$$

The ejection of a proton, except in a few cases, is a rather improbable result of neutron bombardment. When the reaction occurs at low neutron energies, it may be attributed to a resonance absorption process forming a nuclear energy state especially suited to proton ejection as in the cases

$$S^{32}(n, p)P^{32}, \beta-, 14.3 \text{ days}$$

and

$$N^{14}(n, p)C^{14}, \beta-, 5500 \text{ years}$$

The ejection of an alpha particle after neutron capture is also a rather inefficient reaction, owing to the coulombic barriers. It is observed chiefly with the elements of low atomic number, such as

$$Na^{23}(n, a)F^{20}, \beta-, 72 \text{ sec}$$

ARTIFICIAL ELEMENTS

Prior to the discovery of artificial radioactivity, some eighty-eight elements were known, either as stable and semi-stable nuclides present in weighable quantities, or as members of the natural decay chains beginning with uranium and thorium. Elements 85 and 87 were unknown, and considerable doubt as to the existence of stable forms of elements 43 and 61 was felt. No elements beyond uranium were known.

The transmutations accomplished by the various reactions given in the preceding section offer opportunities for synthesis of certain isotopes of these "artificial" elements. If they do not occur in nature, their isotopes may be presumed to be unstable, rendering them detectable even in the minute quantities produced by the bombardment reactions.

Element 43.[5] Slow neutron bombardment frequently produces an unstable nuclide which decays by beta emission. This latter process is accompanied by an increase in atomic number, and therefore the n, γ reaction on Mo^{99} can lead to the formation of an isotope of element 43 as follows:

$$_{42}Mo^{98}(n, \gamma)_{42}Mo^{99} \xrightarrow[\text{67 hr}]{\beta^-} _{43}Tc^{99*} \xrightarrow[\text{6.6 hr}]{\text{I.T.}} _{43}Tc^{99} \xrightarrow[\text{2} \times 10^6 \text{ years}]{\beta^-}$$

The long half-life of the lower state offers the possibility of isolating milligram quantities of this element. Tc^{99} and other isotopes occur in the fission product chains (see the following).

Element 61.[6] In a similar fashion, an isotope of element 61 can be formed after neutron capture by an isotope of neodymium.

$$_{60}Nd^{146}(n, \gamma)_{60}Nd^{147} \xrightarrow[\text{11 days}]{\beta^-} _{61}Pm^{147} \xrightarrow[\text{4 years}]{\beta^-}$$

Since this is apparently the longest-lived isotope of promethium, isolation of more than microgram quantities of this element is not likely.

Elements 85[7] and 87.[8] Since there are no stable or semistable nuclides adjacent to elements 85 and 87, they cannot

---

[5] The name Technetium (Tc) has been proposed for element 43. See *Nature* **159**, 8, 24 (1947).

[6] The name Promethium (Pm) has been proposed for element 61. See *Chem. Eng. News* **26**, 2346 (1948).

[7] The name Astatine (At) has been proposed for element 85. See *Nature* **159**, 8, 24 (1947).

[8] The name Francium (Fa) has been proposed for element 87. See *Nature* **159**, 8, 24 (1947).

be synthesized by the methods described above. An isotope of element 85 has been produced by alpha particle bombardment of bismuth as follows:

$$Bi^{209}(\alpha, 2n)At^{211}, \alpha \text{ and } K\text{-capt.}, 7.5 \text{ hr}$$

Element 87 appears as a short-lived member of the $4n + 3$ radioactive decay series. Short-lived isotopes of both elements appear in the artificial $4n + 1$ decay series (see Fig. 4.16).

Trans-Uranic Elements.[9] Elements 93 and 94 may be produced by various bombardment and decay reactions on the more abundant isotope of uranium, U^{238}. A long-lived isotope of element 93 is formed by the process

$$_{92}U^{238}(n, 2n)\,_{92}U^{237} \xrightarrow[6.8 \text{ days}]{\beta^-} \,_{93}Np^{237} \xrightarrow[2.2 \times 10^6 \text{ years}]{\alpha}$$

This nuclide is one starting point for the artificial $4n + 1$ decay chain.

Slow neutron capture by U^{238} induces a two-member beta decay chain, given later, which yields a long-lived isotope of element 94. Another isotope of this element may be produced by the reaction

$$_{92}U^{238}(d, 2n)\,_{93}Np^{238} \xrightarrow[2.0 \text{ days}]{\beta^-} \,_{94}Pu^{238} \xrightarrow[50 \text{ years}]{\alpha}$$

Element 95 may also be produced by a bombardment reaction on uranium, namely,

$$_{92}U^{238}(\alpha, n)\,_{94}Pu^{241} \xrightarrow[10 \text{ years}]{\beta^-} \,_{95}Am^{241} \xrightarrow[500 \text{ years}]{\alpha}$$

---

[9] The transuranic elements have been named Neptunium (Np), Plutonium (Pu), Americium (Am) and Curium (Cm) in order of increasing atomic number. See Seaborg, *Chem. and Eng. News.* 24, 1192 (1946).

but element 96 is obtained by bombardment of small amounts of element 94 produced in the chain-reacting pile.

$$_{94}Pu^{239}(\alpha, n)_{96}Cm^{242} \xrightarrow[\sim 150 \text{ days}]{\alpha}$$

The formation and decay properties of some nuclides in this region are indicated in Table 5.1.

NUCLEAR FISSION

The first recognition of the process of nuclear fission arose from a study of the numerous activities produced by slow neutron bombardment of uranium. Heroic attempts were made to fit these unstable nuclides into spaces immediately around the two uranium isotopes, since all nuclear reactions known at that time involved only small changes in mass and atomic numbers. As a result of experiments on the chemical behavior of these activities, Hahn and Strassmann [10] came reluctantly to the conclusion that they were chemically identical with elements such as barium and lanthanum, having atomic number about half as great as uranium. With this clue, the nature of the fission process was quickly outlined.

Fission Energy. The division of a heavy nucleus into two approximately equal fragments will be a highly exoergic process, as can be seen by reference to Fig. 1.8. The binding energy per nucleon in the region of uranium is about 7.6 mev, while for nuclei half as heavy it is about 8.6 mev, an increase of about 1 mev per nucleon. Thus two nuclei of $A = 100$ are about 200 mev more stable than one nucleus of $A = 200$. From further inspection of Fig. 1.8 one would gather that the fission of all nuclei above $Z \approx 100$ would be exoergic, and yet no nuclides undergo this reaction spontaneously at a large

---

[10] Hahn and Strassmann, *Naturwiss.* **27**, 11, 89 (1939).

TRANSURANIC NUCLIDES.

	242	241	240	239	238	237	236	235	234	233
96-Cm	α 150 days $Pu^{239}(\alpha, n)$ decay of Am 242	α 55 days $Pu^{239}(\alpha, 2n)$	α 27 days $Pu^{239}(\alpha, 3n)$							
95-Am	β^- 16 hr $Am^{241}(n, \gamma)$ $Pu^{239}(\alpha, p)$	α 490 years decay of Pu 241								
94-Pu		β^- 10 years $U^{238}(\alpha, n)$		α 2.4×10^4 yrs decay of Np 239	α 92 years decay of Np 238	K-capt. 40 days $U^{238}(\alpha, 5n)$	α 2.7 yr decay of Np 236			
93-Np				β^- 2.3 days $U^{238}(d, n)$ decay of U 239	β^- 2.1 days $U^{238}(d, 2n)$ $U^{235}(\alpha, p)$	α 2.20×10^6 yrs decay of U 237	β^- 22 hr $U^{235}(d, n)$ $Np^{237}(d, H^3)$	K-capt. 435 days $U^{235}(d, 2n)$ $U^{235}(\alpha, p3n)$	K-capt. 4.4 days $U^{235}(d, 3n)$ $Pa^{231}(\alpha, n)$	
92-U				β^- 23 min $U^{238}(n, \gamma)$	α 4.5×10^9 yrs occurs in nature	β^- 6.8 days $U^{238}(n, 2n)$		α 8.9×10^8 yrs occurs in nature	α 2.4×10^5 yrs decay of Pa 234	α 1.6×10^5 yrs decay of Pa 233
91-Pa									β^- 1.1 min decay of Th 234 I.T., 6.7 hr decay of Th 234	β^- 27 days decay of Th 233
90-Th									β^- 24 days decay of U 238	β^- 23 min $Th^{232}(n, \gamma)$
	242	241	240	239	238	237	236	235	234	233

rate. The half-life for this reaction in U^{235} is about 10^{17} years in contrast to the half-life of 7×10^8 years for alpha decay The failure of the reaction is explainable in terms of a "liquid drop" model of the nucleus. The unbalanced forces on particles at the surface tend to make the aggregate assume the shape of smallest surface (spherical). In order to divide the drop (fission) the surface must be increased, which requires energy, and although the overall process may be exoergic, the required surface energy increase imposes a barrier analogous to the activation energy effect in chemical reactions. This energy can be supplied in some cases by an energetic particle or radiation, or by the capture of a thermal neutron. The naturally occurring nuclide U^{235} and the two artificially produced nuclides U^{233} and Pu^{239} undergo the fission reaction on thermal neutron capture. The cross section for this reaction in the case of U^{235} is about 400 barns. Bombardment of these nuclei and others in the same region with energetic neutrons gamma rays, and charged particles also gives rise to the fission reaction.

The ionization produced in a gas by the fission fragments has been used as a measure of their energy in experiments by Jentschke [11] and others. The apparatus used is indicated in Fig. 5.4. A very thin foil of a fissile element (uranium) is subjected to neutron bombardment. The energetic fission recoils travel in opposite directions into two identical ionization chambers, where the pulse size is taken as an indication of the energy of the particles. Neglecting the effect of any light fragments (neutrons, etc.) emitted in the process, the total energy of the two heavy fission fragments and the partition of energy and mass between them may be deduced, since

$$m_1 V_1 = m_2 V_2$$

and therefore

$$E_1/E_2 = m_2/m_1 \qquad (5.6)$$

[11] Jentschke, *Zeits. f. Physik.* **120**, 165 (1943).

Fig. 5.5 shows the energy and mass distribution observed when uranium is bombarded with thermal neutrons. The broad distribution of energies and masses observed indicates the variety of the ways in which the nucleus divides in fission, and the most probable ratio of masses appears to be about 141/93. For this most probable division the total energy of the two fragments is about 160 mev.

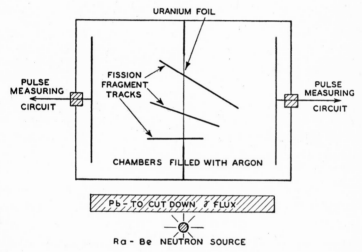

FIG. 5.4.   Energy of fission fragments.

An average of about two neutrons, with a total energy of about 5 mev, is emitted in the fission process, along with several mev of gamma radiation. These two items, with the energy of the heavy fission fragments, account for the energy released in the fission act. The exoergic absorption of the fission neutrons and the radioactive decay of the heavy fission fragments (see p. 162) also contribute to the fission energy, as shown in Table 5.2.

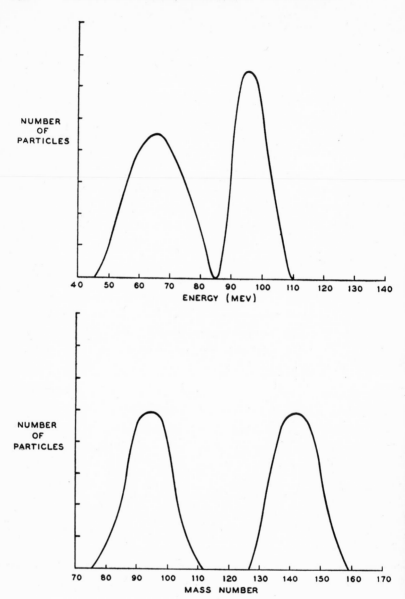

F IG. 5.5. Energy and mass distributions in fission.

TABLE 5.2. ITEMIZED FISSION ENERGY

Heavy fission fragments	~160 mev
Fission neutrons	~ 5
Neutron absorption	~ 10
Fission gammas	~ 5
Radioactive decay of heavy fission fragments $(\beta^- + \gamma)$	~ 20
	~200 mev

Fission Products. The two heavy fragments formed in the fission reaction (to which the term "fission products" is usually restricted) will have a neutron-proton ratio characteristic of the uranium region and somewhat greater than that of the stable nuclides around mass 100 (see Fig. 1.6). This neutron excess will give rise to beta decay reactions of decreasing energy as the stable isobar is approached. Choosing the most probable mass ratio of the fission products as indicated in Fig. 5.5, and assuming that the neutron-proton ratio in these two fragments is approximately the same, the fission reaction for slow neutrons on U^{238} may be written

$$_0n^1 + _{92}U^{235} \rightarrow 2_0n^1 + \gamma + _{55}Cs^{141} + _{37}Rb^{93}$$

The fission product nuclei formed in this reaction will give rise to the following beta decay chains. The first members are too short-lived to permit direct measurement of their half-lives and decay energies.

$$_{55}Cs^{141} \xrightarrow{\beta^-} _{56}Ba^{141} \xrightarrow[18 \text{ min}]{\beta^-} _{57}La^{141} \xrightarrow[3.5 \text{ hr}]{\beta^-} _{58}Ce^{141} \xrightarrow[30 \text{ days}]{\beta^-} _{59}Pr^{141} \text{(stable)}$$

$$_{37}Rb^{93} \xrightarrow{\beta^-} _{38}Sr^{93} \xrightarrow{\beta^-} _{39}Y^{93} \xrightarrow{\beta^-} _{40}Zr^{93} \xrightarrow[2.5 \text{ min}]{\beta^-} _{41}Cb^{93} \text{(stable)}$$

Since the chain members are isobaric, a determination of the relative amounts of some of the longer-lived members of different chains can be used for direct establishment of a mass distribution or "fission yield" curve. The chemical methods involved in this type of determination are discussed in the next chapter. Similar determinations of yield along the individual chains indicate that there is some variation in the neutron-proton ratio, i.e., in a given mass chain, the primary fission yield is distributed among several nuclides.

In a few of the fission product decay chains there occur unstable nuclides which emit neutrons in their decay reactions. As indicated in Chapter IV, neutron decay occurs as a result of the formation of a highly excited state of the daughter nucleus following a beta decay reaction. The neutron emission process usually follows rapidly after the formation of the excited state, and so the apparent half-life for this decay is that of the beta-emitting parent. Table 5.3 lists a few of the known neutron-emitters and their half-lives. Note that the half-lives are all rather short and that this reaction occurs

TABLE 5.3. SOME NEUTRON EMITTERS IN FISSION CHAINS

Probable Parent Nuclide	Half-Period
Br^{87}	55.6 sec
I^{137}	22 sec
?	5 sec

with nuclei well removed from a stable neutron-proton ratio. It is only in such cases that the beta decay energy will be sufficient to give the necessary excitation energy (several mev) to the daughter nucleus. Although these decay reactions only occur in a small fraction of the fission chains, the "delayed neutrons" arising from them are very important to the operation of a chain-reacting pile.

Nuclear Chain Reactions. Among the many exoergic nuclear reactions known, the fission process is unique not only in the magnitude of the energy term, but also in that the reaction gives rise to agents capable of repeating the reaction. These are, of course, the fission neutrons.

If, in a large mass of some fissile nuclide such as U^{235}, a single nucleus undergoes fission, the fission neutrons released in the reaction are available to cause further reactions. Since the fission process produces about two neutrons on the average, these may each cause another fission in the ideal case. Each succeeding generation of fissions may therefore be larger by a factor of two if no neutrons are lost.

In order to achieve maximum efficiency in inducing fission, the energetic fission neutrons must be moderated to thermal velocities, since the neutron capture cross section increases with decreasing energies. The moderation may be accomplished by collision with uranium nuclei, or with the nuclei of a substance specifically chosen to fulfill this function. In the latter case, the fissile material may be distributed in a quantity of the moderator as indicated in Fig. 5.6. The sketch is a cross-sectional view showing rods or bars of the fissile material constituting a regular lattice in the moderator. The spacing is determined by the path length required to bring the fast neutrons to thermal velocities.

The criterion of a self-sustaining chain reaction is the neutron inventory in the device. If the number of neutrons increases with time the fission rate, and therefore the energy output, will increase. Each succeeding generation of fissions will be larger, and a reaction of explosive violence will be achieved unless some natural or artificial agent intervenes. On the other hand, if each generation of neutrons causes so few fissions that the next generation of neutrons is smaller, the reaction will die out. A balanced state may be achieved where the concentration of neutrons and the rate of fission remains constant.

The neutrons of each generation disappear in one of three ways: (1) In a device of finite size, neutrons may escape at the surfaces. (2) Nuclei of the moderator and constructional materials may capture neutrons. (3) The neutrons may be captured by a fissile nucleus and thus perpetuate the reaction. In order for the neutron inventory to remain constant or increase, at least one neutron per fission must go on to cause

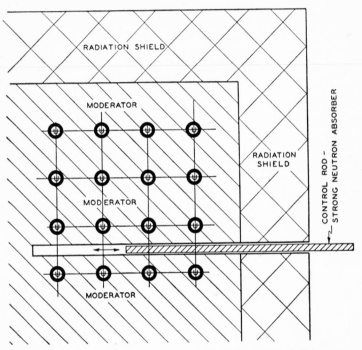

FIG. 5.6. Arrangement for nuclear chain reaction (pile).

another fission. Item (1) makes it apparent that there will be some "critical size" for the reactor above which the loss of neutrons at the surface is tolerable, and below which this loss is so great that the reaction cannot be maintained. Item (2) indicates that the moderator and construction materials must be chosen so as to avoid materials of high capture cross section. Although hydrogenous materials such as ordinary water would be the best moderators, the capture cross.section of the proton is too large. Heavy water (D_2O) and graphite have both been successfully used as moderators.

The rate of fission and the neutron concentration in the reactor may be controlled by the insertion of materials of high capture cross section, such as cadmium. By proper adjustment of the amount of such material, and therefore of the fraction of neutrons lost in this way, the reactor may be maintained in a steady state. Addition of more cadmium will stop the chain reaction and removal will cause the rate of reaction to increase. Since the fission reaction and the neutron diffusion processes are extremely rapid, the chain reaction would be difficult to control if it were not for the delayed neutrons emitted in a few of the fission product chains. Although these constitute only an extremely small fraction of the total number of neutrons per fission, the small delay in their appearance makes the rate of increase or decrease in reaction rate comparable to the half-life of their emission.

Nuclear Power. The fission of each U^{235} nucleus releases approximately 200 mev of energy, and therefore, the fission of one gram of U^{235} releases 5×10^9 kg cal. This energy content is many orders of magnitude above that of any of our ordinary fuels or explosives, and the nuclear fission reaction is therefore receiving considerable attention as a military weapon and as a commercial power source. Official reports state that a nuclear chain reaction has been maintained at a power level in excess of 10^6 watts. This figure corresponds to the fission of approximately 3×10^{16} nuclei per second and to the consumption of 1.17×10^{-5} grams of U^{235} per second.

The principal item of the fission energy is the kinetic energy of the heavy fission fragments. These heavy particles have a very short range and cause dense ionization and excitation along their paths, which would be entirely within the fuel rods in an arrangement such as indicated in Fig. 5.6. In a metallic substance this energy eventually degrades to thermal agitation and may be removed by a cooling fluid passed over

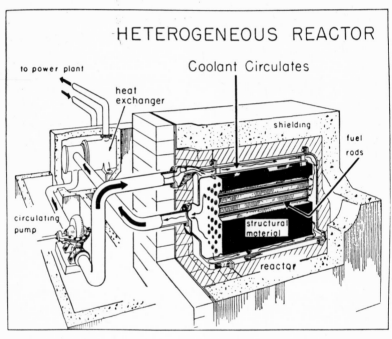

FIG. 5.7. Heterogeneous reactor with solid diluent and circulating coolant. (From *Science and Engineering of Nuclear Power*, 1947, edited by Clark Goodman. Reproduced with permission of the publishers, Addison-Wesley Press, Inc., Mass.)

the fuel rods. A more detailed drawing of an imaginary nuclear power plant is given in Fig. 5.7. Heavy shielding is necessary to protect operating personnel from the penetrating gamma radiations emitted in the fission reactions.

The radioactive decay energy of the heavy fission fragments, although not a major energy source, constitutes a very troublesome component of the pile radiations. Not only present during the progress of the chain reaction, it continues to be important after the reaction has stopped, owing to the relatively long half-lives of the unstable nuclides formed. Summarizing data for all the fission products, Way [12] has given empirical relations for the energy dissipation as a function of time in the form

$$E_\beta = 1.40 \ t^{-1.2} \qquad 10 < t < 10^7 \ \text{sec}$$
$$E_\gamma = 1.26 \ t^{-1.2} \qquad\qquad\qquad (5.6)$$

E_β[13] and E_γ are given in mev/sec/fission for a decay time of t sec. These equations may be used to compute the power dissipated by the radioactive fission products at a time t after the end of a period of operation T. The contribution of each increment of operation time dT will be given by

$$dE = 3 \times 10^{16} \times 2.66 \times (T + t)^{-1.2}dT \qquad (5.7)$$

for a pile operating at 1000 kw. Integrating this expression from the end of operation (shutdown) back to starting time we obtain

$$E_{\beta+\gamma} = \frac{3 \times 10^{16} \times 2.66}{-0.2} \ [(t + T)^{-0.2} - t^{-0.2}] \ \text{mev/sec}$$

or

$$E_{\beta+\gamma} = 64[t^{-0.2} - (T + t)^{-0.2}]\text{kw} \qquad (5.8)$$

Fig. 5.8 is a graphical representation of this function.

In further illustration consider the case of an individual nuclide such as 12.5-day Ba^{140}. The 140 chain occurs with a yield of 6.1%, and by applications of equation 4.13 we may compute that a pile operating at 10^6 watts will contain a Ba^{140} activity of 50,000 curies at saturation. This tremendous activity as well as that due to all the other fission products must be guarded against by heavy shielding both during and after

12 Way, *Phys. Rev.* **70**, 115 (1946).
13 E_β does not include neutrino energy, since this is not absorbed in the system.

the operation of the chain reaction. Considerable activity may also be induced in the cooling fluid if it has an appreciable neutron capture cross section.

The difficulties involved in the adaptation of nuclear energy as a commercial power source are very considerable. The capital investment in nuclear power plant probably will be very large, even when the development is fairly advanced. This is due in part to the great precautions which must be

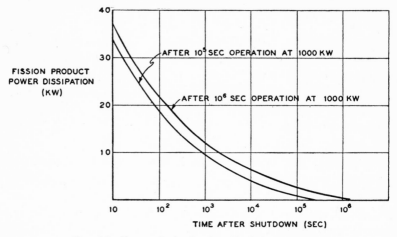

FIG. 5.8. Power dissipation by pile fission products.

taken to provide protection against the energetic radiations. A great many operations must be conducted by remote control, and internal repairs may be difficult or impossible. In addition, the necessity for having some minimum amount (the "critical size") of fuel material present indicates that a nuclear power plant cannot be made very compact or light. Three possible fuel materials are known. One of these, U^{235}, is a rare isotope of the element uranium and must be enriched by the tedious and expensive processes of the type described in Chapter II. The other two fuel materials, U^{233} and Pu^{239}, do not occur appreciably in nature but may be produced in a chain-reacting unit by neutron capture reactions and then isolated in complicated chemical processes. These facts make the cost per unit weight of nuclear fuels vastly greater than ordinary fuels and indeed put the cost per unit energy on the same level. Furthermore, the cost of present-day commercial power to a consumer is nearly two-thirds a distribution rather than a production charge. However, the great saving in fuel weight makes nuclear fuels still very interesting.

Production of Unstable Nuclides. The enormous fission product activities generated in a chain-reacting pile have already been mentioned. Many of these have the nuclear and chemical properties which make them useful in applied nuclear chemistry (see Chapter IX). Large amounts of the fission product activities may be isolated from uranium fuel rods by methods discussed in the next chapter.

The enormous rate of neutron production in the chain-reactting pile makes it possible to conduct the neutron capture reaction on a large scale without seriously interfering with the chain reaction. Many substances may be inserted into the device and activated by means of this reaction. A single "pile" at Oak Ridge, Tennessee, is supplying artificial activities to many laboratories in this country and in other parts of the world.[14] The service rendered by supplying radioactive nuclides at low cost to industrial and academic laboratories is very great.

A self-sustaining fission reaction may be maintained with natural uranium, whose isotopic composition is 0.006% U^{234}, 0.710% U^{235} and 99.28% U^{238}. In this case, a significant fraction of the neutrons are captured by the heavier isotope, pro-

---

[14] Isotopes Distribution Catalogue, Atomic Energy Commission, see *Nucleonics,* Sept., 1947.

ducing U^{239}. This nuclide is unstable to beta decay and so is its daughter, Np^{239}.

$$_{92}U^{238}(n, \gamma)_{92}U^{239} \xrightarrow[\text{23.5 min}]{\beta^-} {}_{93}Np^{239} \xrightarrow[\text{2.33 days}]{\beta^-} {}_{94}Pu^{239} \xrightarrow[\text{2.4} \times 10^4 \text{ years}]{\alpha}$$

The long-lived alpha-emitter Pu^{239} is accumulated in the uranium of the pile, from which it may be extracted by chemical methods for subsequent use as a nuclear fuel.

The drain upon the neutron economy of the pile imposed by the capture reaction given above requires the use of a larger amount of U^{235} to to sustain the reaction than would be necessary in its absence. The uranium, moderator, and other materials in the pile must be especially free from extraneous neutron-capturing impurities in order to maintain the chain reaction. In addition, the spacing of the uranium lattice is very critical, since U^{238} exhibits a strong resonance capture at a neutron energy of about 25 volts. Energetic fission neutrons leaving one piece of uranium must pass through sufficient moderator to take them below this energy, lest an intolerably large fraction of them be captured without inducing further fission.

The nuclide U^{233} may be produced in a fashion similar to that employed for plutonium production, although the source material is, in this case, the rather abundant element thorium. When placed in a chain-reacting pile, this substance captures thermal neutrons to form a two-member beta decay chain as follows:

$$_{90}Th^{232}(n, \gamma)_{90}Th^{233} \xrightarrow[\text{23.5 min}]{\beta^-} {}_{91}Pa^{233} \xrightarrow[\text{27.4 days}]{\beta^-} {}_{92}U^{233} \xrightarrow[\text{1.63} \times 10^5 \text{ years}]{\alpha}$$

Again the long-lived alpha-emitter U^{233} accumulates in the thorium, from which it may be chemically extracted.

The chemical separations referred to above are much more difficult than most, for two principal reasons. First, the extent of transmutation is always very small and the minute amount of the desired nuclide must be extracted from a large amount of source material of rather similar chemical properties. Second, for every gram of U^{233} or Pu^{239} produced, about one gram of intensely radioactive fission product nuclei is formed. The associated radiation effects make the operation of any chemical extraction process extremely costly and difficult.

SUPPLEMENTARY READING

Paneth, "The Making of the Missing Chemical Elements," *Nature* **159**, 8 (1947).

The Science and Engineering of Nuclear Power, Vols. I and II. Addison-Wesley Press, Cambridge, Mass., 1947 and 1949. The following chapters are especially recommended to supplement the present work:

1. *The Fundamentals of Nuclear Physics*, Evans.
2. *The Fission Process*, Deutsch.
7. *Chemistry of the Fission Process*, Coryell.
11. *Heavy Elements and Nuclear Fuels*, Irvine.
13. *Effects of Radiation on Materials*, Allen.
14. *Production of Radionuclides*, Irvine.
16. *Health Physics: Instrumentation and Hazard Evaluation*, Evans.

NUMERICAL EXERCISES

1. A 75-mg sample of a monoisotopic element of atomic weight 75 is subjected to a slow neutron flux of 10^7 n/cm²/sec for 13 hr. After bombardment, the sample is counted in an arrangement estimated to have an over-all counting efficiency of 10% and registers beta particles at the following rates:

End of bombardment	2000
+ 13 hr	1420
+ 26 hr	100
+ 39 hr	71
+ 52 hr	50
+ 65 hr	36

Compute the activation cross section.

2. Equal weight samples of iodine and arsenic are irradiated in the same neutron flux. The following reactions take place exclusively:

$$I^{127}(n, \gamma)I^{128}, \ t_{1/2} = 25 \text{ min}, \ \sigma_a = 6.8 \times 10^{-24} \text{ cm}$$

$$As^{75}(n, \gamma)As^{76}, \ t_{1/2} = 26.8 \text{ hr}, \ \sigma_a = 4.6 \times 10^{-24} \text{ cm}$$

Assuming that the samples are counted with equal efficiency, and that the active isotopes are simple beta-emitters, calculate the ratio of activities in the two samples immediately after a short bombardment. Calculate the ratio 5 hr after bombardment.

3. A 55-mg sample of Mn and a 75-mg sample of As were irradiated simultaneously in a slow neutron flux for 26 hr. The two samples were counted under identical conditions 2.5 hr after bombardment, and the counting efficiencies were assumed equal. The following data are available:

$$Mn^{55}(n, \gamma)Mn^{56}\beta^{-}, 2.5 \text{ hr } \sigma_a = 12.8 \times 10^{-24} \text{ cm}$$

Sample gave 5000 cpm.

$$As^{75}(n, \gamma)As^{76}\beta^{-}, 26 \text{ hr}$$

Sample gave 2000 cpm.

Compute the activation cross section of As^{75}.

4. A sample of antimony metal weighing 100 mg was subjected to a slow neutron flux of 10^6 n/cm/sec for a period of 60 days. The activity of the sample was determined twice after the end of bombardment, and, after corrections for counting efficiency, background, and absorption had been made, the following *total* activities in the sample were computed.

2.8 days after bombardment—1200 d/s.

60 days after bombardment— 133 d/s.

What are the capture cross sections of the two antimony isotopes?

5. A 100-mg sample of gold is subjected to an unknown slow neutron flux for a period of 24 hr. The sample is immediately counted at a geometry of 10%. The observed counting rate is $10,000\beta$ c/m. Assume 100% counting efficiency and a decay scheme of 1β per disintegration. The activation cross section for gold is about 10^{-22} cm². Calculate the slow neutron flux.

6. The activation cross section for 18-min Br^{80} is 8×10^{24} cm² and for 34-hr Br^{82}, 1×10^{-24} cm². Assuming that these are the only activ

ties formed by slow neutron bombardment of bromine, compute the number of disintegrations per minute in a sample containing 100 grams of bromine after 20 min; 20 hr bombardment in a flux of 10^8 n/cm/sec. If counting is delayed 20 min after end of bombardment, what disintegration rate will be present?

7. The cross section of U^{235} for fission by slow neutrons is approximately 400×10^{-24} cm^2. Estimate the total barium activity present in a one-gram sample of natural uranium after one-hour exposure to a slow neutron flux of 10^9 n/cm^2/sec. Estimate the activity at the end of bombardment, one hour later and one day later.

8. A sample of uranium is bombarded with slow neutrons for 10 days and allowed to decay an equivalent period. Samples of barium and strontium are immediately isolated from equal portions of the uranium and show activities of 1120 dpm and 200 dpm respectively. Assuming that the principal activities are 12.5-day Ba^{140} and 53-day Sr^{89}, calculate the relative fission yields of the 140 and 89 chains. What activities of these two nuclides will be present after 30-day bombardment and 30-day decay?

CHAPTER VI

CHEMICAL OPERATIONS WITH UNSTABLE NUCLIDES

CHEMICAL operations with unstable nuclides may be divided into three groups, according to general purpose: (1) the isolation and purification of unstable nuclides after preparation by some nuclear reaction, (2) the analysis of mixtures of unstable nuclides, and (3) the study of the chemical properties of the artificial and unstable elements. The nature of the operations will depend strongly on the amount of material involved. Because of the extreme sensitivity of detection methods, amounts ranging far below the regions of macro- and microchemistry may be handled. Such situations will receive our greatest attention in dealing with the radioactive isotopes of stable elements, since operations with larger amounts of these elements are already relatively well studied. In the consideration of elements which have no stable isotopes, however, the discussion will follow a more conventional pattern, describing the overall chemical properties of these materials.

PRINCIPLES

The weight or concentration of an active sample may be computed by application of the rate equations 4.5 and 4.7. Choosing as a typical example a sample decaying at the readily measurable rate of 10^2 disintegrations per second, with a half-life of 10^5 sec, we find that the amount of unstable nuclide present is about 2.4×10^{-17} mole. If no significant amount of the stable isotopes of such a sample is present, this extremely small value precludes some of the ordinary chemical operations such as gravimetric and volumetric analysis.

Using the term "tracer" concentration or amount to designate the extremely small amounts of material indicated above, we may inquire, by means of a few examples, how the chemical behavior of such materials may be expected to deviate from that observed at ordinary concentration levels. If the 2.4×10^{-17} mole of unstable nuclide were dissolved in one milliliter of water, the concentration would be about 2.4×10^{-14} molar. At this concentration a weak electrolyte such as $HgCl_2$ would be largely dissociated, but the halogens, with dissociation constants of around 10^{-20}, would be expected to remain in molecular form. On the other hand, the hydrolysis of molecular bromine

$$Br_2 + H_2O = OBr^- + Br^- + 2H^+$$

$$K = 6 \times 10^{-9}$$

would be very extensive, even in acid solutions, precluding extraction into organic solvents as with macroscopic amounts. In general, abnormal values of the true distribution coefficients are not expected at tracer levels, but, where the molecular form is different in the two phases, the net effect may be a function of concentration. For example, macroscopic amounts of iron are readily extracted from aqeuous hydrochloric acid solutions into isopropyl ether solutions, but at tracer concentrations this process is not very effective. It has been suggested that this behavior is due to extraction of $FeCl_3$ in the form of a polymer, which would not be appreciably formed at small concentrations. Finally, precipitation of trace amounts as insoluble salts may be feasible in the sense that the solubility product may be exceeded in certain cases such as LaF_3 ($K_{sp} = 3.4 \times 10^{-20}$), but it would be impossible to locate and collect the precipitate.

Isotopic Carrier. Many of the difficulties inherent in chemical operations conducted at tracer levels can be avoided by the use of macroscopic quantities of the stable isotopes of the element in question. In dealing with a mixture of unstable nuclides, such amounts of each element involved may be used, thus transferring further procedures to the usual macroscopic levels.

The use of an isotopic carrier depends upon the assumption that the unstable atoms will exhibit a chemical behavior identical with that of the stable isotopes, which are, of course, present in overwhelming excess. While the slight variations in behavior due to different nuclear masses need not concern us here, the fact that many elements are capable of existence in two or more mutually stable and separable forms (e.g., IO_4^-, IO_3^-, I_2, I^-) imposes an additional requirement. In order to undergo all chemical reactions in the same proportion, the stable and unstable atoms must be distributed among the various forms in the same proportions. Fortunately, the task of achieving this situation is considerably facilitated by the existence of rapid isotopic exchange reactions.

As indicated in Chapter II, an isotopic exchange reaction may be generalized as

$$A^*B + AC = AB + A^*C$$

where the asterisk represents the unstable nuclide present in very much smaller amount than the stable nuclide. With most elements the value of the equilibrium constant in such a case is not significantly different from unity.

$$K = \frac{AB \cdot A^*C}{A^*B \cdot AC} = 1 \qquad (6.1)$$

If the exchange reaction is rapid, the introduction of a macroscopic quantity of AC will quickly result in the attainment of the state where

$$\frac{A^*B}{A^*C} = \frac{AB}{AC} \quad \text{or} \quad \frac{A^*C}{AC} = \frac{A^*B}{AB} \qquad (6.2)$$

although no detectable quantity of AC may be transformed. Since the distributions of stable and unstable atoms produced by this process are identical, the existence of such a reaction permits the use of AC as an isotopic carrier for A*B. To illustrate: A rapid exchange reaction occurs between all the reduced states of iodine, IO^-, I_2, and I^-, and therefore any one of the three forms is a satisfactory isotopic carrier for the others. On the other hand, the exchange reaction between IO_3^- and IO_4^- is very slow. In such cases carriers for each state may be added or a single addition of carrier may be oxidized and reduced through the various valence states to permit exchange.

The rate of a particular isotopic exchange reaction may frequently be predicted qualitatively. Two valence states which form a reversible oxidation-reduction couple may be expected to undergo rapid exchange. On the other hand, the central atom of an oxygenated anion usually exchanges very slowly with the free ion, and exchanges between ionic and covalent forms are usually slow. Many isotopic exchange reactions have been studied, and the rates have been correlated with molecular structures. Information of this type is included in Chapter IX.

Nonisotopic Carriers. Precipitation reactions in aqueous solution are common as well as convenient operations in nuclear chemistry. Although they may be accomplished by use of isotopic carriers, this is frequently undesirable, since it considerably decreases the specific activity of the product. However, many instances are known where the precipitation or presence of a nonisotopic solid serves to remove or carry a considerable fraction of the active atoms from solution. Such phenomena have been called coprecipitation reactions, and they are roughly divisible into two classes: mixed crystal formation and adsorption.

Mixed Crystal Formation. The formation of mixed crystals is well known in macroscopic systems. The formation of an ionic crystal $A^+ C^-$ in the presence of another positive ion of similar size and charge B^+ may result in the incorporation of an appreciable quantity of the second ion B^+ into the crystal lattice, presumably in positions normally occupied by A^+. This phenomenon usually occurs when the compounds A^+C^- and B^+C^- are isomorphous as in the case of $ZnSO_4 \cdot 7H_2O, MgSO_4 \cdot 7H_2O$. Not only must the salts show the same crystal habit, but the substituting ion must have approximately the same ionic radius, in order for macrosubstitution to be possible.

The conditions for incorporation of trace amounts of material by this mechanism are considerably less stringent. Greater divergence in ionic size is permitted, and the macroscopic forms need not necessarily have the same crystal habit. For instance, macroscopic amounts of barium chloride precipitate as $BaCl_2 \cdot 2H_2O$-monoclinic, whereas lead chloride precipitates as $PbCl_2$-rhombic, and these substances do not form mixed crystals in macroscopic amounts. On the other hand, barium chloride precipitates carry trace amounts of lead very well.

If, in the formation of the mixed crystal $A^+ (B^+)C^-$, the whole solid phase comes to equilibrium with the solution, the distribution of A and B between the two phases may be described by the Berthelot-Nernst distribution law:

$$\frac{x}{y} = D\frac{a-x}{b-y} \qquad (6.3)$$

where

$a =$ initial amount of A in solution
$b =$ initial amount of B in solution
$x =$ amount of A precipitated
$y =$ amount of B precipitated

and D is the characteristic distribution coefficient. This relation implies that the two substances A and B will be uniformly distributed in the solid phase. However, if the formation of the solid phase takes place in such a fashion that each infinitesimal increment is in equilibrium with the solution from which it forms, but is thereafter fixed in composition, the differential equation

$$\frac{dx}{dy} = \lambda \frac{a - x}{b - y} \tag{6.4}$$

may be used to describe the distribution. λ is the characteristic distribution coefficient. The integrated form of this equation

$$\ln \frac{a}{a - x} = \lambda \ln \frac{b}{b - y} \tag{6.5}$$

due to Doerner and Hoskins,[1] is known as the logarithmic distribution law. It indicates that the substances A and B may not be uniformly distributed in the solid phase. For example, if the distribution coefficient λ is greater than unity, early formation of the solid phase will deplete the solution in A and the last solid formed will have a smaller proportion of A than the first.

Fig. 6.1 is a graphical representation of the predictions of the two equations in coprecipitation processes where various values of λ and D are observed. Note that when λ or D equals unity, the two substances A and B precipitate in the same ratio. When λ or D is less than unity, the logarithmic distribution concentrates B more effectively in the solid phase for a given amount of A precipitated. On the other hand, when λ or D is greater than unity, the homogeneous distribution concentrates B more effectively.

Precise prediction of the distribution law which will hold under various experimental conditions is difficult and, in fact, a distribution intermediate between the two ideal cases is

---

[1] Doerner and Hoskins, *J. Am. Chem. Soc.* **47**, 662 (1925).

frequently observed. We may, however, describe some experiments which favor one or the other of the two laws stated above. A very slow and continuous formation of solid by evaporation of a saturated solution leads to the Doerner-Hoskins or logarithmic distribution, since the slow formation

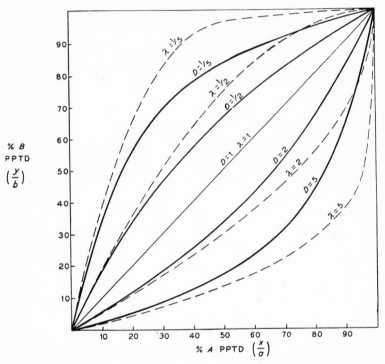

FIG. 6.1. Distribution laws in mixed crystal formation.

of the solid phase permits equilibration of the new surfaces with the solution and yet recrystallization of deeper layers is repressed by the continuous deposition. The coprecipitation of radium with barium chloride was studied under these conditions by Riehl and Kading [2] and, as shown in Fig. 6.2, the

[2] Riehl and Kading, *Zeits. f. physikal. Chemie* **A149**, 180 (1930).

distribution obeys the Doerner-Hoskins equation. With the same chemical system Mumbrauer [3] obtained a homogeneous (Bethelot-Nernst) distribution by extensive digestion of precipitates at constant solution volume and temperature (see Fig. 6.3). Under such conditions considerable recrystalliza-

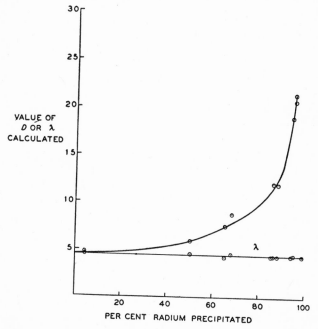

FIG. 6.2. Logarithmic distribution in precipitation of Ra-BaCl$_2$[2].

tion takes place, permitting equilibration of the whole solid phase with the solution. Experiments of this type lead to the conclusion that continuous precipitation with little digestion will favor the logarithmic distribution and that rapid precipitation (to form small crystals) with long digestion will favor the homogeneous distribution.

[3] Mumbrauer, Zeits. f. physikal. Chemie A156, 113 (1931).

At first glance it would seem that the distribution coefficient should be the same for both homogeneous and logarithmic cases and, further, that its magnitude might be predicted from the relative solubilities of the two salts AC and BC. Unfortunately, these simple generalizations are subject to

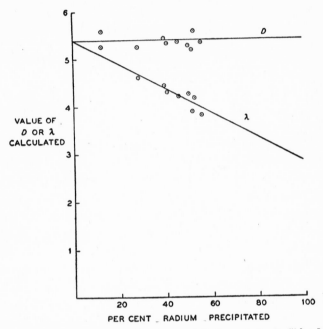

Fig. 6.3. Homogeneous distribution in precipitation of Ra-BaCl$_2$^{3}. *Legend:* Points represent values of D and λ calculated from Ba and Ra analyses at various stages of the precipitation.

many exceptions. The value of λ (heterogeneous) approaches that of D (homogeneous) only when the precipitation is accomplished very slowly. This is probably due to the entrance of a rate process, such as diffusion from the body of the solution to the surface of the solid, when the precipitation is carried out rapidly. As for the second generalization, the relative solubilities of the two salts involved cannot be safely used to predict the value of the distribution coefficient. In general, the more insoluble salt may be expected to concentrate in the solid phase, but even this statement has its exceptions.

Adsorption. The adsorption of solutes at macroscopic concentrations on the surface of solids can frequently be described by the Freundlich adsorption isotherm, an empirical relation of the form

$$\frac{x}{m} = kc^{1/n} \tag{6.6}$$

where

x = amount of solute adsorbed
m = amount of adsorbent
c = concentration of solute

k and n are constants characteristic of the nature of the solute and the adsorbent, and n is greater than unity. While the absolute amount of solute adsorbed decreases with decreasing solute concentration, the fraction of solute adsorbed increases with decreasing concentration. Therefore, at trace concentration levels, adsorption becomes an important mechanism of coprecipitation. It is sometimes possible to remove a trace species from a mixture of active nuclides by precipitation of a solid with especially great affinity for the desired element. More frequently, however, the phenomenon of adsorption lacks the specificity for such an application and may be used to remove a group of undesirable elements from the solution containing the species of interest. In such an application isotopic carrier for the trace element which is not to be adsorbed is usually added. The absolute amount of the element adsorbed increases in accordance with equation 6.6, but the fraction adsorbed (assumed identical for active and inactive isotopes) decreases. This technique, sometimes refrred to as use of "holdback" carrier, may also be employed to prevent contamination of a product precipitate by undesired activities.

Since absorption is a surface phenomenon, coprecipitation by this mechanism will be very sensitive to the character and extent of the surface involved. Hahn [4] and others have formulated rules to describe the influence of various factors on the adsorption of ions from solution, stating that an ion will tend to be adsorbed by a precipitate if that precipitate has acquired a surface charge opposite in sign to that of the ion to be adsorbed, and if the adsorbed compound is slightly soluble in the solvent involved. These generalizations are exemplified in Table 6.1. The excess of one of the precipitating reagents serves to give the surface of the precipitate a corresponding charge, a phenomenon utilized in the application of the Fajans adsorption indicators.

TABLE 6.1. ADSORPTION OF THORIUM B (LEAD)[4]

Precipitate	% ThB Carried
$CaSO_4$—excess H_2SO_4	90
$CaSO_4$—excess $CaCl_2$	5
AgI—excess KI	75
AgI—excess $AgNO_3$	4

Early investigations centered considerable attention upon the "radiocolloid" apparently formed by some of the thorium and uranium decay products at trace concentrations. For instance, solutions containing trace amounts of ThB (lead) or ThC (bismuth) showed discontinuous distributions of activity which could be concentrated by centrifugation or filtration. It is now generally assumed that this behavior, which is not uncommon with various other readily hydrolyzable elements, is due to adsorption on dust particles and other small solid

[4] Hahn, see Supplementary Reading.

particles suspended in the liquid phase. Careful purification of the solvent considerably reduces the effect, but tracer materials may still deposit on the walls of the container, leading to apparent "losses" of activity.

PURIFICATION AND ANALYSIS

Having discussed some of the special considerations which apply to operations with unstable nuclides, we will now proceed to describe, largely by example, some of the more common applications of these principles to the purification and analysis of unstable nuclides.

Nuclear bombardment reactions (see Chapter V) in practice rarely yield a single unstable nuclide. The nuclear projectile may induce more than one type of rearrangement. If the target element is not monoisotopic, a variety of products is possible from each of its isotopes. In addition, it may be necessary to bombard the target element in the form of a polyatomic molecule, introducing still more possible products. Some of the extraneous products may be present in insignificant amounts, others may be neglected through proper choice of bombardment and decay times, but there frequently remain one or more "contaminating activities" from which the activity of interest must be freed.

The ultimate use of the radioactive material to be isolated frequently requires a product of the maximum specific activity, and therefore the use of isotopic carriers in the chemical operations may be undesirable. If the nuclear reaction for the production of the unstable nuclide is one which involves no change in atomic number (for example, $n, \gamma,$ or d, p), isotopic carrier is present at the outset. When the activation is accomplished in a rather small projectile flux, this may make the specific activity too small for use. However, in favorable cases, even this unfortunate correspondence of target and product can be circumvented by use of the *Szilard-Chalmers reaction*, in which the unstable nuclide appears in a form which is distinct and separable from the large mass of unchanged target atoms.[5] Here again the ultimate use requirements will determine the advisability of the use of isotopic carrier.

A wide variety of methods has been used in the purification and analysis of unstable nuclides and, although they are largely based on the previous knowledge of inorganic chemistry, two new aspects should be noted: the common use of trace amounts of material, as previously emphasized, and the shift of attention to rather neglected portions of the periodic system, which is particularly notable in connection with the fission reaction. The following discussions will serve to illustrate these points and to enumerate some of the more commonly used methods.

Identification of Unstable Nuclides. When bombardment of a stable element yields a variety of activities of various energies and half-lives, the methods of physics and chemistry are combined to establish the atomic and mass numbers of the various unstable nuclides involved. The element tellurium, studied by Seaborg, Livingood, and Kennedy,[6] will furnish a suitable example.

Slow neutron (n,γ) or deuteron (d,p) activation of tellurium induces activities with half-periods of 25 min, 70 min and 9.3 hr. These were shown to be isotopes of tellurium by a chemical operation designed to separate tellurium from all neighboring elements. The tellurium target was dissolved in nitric acid, and macroscopic amounts of tin, antimony, and iodine were added as carriers. Iodine was removed by distillation from this solution. After removal of nitric acid by evaporating to small volume and adding hydrochloric acid,

[5] For a more complete discussion of this reaction, see Chapter VII.
[6] Seaborg, Livingood, and Kennedy, *Phys. Rev.* **57**, 363 (1940).

tellurium was precipitated as the metal by treating the solution ($3 N$ in HCl) with sulfur dioxide. Tin and antimony are not precipitated by this reagent. Selenium contamination in the target material might have given rise to one or more of the activities observed in the tellurium precipitate, since trace amounts of selenium might coprecipitate with tellurium metal. This possibility was ruled out by precipitation of selenium metal by sulfur dioxide in $12 N$ HCl, a concentration at which tellurium does not precipitate. This precipitate proved to be inactive.

Having identified the three activities as tellurium isotopes, the question of mass assignment remains to be decided. Fig. 6.4 shows the stable isotopes of tellurium and other near-by elements and shows that tellurium activities produced by d,p or n,γ reactions must be assigned mass numbers 121, 127, 129, or 131. The next element, iodine, is monoisotopic and, when bombarded with fast neutrons, yields the tellurium activity of 9.3-hr half-life. Since the only stable iodine isotope has mass number 127, and the nuclear reaction is probably $n,p,$ the 9.3-hr activity may be assigned mass number 127.

Fast neutron and gamma ray bombardment of tellurium give rise to two of the three tellurium activities, 9.3-hr and 70-min, but not 25-min. Since mass number 131 could not be produced by these reactions, the 25-min activity is assigned to this position. There remains only the decision as to whether the 70-min activity has mass number 121 or 129. Bombardment of antimony with protons and deuterons yields still another tellurium activity with a half-life of 125 days. This is presumed to have mass number 121, being formed by p,n and $d,2n$ reactions. The same activity, along with the 9.3-hr activity, is produced by alpha bombardment of tin (a,n reactions). Since the latter is already assigned to mass number 127, the 125-day activity must have mass number 121 and the 72-min activity is left to mass number 129.

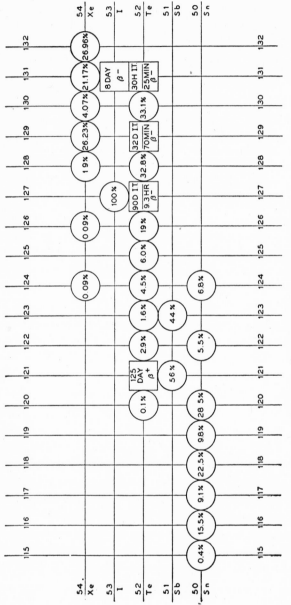

Fig. 6.4. Nuclides in the region of tellurium.

The distinct absorption characteristics of the four tellurium activities mentioned above, as well as the half-lives, serve as additional characterizations. In addition, the three nuclides of mass numbers 127, 129, and 131 have long-lived isomeric states with half-lives of 90 days, 32 days, and 30 hr, respectively. Chemical separation of these isomers will be discussed in the next chapter.

Genetic Relationships. Chemical methods are frequently used to establish genetic relationships, since parent and daughter (except in isomeric transition) have different atomic numbers and are therefore chemically distinguishable.

The nuclide Te^{131}, described previously, decays to I^{131}, which is a beta-emitter of 8-day half-life. This relationship may be established by extraction of iodine carrier samples from slow neutron-activated tellurium.[6, 7] After an initial extraction to remove iodine activity, successive extractions of iodine from aliquots of the tellurium solution at measured intervals of time establish that the amount of 8-day iodine increases rapidly in the first hour, then more slowly for a few days, reaching a maximum value 4 days after the bombardment. Then the iodine activity decreases, soon approaching its own 8-day half-life. Application of the equations for radioactive decay indicates that the iodine activity is a decay product of 25-min Te^{131}, which, in turn, is formed from its upper isomeric state, 30-hr Te^{131*}.

The three natural decay chains, whose longest-lived members are Th^{232}, U^{235}, and U^{238}, furnish many interesting and useful examples of chemically separable, genetically related nuclides. The occurrence of Ra^{226} and other decay products of U^{238} in uranium ores is well known and forms the basis for a considerable industry. The relative decay constants of Ra^{226} and U^{238} indicate that the maximum radium content of such

7 Livingood and Seaborg, *Phys. Rev.* **54**, 775 (1938).

ores will be about 1 gram in 4 tons of U_3O_8. This minute amount of radium is isolated by coprecipitation with $BaSO_4$. The barium-radium separation is achieved by fractional crystallization of $Ra\text{-}BaBr_2$, which is selected for the comparatively large divergence of the distribution constant from unity. In this case

$$D = \frac{(Ra/Ba)\,solid}{(Ra/Ba)\,solution} = 10$$

which indicates that the radium concentrates in the solid phase.

The immediate decay product of radium, the rare gas radon, may be isolated by micro-gas handling techniques. It is frequently sealed in small glass or gold capillaries, where, with its short-lived decay products, it furnishes a compact and intense source of radiation. The activity of this source at first decreases with the 3.8-day half-life of radon, depositing the daughter activities on the walls of the tube. The longest-lived of these, Pb^{210} (RaD), with its daughter, Bi^{210} (RaE), may be leached from the walls of such "spent" radon tubes as carrier-free lead and bismuth tracers. Although the radiations of Pb^{210} (22 years) are not easily detected, it is readily followed through the energetic beta radiations of its 5-day daughter and is frequently used as a comparison standard in activity measurements.

For separate use, Bi^{210} is readily isolated from its parent by electrochemical deposition (carrier-free) on nickel metal in hot hydrochloric acid solutions.[8] The nickel metal, with deposited Bi^{210}, may be dissolved in acid and the active species carried from this solution by precipitation of $Fe(OH)_3$ with ammonia, in order that nickel, which forms an ammonia complex, will not precipitate. Iron may be finally removed by extraction of $FeCl_3$ into ether from hydrochloric acid solution.

---

[8] Erbacher, *Z. physik. chem.* **A156**, 142 (1931).

Fission Products. The operation of a chain-reacting pile produces fission product activities measured in thousands of curies in the form of neutron-rich nuclides of mass numbers ranging from 72 to 158. Comparing the neutron-proton ratio of $U^{235} + n$ with that of the stable nuclides in the fission product region, we see that beta decay chains with an average of five members may be expected. Although the early members of these chains are very short-lived, they may occasionally be detected if possessed of some rather special properties. For instance, the presence of a short-lived rare gas member in a fission product chain may be established by sweeping gas through an uranium solution during neutron bombardment. Subsequent beta decay of the rare gas to the succeeding element, an alkali metal, may be detected through the deposition of the active daughter on a charged wire axially suspended in the outlet tube. The charged wire collects daughter activity by virtue of the positive charge induced during beta decay (see Chapter VII), but its small area picks up little activity by simple settling out of other active species which may be swept along in the gas stream. Most of these appear on the much larger area presented by the outer wall of the tube. The distribution of the active daughter deposit along the wire may be used to estimate the half-life of the rare gas parent.

In connection with the development of nuclear reactors, procedures have been developed for quantitative isolation and measurement of a number of the longer-lived nuclides produced by the fission reaction. Such radiochemical analytical methods may be used to establish a fission yield curve similar to that shown in Fig. 5.3. From a sample of uranium in which a known number of fissions have taken place a certain element is isolated, say barium, and the activity of this sample is determined. Since the only moderately long-lived fission isotope of barium is Ba^{140} (12.5-day), application of the usual growth and decay equations permits the calculation of the fission yield of the 140 chain. The yield in other chains is usually determined by comparison and the results are shown in Fig. 6.5.[9]

In brief, the isolation of barium may be accomplished as follows: To a solution of bombarded uranium, a known amount

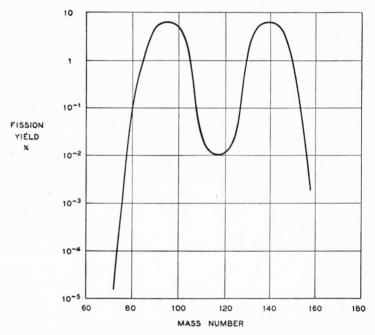

FIG. 6.5.   Fission yield curve for U^{235}.

of stable barium carrier is added and precipitated as barium nitrate with fuming nitric acid. This precipitate should be redissolved and reformed several times to reduce contamination by other fission products. Further purification may be achieved by precipitation of a small amount of iron hydroxide,

---

9 Plutonium Project, *J. Am. Chem. Soc.* **68**, 2411 (1946).

which carries readily hydrolizable elements forming insoluble hydroxides and trivalent rare earths. Such a procedure is known as "scavenging." The barium carrier is finally precipitated in reproducible form, say as $BaCl_2 \cdot 2H_2O$, for weighing and counting. The procedures need not be quantitative in the usual sense, since the activity of the sample may be corrected for "chemical yield" by multiplying by the ratio of carrier added to carrier isolated. Other radiochemical analyses follow this general pattern: addition of carrier, isolation by repeated precipitation of the carrier or a scavenger, and, finally, determination of chemical yield. In some cases, "holdback" carriers and complexing agents may be necessary to prevent contamination of the product by increasing the solubility of unwanted radiospecies.

Uranium which has been used as fuel material in a chain-reacting pile and which therefore contains large amounts of fission product activities represents a rich source of certain radioactive tracers. In the decay chains which have a fission yield of 1% or more (85-105 and 129-150) there occur many unstable nuclides with convenient half-lives and decay characteristics. Reference to the isotope chart in the Appendix indicates that unstable nuclides of the elements Kr, Sr, Y, Zr, Cb, Mo, Tc(43), Ru, and Rh in the light group and Te, I, Xe, Cs, Ba, Ce, Pr, Nd, and Pm (61) in the heavy group will be important contributors to the fission product activity for periods ranging from days to years. In the process of dissolving the uranium, volatile elements such as Kr, I, and Xe are usually lost, leaving a uranium solution containing large amounts (radiochemically speaking) of the remaining activities.

A particularly successful method of isolating individual fission product elements without isotopic carrier has resulted from the use of cation exchange resins.[10] One commonly used type, designated as IR-1, is a phenol formaldehyde polymer, containing free methyl sulfonic acid, carboxyl, and phenolic groups. The anion is insoluble but holds many ionizable, and therefore exchangeable, cations. When an aqueous solution containing cation M^{+n} is brought in contact with the resin, the cations in solution exchange with those of the resin in a reversible reaction which may be represented by

$$nRH + M^{+n} = R_nM + nH^+$$

The equilibrium concentrations of H^+ and M^{+n} in solution depend on the activities of these ions in solution and the respective affinities of each for the resin. In general, the cation-resin affinity increases with increasing ionic charge and decreases with increasing ionic (hydrated) radius. The equilibrium distribution of an ion between resin and solution may be altered by the use of complexing agents which alter the activity of the ion in solution.

The separation of fission products is accomplished by a technique very similar to that employed in chromatographic separations. The fission product solution, about 0.1 N in HCl, is introduced at the top of a bed of resin, where all major fission products except Ru and Te (present as anions) are adsorbed in a narrow band. This band of fission products is selectively eluted by the flow of solutions containing various concentrations of complexing agents such as oxalate, citrate, and tartrate ions. The presence of fission product activities in the outflow is detected by an ionization chamber placed near the outlet. Fig. 6.6 shows a record of the activity as a function of volume of eluting solution. Radiochemical analysis establishes the chemical identity of the nuclide responsible for each peak. Further refinement of this technique has been used to separate the rare earths and to identify unstable isotopes of element 61 (see below).

ARTIFICIAL ELEMENTS

Technetium (43). The chemical properties of this element were studied, using tracer techniques, by Perrier and Segré.[11] In analogy with other members of its family, Mn and Re, the element exists in aqueous solutions either as a cation (reduced state) or oxygenated anion (oxidized state). The anionic form, probably TcO_4^-, may be reached by $HNO_3 - H_2SO_4$ oxidation and is reduced to the cationic form in HCl solutions

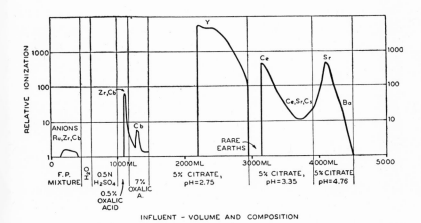

FIG. 6.6. Separation of fission products by elution from cation-exchange resin.[12]

by $SnCl_2$. Reduction to the metal may be accomplished by metallic Zn, Fe, and Ni. Trace amounts of Tc in the oxidized

[11] Perrier and Segré, *J. Chem. Phys.* **5**, 712 (1937); **7**, 155 (1939).
[12] Cohn, Parker, and Tompkins, *Nucleonics* **3**, No. 5, 22 (1948).

anionic form can be deposited on a platinum cathode, probably as the metal, and the deposition potential is -0.146 volt at pH $= 2.36$.[13] This corresponds to a standard electrode potential of -0.41 volt for the reaction

$$Tc + 4H_2O = TcO_4^- + 8H^+ + 7e$$

The cationic form coprecipitates with sulfides such as those of Re, Cu, and Cd in solutions up to 5 N in HCl. When the mixed sulfide with Re is treated with chlorine gas at 200° C, both elements volatilize. The anionic form coprecipitates with $KReO_4$ and $CsReO_4$. The distribution coefficients

$$D = \left(\frac{\text{activity}}{\text{mgRe}} \right)_{\text{soln}} \left(\frac{\text{mgRe}}{\text{activity}} \right)_{\text{solid}}$$

are 3 and 0.75 respectively. This oxidation state also apparently forms a volatile oxide, since the tracer evaporates with ReO_4.

Weighable amounts of the long-lived ground state of Tc^{99} ($\sim 10^6$ years) have been isolated by intensive slow neutron bombardment of molybdenum in the chain-reacting pile.[14] Microchemical studies have generally confirmed the earlier tracer work.

Promethium (61). The atomic number of this element indicates that it will fall in the rare earth series and will have $+3$ as its most important valence state in aqueous solutions. Separation from its neighbors, neodymium and samarium, will be exceedingly difficult. This great similarity to other elements of the series is the source of some controversy concerning the identification of this element as a stable nuclide, a

---

[13] Flagg and Bleidner, *J. Chem. Phys.* **13**, 269 (1945).
[14] Motta, Boyd, and Larson, *Phys. Rev.* **72**, 1270 (1947).

claim put forward by Harris, Yntema, and Hopkins,[15] who proposed the name *Illinium*. As mentioned in Chapter I, there are considerable grounds for believing that no stable isotope of this element exist, and therefore it would seem that the first isolation and correct identification of an unstable isotope of this element, by Marinsky, Glendenin, and Coryell,[16] represent the true "discovery" of this element.

Promethium activities Pm^{147} (3.7-year) and Pm^{149} (47-hour) were isolated from neutron-activated neodymium and from fission product solutions by use of cation exchange resins. A preliminary separation procedure involving repeated carbonate digestions served to remove most of the cerium, samarium, europium, and yttrium activities from the mixtures, leaving only praeseodymium, neodydium, and presumably 61. The most persistent containment of the purified solution was yttrium, and therefore the amount of yttrium in the final solutions was used as an indication of the effectiveness of these preliminary operations. The solution containing only elements 59 through 61 was next adsorbed at the top of a resin column and eluted with citric acid buffer solutions of pH 3. The activity versus volume eluted is shown in Fig. 6.7. Three major activity peaks occur, two of which may be identified as praeseodymium and samarium. A very small activity peak due to yttrium is shown on a magnified scale. The activity peak immediately preceding neodymium is attributed to element 61, since other rare-earth activities must be at least as small as yttrium and the 61 peak falls in the correct sequence with respect to the other two, i.e., the reverse of the sequence of atomic numbers. This principle is established in other elution experiments with rare earths. In addition, the activity peak attributed to element 61 showed the decay and absorption characteristics of a previously unassigned rare-earth activity.

---

[15] Harris, Yntema, and Hopkins, *J. Am. Chem. Soc.* **48**, 1585 (1926).
[16] Marinsky, Glendenin, and Coryell, *J. Am. Chem. Soc.* **69**, 2781 (1947).

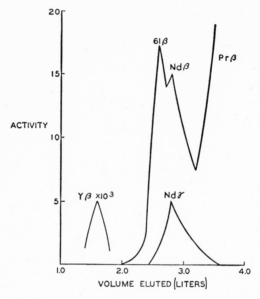

Fig. 6.7. Elution curve of intermediate rare earth fraction.[16]

Astatine (85). Investigations of the chemical properties of this element must be carried out at the tracer level, since no isotope of half-life more than a few hours is known. Such studies [17] have mostly used the 7.5-hr At^{211}. Although it is difficult to draw definite conclusions from experiments at such extremely small concentrations, the chemical behavior of the element appears to correspond well to its position as a member of the halogen family. At least three oxidation states are known in aqueous solutions, corresponding to At^-, At^0 or At_2^0, and probably two oxidized states forming oxygenated anions such as AtO_3^-.

Solvent extraction experiments attest to the existence of a form of astatine having zero valence. In this form the element

---

[17] Johnson, Leininger, and Segré, *J. Chem. Phys.* **17**, 1 (1949).

is volatile, reactive toward noble metals, and extracts readily from acid aqueous solutions into organic solvents. The zero state is reduced by SO_2 to a -1 state which is readily carried by AgI precipitates. In this form it does not extract into organic solvents. Ferric compounds or stronger oxidizing agents such as Br_2 or HClO may be used to attain the oxidized state or states. Oxidation by cold Br_2 produces a form which carries poorly with $AgIO_3$, but HClO oxidation produces a form which carries well with $AgIO_3$.

Francium (87). The chemical properties of this element have been studied on a tracer scale through use of the 21-min AcK (Fa^{223}).[18] In keeping with its position as an alkali metal it coprecipitates readily with rubidium and caesium salts such as the perchlorates, picrates, and chloroplatinates. In concentrated acetic acid solution, caesium acid tartrate can be precipitated without carrying francium. This is in conformity with the increasing solubility of this salt in the series potassium, rubidium, and caesium. Francium is the most electropositive element.

Thorium (90) and Uranium (92). A brief discussion of the chemical properties of these elements, which occur as semi-stable nuclides in the earth's crust, is appropriate here for two reasons: first, these two elements are the source materials for the manufacture of nuclear fuels; and, second, the intensive investigation of the chemical properties of these and succeeding elements has indicated that they are the first members of a new, rare earth-like transition series.

Thorium is a fairly rare element, constituting about $2 \times 10^{-5}\%$ of the earth's crust, occurring chiefly as the complex phosphate, monazite, and as thorite, $ThSiO_4$. The element is monoisotopic in the sense that only one isotope has a

---

18 Perey, *J. chim. phys.* **43**, 262 (1946).

half-life great enough to appear in weighable amounts. This nuclide decays by alpha emission to form the $4n$ series, ending in stable Pb^{208}. The radiation hazards connected with these substances must be considered in the development of refining processes.

In aqueous solutions, thorium is known exclusively as the quadrivalent ion Th^{+4}, forming insoluble salts such as $Th(IO_3)_4$ and $Th(C_2O_4)_2$.

Although the element protoactinium (91) occurs in minute but weighable quantities in nature, it depends for its existence upon its longer-lived parent U^{235} (see Fig. 4.16). Aqueous solutions of this element consist of the ions Pa^{+4} and Pa^{+5}, which are readily hydrolized and adsorbed on solid particles or precipitates such as MnO_2.

Three isotopes of uranium occur in weighable amounts: U^{234}, U^{235}, and U^{238}. All three are long-lived alpha-emitters, and the latter two are the starting points for the $4n + 3$ and $4n + 2$ decay chains. The abundance of the element in the earth's crust is about $8 \times 10^{-5}\%$, and it occurs principally as pitchblende, a uranium oxide, and carnotite, a complex uranium vanadate. Deposits of the former were extensively worked, even prior to the discovery of nuclear fission, for the purpose of extracting a decay product, Ra^{226}, used chiefly in medical therapy.

For recovery of uranium, concentrated pitchblende is commonly treated with concentrated $H_2SO_4-HNO_3$ to yield a solution containing a sulfate complex of the ion UO_2^{++}, free from impurities forming insoluble sulfates. Neutralization with sodium carbonate removes impurities forming insoluble hydroxides and carbonates. Finally, acidification with nitric acid forms a solution of uranyl nitrate hexahydrate (UNH), which is soluble in ether. Solvent extraction yields a very pure uranium salt, which ignites to the mixed oxide, U_3O_8. Reduction of this oxide to the metal may be accomplished with metals such as Al or Mg. The metal is the form commonly used in nuclear reactors, and in this application must be especially pure, particularly with respect to nuclides of high neutron-capture cross section. A gaseous compound UF_6, used in separation of U^{235} (see Chapter II), may be obtained by treatment of the oxide with HF and F_2.

Compounds of uranium corresponding to oxidation states +3, +4, +5 and +6 are known, although only +4 and +6 are at all stable in aqueous solutions. Electrochemical behavior may be summarized by the statement of standard redox potentials as in Table 6.3. The values given indicate that the uranyl

TABLE 6.3. STANDARD REDOX POTENTIALS OF URANIUM IN AQUEOUS SOLUTIONS [19]

Couple	$E°$ (25° C)
$U = U^{+3} + 3e$	+1.5 v
$U^{+3} = U^{+4} + e$	+0.75 v
$2H_2O + U^{+4} = UO_2^{++} + 4H^+ + 2e$	+0.65 v
$UO_2^+ = UO_2^{++} + e$	+0.05 v

ion (UO_2^{++}) is the most stable form in aqueous solutions. Trivalent uranium will be unstable with respect to oxidation by water

$$2U^{+3} + 2H^+ \rightarrow 2U^{+4} + H_2$$

and both U^{+3} and U^{+4} are unstable with respect to oxidation by air to UO_2^{++}. The pentavalent ion UO_2^+ is unstable in solution, disproportionating to U^{+4} and UO_2^{++}. The trivalent and tetravalent states form insoluble salts such as UF_4 and $U(OH)_4$ and coprecipitate with the analogous rare earth salts. On the other hand, the uranyl ion forms few very insoluble salts, a notable exception being $NaUO_2(C_2H_3O_2)_3$. The alkali metal uranates, such as Na_2UO_2, are sparingly soluble.

[19] Betts, *Proc. of Conf. on Nuclear Chemistry at McMaster University*, May, 1947.

Chemical separation of uranium from thorium is an essential step in the production of the nuclear fuel U^{233}, since this nuclide is formed by beta decay after slow neutron capture by Th^{232}. Irvine [20] has pointed out that precipitation reactions are not likely to be successful here, since hexavalent uranium forms no insoluble compounds under conditions that thorium will stay in solution, and in the quadrivalent state uranium resembles thorium very closely. The solution must probably be sought in solvent extraction methods.

Neptunium (93). After the discovery, by Hahn and Strassmann, that most activities induced by neutron bombardment of uranium were associated with lighter elements (fission) there remained at least one beta-emitter of 23-min half-life which was definitely isotopic with uranium. Its decay product, a 2.3-day beta-emitter, could only be an isotope of element 93, Np^{239}, first identified and studied on a tracer scale by McMillan and Abelson.[21] Later, with the tremendous neutron flux of the chain-reacting pile, it became possible to accumulate weighable amounts of 2.25×10^6-year Np^{237}. The low specific activity of this nuclide permits chemical operations with only moderate health precautions.

The earlier tracer-level experiments with neptunium [22] served to indicate that this element has at least two stable oxidation states in aqueous solution, one analogous to the hexavalent uranium ion UO_2^{++}, and the other corresponding to the quadrivalent uranium ion U^{+4}. However, a stronger oxidizing agent was needed to form NpO_2^{++} from Np^{+4} than in the case of uranium. These conclusions were reached from a study of the coprecipitation behavior of the neptunium activity with other heavy elements and rare earth precipitates. In

---

[20] Irvine, see Supplementary Reading, Chapter V.
[21] McMillan and Abelson, *Phys. Rev.* **57**, 1185 (1940).
[22] Seaborg and Wahl, *J. Am. Chem. Soc.* **70**, 1128 (1948).

reducing solutions, neptunium coprecipitates with rare earth fluorides such as LaF_3 and with $Th(IO_3)_4$. After oxidation by strong oxidizing agents such as $HBrO_3$, the activity does not follow such precipitates but on the other hand does coprecipitate with $NaUO_2(C_2H_3O_2)_3$.

Further work with macroscopic amounts of Np^{237} permitted the isolation of pure compounds of this element. The oxidation states Np^{+3} and Np^{+5}, as well as those mentioned above, were identified. In comparison with uranium, there is a general shift in stability toward the lower valence states.

Plutonium (94). The 50-year isotope of plutonium, Pu^{238}, was the first isolated,[23] and early investigations[22] of the chemical behavior of this element were conducted at tracer concentrations. The longer-lived isotope Pu^{239} was produced in weighable amounts by neutron bombardment of U^{238}, from which it must be isolated in chemical operations. The 2.4×10^4-year half-life of Pu^{239} leads to a specific activity of about 10^8 alpha disintegrations per minute per milligram and makes special precautions necessary in handling macroscopic amounts of the material.

Although tracer scale experiments are very informative in many respects, they cannot completely substitute for the usual studies at macroscopic concentration levels, and for the preparation and study of pure compounds. In order to insure as completely as possible the success of the proposed plutonium separation process, Seaborg[24] and his associates developed a remarkable program in ultramicrochemistry, experimenting with microgram quantities of plutonium in microliter volumes of solution. The success of their work is attested to by the fact that the plant scale separations encountered no major difficulties, although they represented a scale-up by a factor of

[23] Seaborg, McMillan, Kennedy, and Wahl, *Phys. Rev.* **69**, 366 (1946).
[24] Seaborg, *Chem. and Eng. News* **24**, 1193 (1946).

10^{10}. Similar techniques have been employed in the studies of other transuranic elements which are so short-lived as to preclude the preparation of more than microgram quantities.

Plutonium[25] in aqueous solutions may have the valence states +3, +4, +5 and +6, the tetravalent state being the most stable, as shown by the standard redox potentials given in Table 6.4. In contrast to the case of uranium, there is little air oxidation of the lower states. In mildly acid solutions, the

TABLE 6.4. STANDARD REDOX POTENTIALS OF PLUTONIUM
IN AQUEOUS SOLUTION

Couple	$E°$ (25° C)
$Pu = Pu^{+3}$	+0.5
$Pu^{+3} = Pu^{+4} + e$	—0.7 v
$2H_2O + Pu^{+4} = PuO_2^{++} + 4H^+ + 2e$	—1.0 v

+4 state disproportionates appreciably to +3 and +6. In solutions of low acid concentration the +5 state (PuO^+_2) appears, in equilibrium with +3 and +6. It is much more stable than the corresponding state of uranium.

Trivalent plutonium solutions are blue and do not reduce water, as in the case of uranium. The hydroxide $Pu(OH)_3$, oxalate $Pu_2(C_2O_4)_3$, and fluoride PuF_3 are insoluble and trace amounts of plutonium in reduced solutions coprecipitate with the analogous rare earth compounds.

Tetravalent plutonium may be formed by mild oxidation of the trivalent state, and its solutions are generally red-brown in color. The hydroxide $Pu(OH)_4$ is a weaker base than $Pu(OH)_3$, and consequently its solutions tend to hydrolyze readily and adsorb on glass walls, dust particles, etc. Insoluble salts of tetravalent plutonium include the the fluoride PuF_4, iodate $Pu(IO_3)_4$, and peroxide Pu_2O_7. Complex compounds

---

[25] Harvey, Heal, Maddock and Rowley, *J. Chem. Soc.* **1947**, 1010 (1947). See also Harvey, Supplementary Reading.

soluble in benzene are formed with acetylacetone, benzoyl acetone, and similar organic molecules.

Hexavalent plutonium (PuO_2^{++}) solutions may be prepared by oxidation of the tetravalent state with strong oxidizing agents such as $Cr_2O_7^=$, MnO_4^-, etc. In analogy to uranium, the compound $NaPuO_2(C_2H_3O_2)_3$ is quite insoluble, and trace amounts of plutonium coprecipitate with the uranium compound. Again, the alkali metal plutonates such as Na_2PuO_2 are sparingly soluble. A few compounds with organic reagents such as 8-hydroxy quinoline are extractable into organic solvents.

Separation of minute amounts of plutonium from uranium after production in a chain-reacting pile may be based upon the contrasting oxidation-reduction properties of the two elements.[20] Plutonium is more readily reduced than is uranium and in the the tetravalent state will coprecipitate with rare earth fluorides, while uranium remains in solution. However, such a process will be complicated by the presence of large quantities of radioactive fission products. Their presence requires that the separation process also "decontaminate" the product. This could be accomplished by precipitating a rare earth fluoride to carry fission products while both plutonium and uranium are in the hexavalent state. A second precipitation to carry plutonium in the reduced state would further decontaminate by leaving in solution those fission products which do not carry on the rare earth fluorides. The whole process would have to be repeated many times with completely remote control and heavy shielding. Waste and uranium solutions would require special storage, since they would be too active for ordinary disposal.

Americium (95) and Curium (96). These two elements have been isolated and studied by Seaborg [26] and his associates

[26]Seaborg, *Chem. and Eng. News* **25**, 358 (1947).

in the course of the development of the plutonium production process. Early investigations were conducted on a tracer scale, but later it was possible to isolate microgram quantities of these elements. The tremendous specific activities involved make the experiments very hazardous and difficult.

Curium and Americium have very similar chemical properties, existing in aqueous solutions exclusively in the trivalent state. They may be separated from the preceding elements by coprecipitation with rare earth fluorides in oxidizing solutions. Separation from each other is comparable to the separation of adjacent rare earths and was accomplished by use of ion-exchange resins.

The Actinide Series. As the properties of uranium and the transuranic elements were more thoroughly understood, it became evident that these elements are not analogs of the immediately preceding period. Rather, these elements exhibit the similarity among themselves which is characteristic of a rare earth-like electronic structure.

The electronic structure which characterizes the lanthanide series is exemplified by the configuration of its first member, as shown in Table 6.5. The filling of an inner ($4f$) shell gives these elements very similar chemical properties. Table 6.5 also includes suggested electronic configurations for the heavy elements, as proposed by Seaborg.[24]

Analysis of the emission spectra of uranium [27] definitely indicates the presence of three $5f$ electrons, in support of the configuration given above. The absorption spectra of the lanthanide series are characterized by the sharpness of the absorption bands, which are presumed to arise from transitions of the $4f$ electrons. Since these electrons are protected by the $5s$ and $5p$ shells, they are not subject to the perturbations of solvation and complex formation. Similar sharp bands in the

---

27 Kiess, Humphreys, and Laun, *J. Res. Natul. Bur. Standards* **37**, 57 (1946).

TABLE 6.5. Electronic configuration of the neutral atoms in the lanthanide and actinide series.

Lanthanide Series

At. No.	Symbol	4s	4p	4d	4f	5s	5p	5d	6s
54	Xe	2	6	10		2	6		
55	Cs								1
56	Ba								2
57	La							1	2
58	Ce				1			1	2
59	Pr				2			1	2
60	Nd				4				2
61	[Pm]								
62	Sm				6				2
63	Eu				7				2
64	Gd	constant	constant	constant	7	constant	constant	1	2
65	Tb				8			1	2
66	Dy				10				2
67	Ho				11				2
68	Er				12				2
69	Tm				13				2
70	Yb				14				2
71	Lu				14			1	2

Actinide Series [Tentative]

At. No.	Symbol	5s	5p	5d	5f	6s	6p	6d	7s
86	Rn	2	6	10		2	6		
87	Fa								1
88	Ra								2
89	Ac							1	2
90	Th				1			1	2
91	Pa				2			1	2
92	U	constant	constant	constant	3	constant	constant	1	2
93	Np				4			1	2
94	Pu				5			1	2
95	Am				6			1	2
96	Cm				7			1	2

absorption spectra of quadrivalent uranium, the lower states of neptunium and all the states of plutonium have been noted [28] and attributed to $5f$ electrons in these elements.

TABLE 6.6. VALENCE STATES OF LANTHANIDE AND ACTINIDE SERIES

Lanthanide Series			Actinide Series		
At. No.	*Symbol*	*Valence States*	*At. No.*	*Symbol*	*Valence States*
57	La	*III,*	89	Ac	*III*
58	Ce	*III*, *IV*	90	Th	*IV*
59	Pr	*III*, *IV*	91	Pa	*IV*, *V*
60	Nd	*III*, *IV, V*	92	U	*III, IV, V, VI*
61	(Pm)	*III*	93	Np	*III, IV, V, VI*
62	Sm	*II*, *III*	94	Pu	*III, IV, V, VI*
63	Eu	*II*, *III*	95	Am	*III*
64	Gd	*III*	96	Cm	*III*

Although chemical properties cannot furnish an unambiguous answer to the question of the electronic structure of the transuranic elements, the facts lend considerable support to the actinide hypotheses. Table 6.6 summarizes the known valence states of the elements of both the lanthanide and actinide series, with the most stable state underlined. The return to the exclusively tripositive form in curium is strong evidence that the series begins with thorium, since this represents a half-filled shell and is analogous to gadolinium. In further analogy to gadolinium, curium shows no absorption at visible wave lengths as do preceding members of both series. The greater variety of valence states in the actinide series is not unexpected, since in these higher shells transitions such as $5f$-$6d$ would not require as much energy as $4f$-$5d$. In fact, a mixed $5f$-$6d$ transition series has been proposed to account more readily for the various oxidation states.

---

[28] Kasha, MDDC 591; Harvey, see Supplementary Reading.

Final determination of the electronic states in the uranium region awaits the completion of extensive studies on the optical and magnetic properties of these elements.

Supplementary Reading

Cohn, "Radioactive Contaminants in Tracers," *Anal. Chem.* **20**, 498 (1948).

Hahn, *Applied Radiochemistry,* Cornell Univ. Press, Ithaca, N. Y., 1936.

Harvey, "The Actinide Elements and the Chemistry of Plutonium," *Nucleonics* **2**, 30 (1948).

Hume, "Radiochemical Activity Analysis, *Anal. Chem.* **21**, 322 (1949).

Pearlman, "The Transuranic Elements and Nuclear Chemistry," *J. Chem. Ed.* **25**, 273 (1948).

Schweitzer and Whitney, *Radioactive Tracer Techniques*, D. Van Nostrand Co., Inc., 1949.

Tompkins, "Laboratory Applications of Ion Exchange Techniques," *J. Chem. Ed.* **26**, 32, 92 (1949).

Chapter VII

CHEMICAL CONSEQUENCES OF NUCLEAR REACTIONS

We have repeatedly emphasized the magnitude of the energy term in nuclear reactions and given several examples where the energy of a particle or radiation emitted in a nuclear reaction is several mev. Up to this point it has generally been sufficient to identify this energy with the nuclear energy change, neglecting the very small fraction of the decay energy imparted to the product atom in accordance with momentum conservation. As small as this fraction is, it may represent a chemically significant amount of energy, since the nuclear decay energy is frequently more than 10^5 times as great as chemical bond energies. In addition, several types of decay reactions, such as isomeric transition and orbital electron capture, involve very important interactions with the extra-nuclear electronic structure and leave the product atom with the chemically significant potential energy of a vacancy in the inner electronic orbitals. Either of these types of energy, which might be called recoil and electronic interaction, can bring about in sufficient amount chemical changes in the product atom which would be unobserved in atoms with thermal energies. Furthermore, if the product nuclide is unstable, the extremely sensitive detection methods for nuclear radiations may be used to study the nature of such chemical changes in a number of atoms which would be undetectable by classical analytical techniques.

PHYSICAL BASIS

Recoil. Conservation of momentum in the emission of a particle or radiation by a nucleus permits us to equate the momentum of the nucleus $M_r v_r$ to the relativistic momentum of the departing particle or radiation thus (see equation 1.14):

$$M_r v_r = \frac{1}{c} \sqrt{E(E + 2m_0 c^2)} \tag{7.1}$$

Solving this relation for the energy of the recoiling nucleus, we have

$$E_r = \frac{E^2}{2M_r c^2} + \frac{m_0}{M_r} \cdot E \tag{7.2}$$

where E is the energy of the departing particle or radiation (very nearly the nuclear decay energy).

Gamma quanta, with zero rest mass, give a simple second-power dependence of recoil energy on gamma energy:

$$E_r = \frac{E_\gamma^2}{2M_r c^2} \tag{7.3}$$

Alpha particles, which usually have velocities small in comparison to that of light, can be treated with the classical form of equation 7.2:

$$E_r = \frac{m_0}{M_r} \cdot E_a \tag{7.4}$$

Since beta particles usually have velocities comparable with that of light, the full form of equation 7.2 must be used in computing the recoil energy. In addition, the neutrino emitted in beta decay will influence the recoil energy. Depending on the mass and angular correlation assumed for this particle, the recoil energy in a beta decay reaction may vary from zero up to the value computed by equation 7.2 (using the maximum beta energy). Fig. 7.1 shows the recoil energy as a function of decay product type and energy, using the maximum value in the case of beta decay. A typical case of $A = 100$ has been chosen. When an energetic particle reacts with a nucleus to produce another particle or radiation, e.g., reactions such as

(n,p), (a,n), etc., the momentum of the projectile must also be taken into account. If no particular angular correlation between projectile and produced particle is assumed, the recoil energy of the product nucleus will vary between the approximate limits

$$\frac{m_1}{M} E_1 + \frac{m_2}{M} E_2 > E_r > \frac{m_1}{M} E_1 - \frac{m_2}{M} E_2 \qquad (7.5)$$

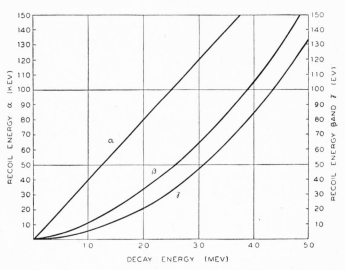

FIG. 7.1. Recoil energy in nuclear decay reactions ($M_r = 100$ amu).

where m_1, m_2 and E_1, E_2 refer to the masses and energies of the projectile and product particles.

The recoil energies given in the figure may be compared with chemical bond energies, which lie in the region 3-4 ev and the energy of thermal motion at room temperatures, about 0.025 ev. Thus it is seen that almost all known alpha decay reactions and many beta and gamma decay reactions will impart sufficient energy to the reacting nucleus to rupture chemical bonds in which the atom may be participating.

Internal Energy. When the recoiling atom is bonded to some other atom or radical, the total recoil energy computed above E_r will appear in part as transitional energy E_t of the whole molecule and in part as internal energy E_i (vibration and rotation). Energy conservation requires that

$$E_r = E_i + E_t \qquad (7.6)$$

and momentum conservation requires that

$$M_r v_r = M_{rx} v_{rx} \qquad (7.7)$$

where M_{rx} and v_{rx} represent the mass and velocity of the whole molecule. Simultaneous solution of these equations yields

$$E_i = E_r \cdot \frac{M_x}{M_{rx}} \qquad (7.8)$$

This relation indicates that only when the mass ratio of the recoiling atom and its bond partner is very great, as in the case of hydrides, will the internal energy be very small. Even in this case, subsequent collisions of the molecule will probably result in further conversion to internal energy.

Electronic Interaction. Several types of nuclear reactions may be expected to cause extra-nuclear electron loss by the reacting atom. The most obvious of these are the reactions in which an extra-nuclear electron interacts with the nucleus in the decay reaction, namely, internal conversion of an isomeric transition and orbital electron capture. In either case, the vacancy in the electronic structure (usually in the K- or L-shell) is followed by a cascade of electrons from more distant shells, emission of X-rays, and emission of several very weak electrons (Auger shower). Cooper [1] has calculated the probability of ionization after K-electron loss in bromine and finds that the average excess charge is $+4.7$ and that this is more than sufficient to dissociate a homopolar bond such as H-Br.

[1] Cooper, *Phys. Rev.* **61**, 1 (1942).

A departing beta particle has a finite though small probability of ejecting an electron from the extra-nuclear structure, according to Feinberg.[2] He calculates that this probability is $0.3/Z^2$ for interaction with K electrons and is "considerably larger" for outer electrons. Davies[3] has pointed out another possible source of ionization or excitation in nuclear reactions where the atomic number changes. In a process such as beta decay, the change in atomic number must be accompanied by appropriate adjustment of the electronic orbitals to the new states corresponding to the new nuclear charge. It is possible that some electronic excitation may result, but it is difficult to say what contribution this effect or the beta particle interaction may make to the chemical behavior of the atom, and, coupled with the uncertainty in the recoil energy in the beta decay process, they make quantitative predictions about the chemical consequense of the beta decay process almost impossible.

NEUTRON CAPTURE

The process of slow neutron capture, with its coincident gamma radiation, is one of the most widely observed types of nuclear bombardment reactions and frequently leads to the formation of an unstable nuclide. Since the active product and the target atoms are isotopic, any chemical change brought about in the course of the activation reaction may be useful in enhancing the specific activity of the radio-nuclide produced.

The Szilard-Chalmers Reaction. Szilard and Chalmers[4] were the first to report a chemical effect following slow neutron capture and the reaction they observed will serve to illustrate the chemical phenomena. They bombarded ethyl iodide

2 Feinberg, J. Phys. (U.S.S.R.) **4**, 423 (1941).
3 Davies, J. Phys. and Colloid Chem. **52**, 595 (1948).
4 Szilard and Chalmers, Nature **134**, 462 (1934).

with slow neutrons and then shook this organic liquid with an aqueous solution containing a small amount of iodide carrier. A considerable fraction of the active iodine (25-min I^{128}) was found in the aqueous layer while essentially all the unchanged target iodine atoms remained as ethyl iodide. Apparently the neutron capture process broke the carbon-iodine bond, liberating active iodine in a water-soluble form. That portion of the iodine activity which remains in the organic form is said to be "retained," although "reformed" would be a better term, since it is quite certain that the nuclear reaction induces bond rupture in almost every instance (see p. 211).

The Szilard-Chalmers reaction is well known with many organic halides and with organic compounds of other elements. For instance, triphenyl stibine has been used for antimony activation and cacodylic acid for arsenic. Certain types of inorganic molecules also show this reaction. Slow neutron bombardment of permanganates yields manganese activity as manganese dioxide, and bombardment of ferrocyanides yields iron activity as free ferrous or ferric ions.

Some empirical criteria for the success of such a reaction may be listed. (1) The element to be activated should be capable of existence in at least two mutually stable chemical forms. (2) These forms should not undergo rapid isotopic exchange. (3) The most suitable target form will probably be a fairly complex molecule or ion, or at least one which cannot readily be resynthesized under the conditions of the experiment.

Primary Processes. The capture of a slow neutron by a nucleus is usually exoergic by about 8 mev, this energy appearing in the form of one or more gamma quanta whose individual magnitudes are largely unknown. Taking the case of a 4-mev quantum, Fig. 7.1 indicates that the recoil energy will be about 85 ev (1900 kcal/mole) when the atomic mass is 100. Except in the case of hydrides, a large fraction of this energy is immediately available for bond rupture, and the newly formed unstable atom departs with a velocity of around 10^7 cm per sec. If two or more quanta are emitted in a random orientation, their momenta may partially cancel and leave the unstable atom with less than sufficient energy for bond rupture in a small fraction of the reactions.

Since the velocity of the recoiling atom is not greater than the orbital velocity of its outer electrons, ionization by collision cannot be expected. However, if any internal conversion of some step in the gamma cascade occurs, ionization is very probable. Formation of ionized active atoms in the reaction Br^{79} (n,γ) Br^{80} has recently been reported by Wexler and Davies.[5] They bombarded gaseous ethyl bromide with slow neutrons in a cylindrical chamber with a central rod. A potential difference of 4000 volts was applied to the rod and cylinder and the gas pressure adjusted to give a mean free path larger than the electrode spacing. Comparison of the active bromine deposited on the wall and rod in the presence and absence of the electric field indicated that approximately 20% of the bromine recoils were charged (positively). This ionization is assumed to be a result of internal conversion as mentioned above.

Hot Atom Reactions. The high-speed recoil atom or ion loses its excess energy by collisions with the atoms of its environment, eventually reaching thermal equilibrium with the system. In a number of cases it is quite clear that chemical reactions must occur while the activated atom is still "hot." A reaction such as

$$Br + CCl_4 \rightarrow CCl_3Br + Cl$$

does not occur at a measurable rate with photochemically pro-

---

[5] Wexler and Davies, Conference on Hot Atom Chemistry, Brookhaven National Laboratory, August, 1948.

duced "thermal" atoms and yet, as reported by Willard,[6] this reaction accounts for about 30% of the active bromine atoms when dilute solutions of Br_2 in CCl_4 are subjected to slow neutron bombardment. To take another illustration, in the bombardment of halogens dissolved in saturated hydrocarbons a small portion of the activity appears as alkyl halide. This is to be contrasted with the well-known thermal reaction

$$Br + CH_4 \rightarrow CH_3Br + H$$

whose activation energy is given as 17.4 kcal.[7]

Retention in Alkyl Halides. Since practically every neutron capture reaction must result in bond rupture, that portion of the active halogen which reappears in organic form must be the result of a re-formation reaction. As mentioned in the previous paragraph, hydrogen substitution has to be a "hot atom" reaction, but this is not the most important re-formation reaction. Radiochemical analysis of the organic activity has shown that it is largely present in the form of the target molecule (see Table 7.1), indicating that the re-formation reaction must be a halogen exchange process rather than hydrogen substitution. This reaction also must be a "hot atom" reaction since the "thermal" exchange reaction

$$X^* + RX = RX^* + X$$

is immeasurably slow at room temperature. This assumption is further justified by noting that the retention decreases as the alkyl halide is diluted with alcohol, which serves to "cool" the energetic atoms without reforming alkyl halide (see Table 7.1).

Libby [8] has given a reasonable description of the re-formation process in terms of the collision properties of the various atoms of the alkyl halide. A collision of the energetic

6 Willard, *J. Phys. and Colloid Chem.* **52**, 585 (1948).
7 Steacie, *Atomic and Free Radical Reactions*, Rheinhold, New York, 1946.
8 Libby, *J. Am. Chem. Soc.* **69**, 2523 (1947).

halogen atom with a hydrogen atom of the alkyl halide can show an energy transfer of from zero to a small fraction (1/80 in the case of bromine) of the recoil energy. The radical formed in this collision might combine with the halogen recoil were it not for its considerable remaining energy, which enables it to leave the scene of the collision. It is this poor energy transfer which is assumed to account for the absence of active dihalogen in the "retained" portion.

In contrast, the collision of the energetic halogen recoil atom with the equally massive halogen atom of the alkyl halide may result in energy transfer from zero to the total, the average being one-half. When the transfer is large, the recoil atom may remain in the vicinity of the radical which it formed and may subsequently combine with it to reform the target molecule. This reaction will be favored in the liquid phase, where a "cage" of molecules about the pair will keep them together and absorb any excess energy. In gas phase bombardments, the absence of this cage effect reduces retention to very low values (see Table 7.1).

TABLE 7.1.   RETENTION IN ALKYL HALIDES [8]

A.   COMPOSITION OF RETAINED ACTIVITY

Compound Bombarded	% Retention	Composition of Retained Activity %			
$C_6H_5Br(l)$	70	99.5	C_6H_5Br,	0.5	$C_6H_4Br_2$
$C_6H_5Cl(l)$	50	70	C_6H_5Cl,	30	$C_6H_4Cl_2$
$CH_3I(l)$	56	81	CH_3I,	19	CH_2I_2
$CH_2Br_2(l)$	57	75	CH_2Br_2,	25	$CHBr_3$
$CHBr_3(l)$	66	71	$CHBr_3$,	29	CBr_4

B.   EFFECT OF DILUTION BY ETHANOL ON RETENTION BY CBr_4

Mole per cent CBr_4	Retention (%)
100.0	60 ± 5
1.15	28 ± 5
0.74	13 ± 5
0.45	2 ± 2
0.064	0 ± 2

TABLE 7.1. (Continued)

C. Effect of Vaporization on Retention by Organic Halides

Compound	Retention (l)%	Retention (g)%	Pressure(cmHg)
C_2H_5Br	75	4.5 ± 0.4	39 + 37 air
CH_2BrCH_2Br	31	6.9 ± 0.6	4 + 72 air

The substance of this argument is, therefore, that only in collisions with the halogen atom of the alkyl halide can the recoil atom be expected to lose enough energy to be trapped in a liquid cage and combine with the radical formed by this collision. Of course, in a certain fraction of the collisions, the recoil atom may still retain sufficient energy to leave the cage and yet not have enough energy to dissociate another alkyl halide molecule. Such atoms probably settle down in some inorganic form and are extractable in aqueous solutions.

Of considerable practical importance is the fact that a small percentage of aniline added to the liquid alkyl halide considerably decreases the retention. Libby has ascribed this to a reaction of the Menschutkin type

$$RX + \phi NH_2 = \phi NH_2R^+ + X^-$$

which normally occurs only at elevated temperatures. The excitation energy of the molecule newly formed from a radical and the recoil atom may give rise to this reaction, yielding free and "cool" halogen, which no longer has the energy necessary to enter organic combination.

Gas Phase Experiments. Since the absence of a cage effect in gas phase bombardments would decrease the importance of hot atom re-formation reactions of the type discussed above, it might be presumed that the recoil atoms reach thermal equilibrium and react in ordinary fashion. This viewpoint was adopted by Suess [9] and later by Hamill and Williams [10] in studying the behavior of bromine recoil atoms in reactions with hydrogen bromide and acetylene (or ethylene). The first reagent is presumed to fix active bromine in inorganic form by virtue of an exchange reaction

$$Br^* + HBr \xrightarrow{k_1} HBr^* + Br$$

and the second to yield an organic bromide by the reactions

$$Br^* + C_2H_4 \underset{k_3}{\overset{k_2}{\rightleftharpoons}} C_2H_4Br^*$$

$$HBr + C_2H_4Br^* \xrightarrow{k_4} C_2H_5Br^*$$

The source of bromine recoil atoms may be either ethyl bromide or hydrogen bromide.

The partition of the activity between organic and inorganic form appears to be independent of HBr concentration above a small minimum value. This makes it necessary to postulate that reaction 3 is much faster than reaction 4. Thus both inorganic and organic yield increase with increasing HBr concentration (k_1 and k_4).

Fig. 7.2 shows the dependence of the activity partition on the ethylene pressure. Apparently the organic activity does not approach 100% at large ethylene pressures and therefore it is necessary to postulate a reaction such as

$$[Br^*] + C_2H_5Br \rightarrow HBr^* + C_2H_4Br$$

where the brackets indicate a "hot" bromine atom. Such a reaction would form inorganic bromine activity in a proportion independent of the HBr and C_2H_4 concentrations. The behavior of the activity partition shown in Fig. 7.2 indicates

9 Suess, *Z. physikal. chemie* **B45**, 297, 312 (1939).
10 Hamill and Williams, *J. Chem. Phys.* **16**, 1171 (1948).

that approximately 20% of the active bromine recoil atoms react by this path before being moderated to thermal energies to participate in reactions 1 through 4.

Aqueous Solutions. Several successful Szilard-Chalmers reactions have been carried out in aqueous solutions, and the

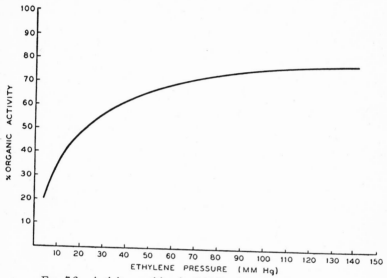

Fig. 7.2. Activity partition in $C_2H_5B_2$—HB_2—C_2H_4 mixtures.

target substance is usually an oxygenated anion or a Werner complex. The omnipresent solvent, water, is undoubtedly the chief reagent in determining the ultimate fate of the recoil fragments, although several cases are known where small changes in hydrogen ion concentration markedly affect the course of the reaction.

As examples of cases where the retention is not a function of pH, we may mention the reactions

$$ClO_4(n, \gamma)Cl_2^* \text{ or } Cl^{-*} \text{ Retention nearly 0}$$
$$PO_4{\equiv}(n, \gamma)P^*O_3{\equiv} \quad \text{Retention 50\%}$$

Mechanisms proposed [11] in these cases involve primary expulsion of O or O^- to produce a metastable ion which is reduced or oxidized, according to its properties, by the solvent.

The retention of manganese activity by permanganate is strongly dependent on pH, as shown in Fig. 7.3. The fact that a concentration of hydroxide ions of only 0.01 N can profoundly alter the fate of the recoils is taken to mean that the

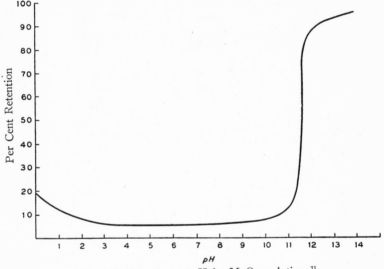

Fig. 7.3. Retention vs. pH for MnO_4^-—solutions.[11]

corresponding reaction cannot be a hot atom reaction, since the recoil energy could hardly be retained through a sufficient number of collisions. Libby [11] proposes that the initial neutron capture reaction forms an intermediate such as MnO_3^+ or perhaps MnO_2^{+3}, which is rapidly reduced by water in neutral or dilute acid solutions. In weakly alkaline solution the reaction

$$MnO_3^+ + OH^- = H^+ + MnO_4^-$$

competes and results in retention.

11 Libby, *J. Am. Chem. Soc.* **62**, 1930 (1940).

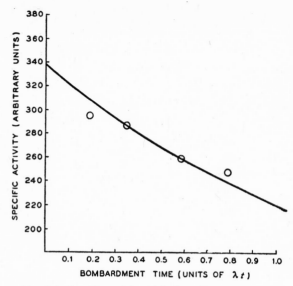

FIG. 7.4. Specific activity of Szilard-Chalmers iron.[12]

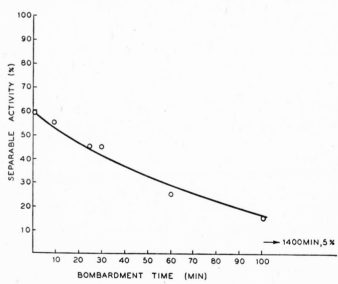

FIG. 7.5. Separable activity in bombardment of SbF$_5$.[12]

The low retention (in acid solutions) and well-known nuclear properties of manganese (see Appendix) permit the use of this system for the determination of very small slow neutron fluxes. If a liter of 1 N $KMnO_4$ (pH < 10) is exposed to a slow neutron flux for one half-life, and if the activity is efficiently collected with a small precipitate of MnO_2, a readily measurable disintegration rate of 10μ rd corresponds to a neutron flux of about 3 neutrons per cm^2/sec (see equation 5.2).

Radiation Effects. Slow neutron bombardment is almost always accompanied by gamma radiation from the neutron source. The effects of such radiations are discussed in detail in the next chapter, but for our present purpose it is sufficient to note that nonactivating radiation decomposition of the target substance may produce inactive atoms isotopic with the product of a Szilard-Chalmers reaction. This will lower the specific activity of the extracted material, especially in long or high-intensity bombardments. This has been observed and measured [12] in the case of ferrocyanide bombardment to produce active iron, as shown in Fig. 7.4.

Another but less common effect of radiation appears to be a return of the separable activity to the target form. When antimony activity is enriched by bombardment of SbF_5 (separable activity appears in less volatile form, probably SbF_3), little or no radiation decomposition of the target substance occurs, but the percent of separable activity rapidly decreases with bombardment time as shown in Fig. 7.5.

ISOMERIC TRANSITION

The process of isomeric transition is similar to neutron capture in that no change in atomic number occurs, and therefore

---

[12] Williams, Jenks, Leslie, Richter, and Larson, Paper #3.2.2 and Tompkins, Adamson and Williams, Paper #3.2.3. The Plutonium Project Record, Vol. 9B; see Williams, *J. Phys. and Colloid Chem.* **52**, 603 (1948).

any chemical effect accompanying the nuclear reaction offers almost the only means of separating parent and daughter. Cases of isomeric transition suitable for chemical study are rather rare, since several qualifications must usually be fulfilled: (1) the excited state must be fairly long-lived, to permit chemical manipulations; (2) the lower isomeric state must also be unstable, and shorter-lived than the parent, in order that radiochemical analysis may be used to establish its chemical behavior; (3) the element must be capable of existence in at least two mutually stable, separable, and nonexchanging forms.

Internal Conversion versus Gamma Recoil. Most of the longer-lived isomeric transitions involve decay energies of only a few hundred kilovolts. If the transition proceeds by gamma emission, the recoil energy, as indicated by Fig. 7.1, will be quite small, probably insufficient to cause bond rupture. On the other hand, the ionization which follows internal conversion can be expected to cause bond rupture in practically every case. Therefore, we may postulate that internal conversion is at least a necessary, and probably a sufficient, condition for chemical change accompanying isomeric transition.

This point has been experimentally demonstrated by comparison of the chemical effect in the isomeric transitions of Zn and Te.[13] Conversion is apparently negligible in the Zn case and is present to the extent of 50-100% in the Te case. Gaseous diethyl compounds containing these two active species were allowed to stand in glass vessels for several hours, after which the gases were withdrawn and the walls of the vessel examined for beta activity. This was observed in the case of Te but not with Zn. In spite of the greater recoil energy furnished by the Zn transition, bond rupture apparently did not

---

[13] Seaborg, Friedlander, and Kennedy, *J. Am. Chem. Soc.*, **62**, 1309 (1940).

occur. The Te transition, with its smaller recoil energy and internal conversion, was able to decompose the molecule and deposit 70-minute daughter Te on the walls of the vessel.

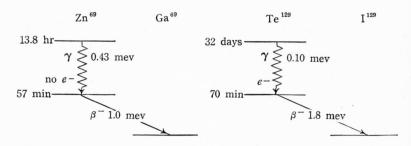

Internal Conversion in Br⁸⁰. This nuclide is readily produced by slow neutron bombardment of stable bromine and is well adapted to chemical studies.

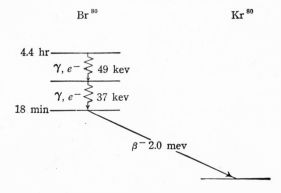

Early experiments indicated that the maximum chemical effect was about 85%, i.e., this portion of the isomeric transitions produced a recognizable chemical reaction. Recently, Hamill and Young [14] have reported a nearly complete chemical separation of these isomers. They synthesized methyl bromide containing the 4.4-hr parent and allowed

---

[14] Hamill and Young, *J. Chem. Phys.*, **17**, 215 (1949).

this to stand in the vapor state with hydrogen bromide, which is expected to exchange rapidly with any bromine fragments. During the course of about two hours, practically all 18-min daughter atoms initially present decay away, and a new generation is formed under the conditions of the particular experiment. After this period the gas mixture is drawn over soda-lime and thence into a small chamber near a Geiger counter. Since hydrogen bromide, and any active bromine associated

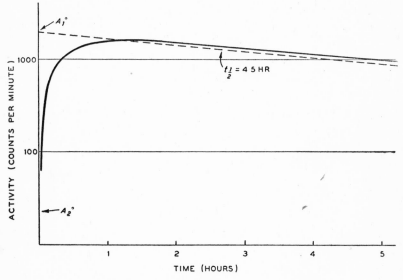

FIG. 7.6.   Activity vs. time in methyl bromide.

with it, will be removed by the soda lime, the sample to be counted contains only 4.4-hr parent activity plus any 18-min daughter activity which was not ejected from the methyl bromide molecule. The very weak radiations of the former (conversion electrons, low-energy gammas, and X-rays) are not detected by the counter. The activity observed in the methyl bromide is due exclusively to the beta-emitting 18-min daughter and varies with time as shown in Fig. 7.6.

The time dependence of the activity is described by equation 4.14, and the values of A^0_2 and A^0_1 obtained from the experimental data. This has been done graphically in the figure. Several experiments, with varying ratios of methyl bromide and hydrogen bromide, indicate that the extent of chemical separation of the isomers is $98 \pm 2\%$. This agrees with recent physical measurements indicating that the extent of conversion in the 49 kev transition is nearly 100%.[15]

Chemical Mechanisms. Bromine isomer separation has been observed in a variety of systems such as gaseous and liquid alkyl bromides, aqueous solutions of bromate ion, and solutions of bromine in carbon tetrachloride. Separation yields vary from zero to 100%, depending on conditions. DeVault and Libby [16] have reported a charged plate experiment which indicates that the daughter atoms lose their charge very quickly. However, since recoil energy is negligible, the process of charge neutralization must account for the reaction of daughter atoms with carbon tetrachloride molecules when the parent is present as molecular bromine dissolved in this substance. Willard [6] attributes this reaction to a process such as

$$CCl_4 + Br^{80}(18 \ min)^+ + e \rightarrow CCl_3 + Br^{80}(18 \ min) + Cl$$

$$CCl_3 + Br^{80}(18 \ min) \rightarrow CCl_3Br^{80}(18 \ min)$$

This reaction is important only in the liquid phase where the "cage" of solvent molecules can keep the radical and atom together. The activation accompanying charge neutralization may also be responsible for the very efficient reduction of bromate to bromide by isomeric transition.[16]

Many other chemical reactions induced by isomeric transitions are satisfactorily explained in terms of the reactions of

---

[15] Grindberg and Rossinow, *Phys. Rev.* **58**, 181 (1940); Berthelot, *Ann. physique* **19**, 219 (1944).
[16] DeVault and Libby, *J. Am. Chem. Soc.* **63**, 3216 (1941).

bromine atoms formed by charge neutralization. When the parent activity is present in the form of an alkyl bromide as in the experiments of Hamill and Young, the daughter bromine atoms liberated by the internal conversion process may be fixed in inorganic form by exchange with hydrogen bromide as described previously, or may add to unsaturated molecules such as ethylene, in analogy with the reactions proposed for the neutron capture process. In the absence of either type of reagent, the free atoms probably react with impurities or adsorb on the walls of the vessel, yielding chiefly inorganic forms.

Isomeric Transition in Tellurium. Three cases of isomeric transitions are observed in the element tellurium, as indicated below. The chemical effects of these nuclear reactions have been studied chiefly in aqueous solutions [17,18] where the major

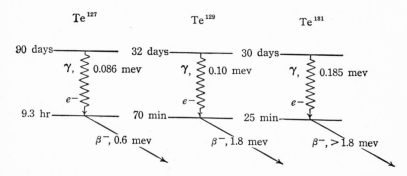

chemical effect observed is reduction from tellurate to tellurite, i.e., parent activity in the higher valence state yields daughter in the lower valence state. The yields are a function of pH, achieving their maximum values in acid solutions, and are given for each of the three transitions in Table 7.2. Since the chemi-

[17] Segré, Halford, and Seaborg, *Phys. Rev.* **55**, 321 (1939).
[18] Williams, *J. Chem. Phys.* **16**, 513 (1948).

cal processes involved are identical in all three cases, these figures have been taken to indicate that the maximum extent of conversion in the three cases is 100, 65, and 45% respectively and that the figures given in the table probably represent the actual conversion.

TABLE 7.2. MAXIMUM DAUGHTER REDUCTION YIELDS IN TELLURIUM I. T.[18]

Isomeric Pair		Yield %
90 day—9.3 hr	Te^{127}	85
32 day—70 min	Te^{129}	55
30 hr—25 min	Te^{131}	35

OTHER REACTIONS

Beta Decay. The change in atomic number accompanying this reaction produces a most obvious chemical change, and therefore the study of this process centers upon determinations of the chemical state of the daughter activity as governed by the nuclear reaction and the properties of the environment. Since the nuclear charge increases by one unit in negative beta decay while, in the absence of other effects, the number of extra-nuclear electrons remains the same, the daughter activity might be expected to appear in a valence state one unit higher than the parent. This effect was sought and found in the decay of 19-min La^{143} to 33-hr Ce^{143}. Starting with +3 lanthanum in acid solution, at least 60% of the cerium daughter was found in the ceric form (+4).[3]

Recoil and ionization are undoubtedly important in the beta decay process, although it is difficult to assess the importance of these effects. That they must produce chemical effects is apparent from further experiments reported on the beta decay from selenium to bromine and from tellurium to iodine. Starting in both cases with an oxidized form of the parent, considerable amounts of daughter in lower valence states are formed as shown in Table 7.3.

TABLE 7.3. DISTRIBUTION OF DAUGHTER ACTIVITY IN BETA DECAY [19]

Parent Form	Daughter Distribution
$SeO_3^=$	40% BrO_3^-, 60% reduced forms
$SeO_4^=$	40% BrO_3^-, 60% reduced forms
$TeO_3^=$	11% IO_4^-, 14% IO_3^-, 75% reduced forms
$TeO_4^=$	12% IO_4^-, 28% IO_3^-, 60% reduced forms

Reduced forms = x^-, x° or xo^-, which rapidly exchange and therefore cannot be distinguished.

Recoil or ionization effects seem to be absent in a case investigated by Edwards [20] where the beta decay reaction (decay scheme given below) was observed in a gaseous system. Gase-

ous lead tetramethyl, containing the weak beta-emitter Pb^{210}, was allowed to stand several days to permit growth of Bi^{210},

[19] Gest, Edwards, and Davies, Paper No. 3.3.4, The Plutonium Project Record, Vol. 9B; Edwards, Gest, and Davies, Paper No. 3.3.5, *ibid.*; Burgus and Davies, Paper No. 3.3.2, *ibid.*; see also Davies, *J. Phys. and Colloid Chem.* 52, 595 (1948).

[20] Edwards, Conference on Hot Atom Chemistry, Brookhaven National Laboratory, August, 1948.

which is readily counted. Only about 8% of the daughter bismuth left the gas phase, the unseparated portion presumably remaining as gaseous bismuth trimethyl. Fig. 7.1 indicates that the maximum recoil energy in this case would be only 0.065 ev, and therefore it is reasonable to attribute the small separation to the internal conversion process.

n,p Reactions. A few *n,p* reactions have fairly high cross-sections with low-energy neutrons. One of these, N^{14} (n,p) C^{14}, is especially important since it gives rise to a long-lived carbon isotope which is extremely useful in chemical and biological studies (see Chapter IX). The chemical form of the radioactive carbon produced by neutron bombardment of various nitrogenous materials has been studied by Yankwich, Rollefson, and Norris,[21] with the approximate results shown in Table 7.4. The analytical methods used distinguished only

TABLE 7.4. FRACTIONAL DISTRIBUTION OF C^{14} ACTIVITY [21]

Bombarded Form	Percentage Distribution in Fractions						
	CO_2	CO	CH_4	HCN	HCHO	CH_3OH	HCOOH
NH_4NO_3(aq.)	60	30	0.1	0	0	1.4	9.6
NH_4NO_3(s)	81	19	0	0	0	0	0
$(NH_2)_2CO$(s)	40	5	0	55	0	0	0
$N_2H_4\cdot 2HCl$(s)	18	8	4	71	0	0	0
NH_2CH_2COOH(s).	8	0	0	15	0	47	30

between aldehydes, alcohols, and carboxylic acids, without regard to carbon chain length.

The data indicate that oxygen-bound carbon is the most likely product form. The presence of a small amount of this form even in hydrazine-dihydrochloride is attributable to the presence of water in the bombarded crystals. Nitrogen-bound

---

[21] Yankwich, Rollefson, and Norris, *J. Chem. Phys.* **14**, 131 (1946).

carbon does not appear with ammonium nitrate but in other compounds increases with increasing nitrogen content. Glycine is the only compound studied which yields appreciable quantities of relatively complicated carbon compounds, suggesting its use to by-pass some of the steps necessary in syntheses beginning with carbon dioxide.

SUPPLEMENTARY READING

Edwards and Davies, "Chemical Effects of Nuclear Transformations," *Nucleonics* **2**, 44 (1948).
Libby, "Chemistry of Energetic Atoms Produced by Nuclear Reactions," *J. Am. Chem. Soc.* **69**, 2523 (1947).

Chapter VIII

CHEMICAL AND BIOLOGICAL EFFECTS
OF NUCLEAR RADIATIONS

THE ENERGETIC particles (except neutrons) and radiations associated with nuclear reactions dissipate their energy almost exclusively by interaction with the electronic systems of the matter through which they pass. Even in the case of neutrons, where collision and absorption are exclusively nuclear processes, the nuclear recoil effects and the capture gammas will transfer considerable energy to electronic systems. The excitation and ionization which result from the action of nuclear radiation is of considerable chemical and biological importance, especially since the development of the chain-reacting pile. However, the study of radiation effects is not inseparably bound to nuclear science, since ionizing radiations are very readily produced without resort to nuclear reactions.

It is the formation of ions which distinguishes this field of radiation studies from photochemistry, although this is not meant to imply that ionization is the only source of chemical and biological action. One widely used unit of radiation exposure is based on the ionization produced in a standard substance. This unit, the *roentgen* (r), is defined as that quantity of gamma radiation such that the associated corpuscular emission per cubic centimeter of dry air (STP) produces, in air, ions carrying one electrostatic unit of electricity of either sign. When experiments involve ionizing agents other than gamma rays, and when materials other than air are considered, related units must be defined. One satisfactory method is simply to state the energy expended per unit weight of absorbing material. The rep unit, or roentgen-equivalent-physical, is defined in this way. Assuming an average value of 32 ev energy expenditure per ion pair, one may calculate that one roentgen corresponds to an energy expenditure of about 83 ergs per gram of air. The rep is defined as that amount of radiation (alpha, beta, gamma, etc.) which expends this energy in a gram of the experimental substance. Other units, such as the rem (roentgen-equivalent-mammal), may take into account the varying biological effectiveness of various radiations. In chemical studies, the effect is frequently stated in terms of the energy expended in the system in electron volt units.

RADIATIONS AND PARTICLES

Radiations. Electromagnetic radiation of great energy (small wave length) is characterized by a low absorption coefficient, and thus, although the energy per quantum is much greater than with visible or ultraviolet radiation, a given quantity of matter will absorb a much smaller fraction of the incident quanta. There are three important processes by which the radiation is absorbed: photoelectron emission, Compton scattering, and pair production. The relative importance of these three processes depends on the energy of the radiation, but it should be noted that all of them result in ionization either in the initial act or in the subsequent travels of the electrons produced. When radiations of many kilovolts energy are used, these secondary electrons are the principal agent in producing ionization and excitation, and therefore the effects may be simulated by bombardment of the system with high-energy electrons. In this event a much larger portion of the incident energy will be absorbed, since the low absorption coefficient of the electromagnetic radiation has been circumvented. Concentrated radioactive substances can be used to furnish gamma ray sources of considerable intensity in the energy region around 1 mev, but the highest intensities of pure gamma radiation of this energy are furnished by the Van de Graaf generator. Lower energies are conveniently available in various types of X-ray machines.

Electrons. Energetic electrons or beta particles dissipate their energy by repeated interaction with the electronic systems of the atoms which they pass, causing both ionization and excitation. Experimental measurements indicate that approximately one ion pair is formed for each 32-ev energy loss, but that the actual formation of ions accounts for only about half this quantity, the remainder being expended in excitation processes. Determinations of the penetrating ability of energetic electrons indicate that the ionizing and exciting events occur many molecules apart, the average separation increasing with increasing electron energy. Useful sources of high-speed electrons include concentrated radioactive materials and devices such as the Van de Graaf generator, which accelerates thermionic electrons through great potential differences.

Ions. Heavy, charged particles such as alphas, deuterons, protons, and fission fragments dissipate their energy in relatively short paths, again producing approximately one ion pair for each 32-ev energy loss. A typical alpha particle may spend its 5 mev of energy in a path of around 5 cm in air indicating that ions are formed every few molecules along the path. The secondary electrons produced in these events also add to the ionization, producing a rather inhomogeneous distribution of ions in comparison to electron absorption. Fig. 3.1 is a reproduction of photographs of the ion tracks produced by these two types of particles in a Wilson cloud chamber. The behavior of protons and deuterons is very similar to that of alpha particles, and all three may be produced with energies

in the mev range by devices such as the Van de Graaf generator or cyclotron.

Neutrons. High-speed neutrons, an important component of
the radiation in a chain-reacting pile, are unique in their action
in that they dissipate their energy almost entirely by collisions
with the nuclei of atoms. In thus transferring their energy to
nuclei they dislodge whole atoms from their positions in solids,
and in liquids and gases create fast-moving atoms and ions
which behave in a fashion very similar to the heavy charged
particles. In fact, some of the chemical effects of fast neutrons
can be simulated by proton, deuteron, or alpha particle
bombardment.

The chemical changes directly produced by the capture of
slow neutrons have been discussed in the previous chapter.
However, in terms of the whole chemical system, the gamma
radiation emitted in the capture process is more important,
since in its absorption it will produce many ion pairs and excited molecules. In addition, the formation of an unstable
nuclide in the reaction introduces another source of beta and
gamma radiation. Therefore, the effects of slow neutrons can
be simulated by irradiation with energetic X-rays and
electrons.

The Chain-reacting Pile. The radiations encountered in
the operation of a chain-reacting pile are numerous and extremely intense. As indicated in Chapter V, they constitute an
important consideration in the construction of such a device.
Using the data given in Table 5.2 we may estimate the time
and space distribution of radiation intensities as follows: The
major item of energy dissipation, the kinetic energy of the
heavy fission fragments, is highly localized. The great initial
velocity of these particles causes them to have charges estimated to be as high as $+20$. Their great kinetic energy is rap-

idly dissipated in collisions, and the ionization and excitation produced are even more dense than with alpha particles. In a heterogeneous pile such as indicated in Fig. 5.6, containing fuel rods of metallic uranium, this energy will degrade to thermal agitation and be completely confined to the fuel rods rather than to their surroundings.

The next largest item, the radioactive decay energy of the fission fragments, amounts to approximately 10% of the fission energy or 10^5 watts in a pile operating at 10^6 watts. The source of this energy is the fission product nuclei produced within the fuel rods, but the penetrating ability of the beta and gamma radiations is such that their energy is expended to a considerable extent in the surroundings. Most of the beta radiations will be absorbed by the moderator if not by the fuel rods, but the gamma radiation is so penetrating that considerable intensities are still present at the surface of the unit. Thus the heavy concrete shielding which surrounds the device is used chiefly for protection of gamma radiations emitted by the fission products and in the fission reaction itself.

The neutrons emitted in the fission process are very energetic and largely escape the original fuel rod. In the course of moderation they collide with the nuclei of the moderating substance, producing measurable physical and chemical changes in this substance. The eventual capture of the moderated neutrons, largely in the fuel rods, is accompanied by the emission of gamma radiation, which amounts to nearly as much as the gamma radiation from the fission product decay.

Aside from the fast neutrons, it appears that the whole structure and contents of a chain-reacting pile are being subjected, during operation at 10^6 watts, to a gamma radiation intensity of at least 10^5 watts, which corresponds to the formation of approximately 10^{24} ions and excited molecules per second. Assuming, in the absence of a stated figure, that the pile weighs 10^3 metric tons, we find that the average energy expenditure from the gamma radiations alone corresponds to approximately 10^5 rep per second.

RADIATION CHEMISTRY

Radiation chemistry is distinguished from photochemistry by the appearance of ionization as an important primary process, in addition to the excitation processes common to photochemistry. If we think of an ion simply as the ultimate state of electronic excitation, capable of all of the various processes observed with lower excited states, we see that, in principle, "radiolysis" is the same as photolysis. All the various consequences, such as fluorescence, collisional deactivation, and various modes of molecular dissociation, may be expected. Whereas with simple diatomic molecules the net result of photolysis and radiolysis may be the same, more complicated molecules may show quite different behavior in the latter case. This may be attributed to the greater variety of excited states available in radiolysis and to a consequently greater variety of primary products. Many complicated molecules, such as the ketones, show a relatively small variety of products when irradiated with light of λ 2537 Å, but a greater variety when subjected to ionizing radiations. Still others, such as benzene, are not altered by light of λ 2537 Å but are decomposed into a complicated mixture by ionizing radiations. These comparisons serve to indicate that radiolysis will be much less specific than photolysis, both in regard to the types of compounds affected and in the nature of the products.

Primary Processes. A detailed analysis of the primary process in the ortho-para hydrogen conversion and also in the synthesis and decomposition of hydrogen bromide by alpha radiations has been given by Eyring, Hirschfelder, and Taylor.[1] In

---

[1] Eyring, Hirschfelder, and Taylor, *J. Chem. Phys.* **4**, 479 (1936) ; *ibid.* **4**, 570 (1936).

the case of ortho-para hydrogen conversion the ratio of molecules converted to ions produced may be as great as 1000, and in the case of hydrogen bromide decomposition this *ion-pair yield* may be as high as 5. To some investigators this suggested an *ion cluster hypothesis* in which a number of molecules clustered about each ion and underwent reaction in this state. Eyring *et al.,* however, by detailed consideration of ionization, neutralization, dissociation, etc., were able to show that the rates of atom production by these processes, coupled with the known reaction rates of such bodies in these systems, adequately explained the observed rates.

In generalized form the types of processes which they considered are the following: The primary ionization of a molecule A may be written

$$A \xrightarrow{\hspace{1em}\text{\tiny WW}\hspace{1em}} A^+ + e$$

where the symbol $\xrightarrow{\text{\tiny WW}}$ is the radiation chemistry equivalent of $h\nu$ in photochemistry. This ion may be relatively stable, or may immediately decompose into a free radical and a radical ion thus:

$$A \rightarrow B^+ + C + e$$

For the moment we will consider only the ions produced in such processes, which eventually disappear by a neutralization reaction such as:

$$A^+ \text{ (or } B^+) + e \rightarrow A^*$$

The asterisk is used to signify that the molecule produced in the neutralization reaction is electronically excited, with an energy equal to the ionization potential of the molecule involved. In complete parallel with photochemistry, this energy of excitation may be emitted as radiation, or may cause rupture of the molecule into free radicals or ultimate molecules. Other paths of reaction are available for the ions, such as ion-molecule reactions thus:

$$A^+ + A \rightarrow D^+ + E$$

which may also produce atoms or radicals. However, the eventual fate of the ion is neutralization to an excited molecule or radical followed by the usual reactions of such species.

The main feature of these proposals is, therefore, the dependence upon excited molecules, atoms, and radicals for the ultimate reactions, rather than upon the ions themselves. Needless to say, the excitation processes which account for about half the energy expenditure of the ionizing radiations simply circumvent the steps involving ions.

The methods of mass spectroscopy hold considerable promise in the study of the primary ionization reactions of radiation chemistry as indicated in Chapter I. In electron bombardment of a complicated molecule several varieties of ions (molecular and radical) will usually be produced. Since, at low electron speeds, doubly charged ions are not important, a measurement of the various e/m values provides information about which ions are formed and in what proportions. These results will, to some extent, be a function of the electron energy and will certainly depend on the molecular structure involved. Some of this information has already been accumulated in connection with purely analytical applications of the mass spectrometer, but largely at electron energies of only a few tens of volts.

The dissociation of metastable ions, a phenomenon of some importance in the primary processes of radiation chemistry, seems to be a study uniquely suited to the properties of the mass spectrograph.[2] The subject first arose as a plausible explanation of diffuse peaks of ion intensity falling at positions in the mass spectrogram corresponding to nonintegral masses. For instance, the molecular ion H_2^+ may dissociate into H^+ and H after electrostatic acceleration and before proceeding far in the magnetic analyzer. The ion H^+ thus has a velocity essentially acquired while endowed with mass 2, but it is curved

[2] Hipple, *J. Phys. and Colloid Chem.* **52**, 456 (1948).

in the magnetic field in a fashion corresponding to mass 1. By application of the equations of mass spectroscopy, it can be shown that the apparent mass would be $\frac{1}{2}$. The rate of this particular ion dissociation is pressure dependent and is therefore presumed to occur in ion molecule collisions thus:

$$H_2^+ + H_2 \to H^+ + H + H_2$$

but Hipple has studied more complicated ions in which the dissociation is apparently first order, as in the case

$$C_4H_{10}^+ \to C_3H_7^+ + CH_3$$

which has a half-period of 2×10^{-6} sec.

Langer [3] has recently called attention to a further type of rearrangement frequently observed in the mass spectra of hydrocarbons. A compound such as neo-pentane gives rise to a strong ion peak at mass 29,

$$
\begin{array}{ccc}
& \text{H} & \\
& \text{HCH} & \\
\text{H} & | \quad \text{H} & \qquad \text{H} \quad \text{H}^+ \\
\text{HC—C—CH} & \to & \text{HC—C} \\
\text{H} & | \quad \text{H} & \qquad \text{H} \quad \text{H} \\
& \text{HCH} & \\
& \text{H} &
\end{array}
$$

presumably an ethyl radical ion. One of the simpler descriptions of this type of rearrangement postulates the migration of one or more protons in the course of ion formation and dissociation.

Hot Atom Reactions. The possibility of the formation of atoms and radicals with kinetic energies in excess of those of the molecules of the substrate must be considered in radiation and photochemistry as well as in nuclear reactions (see Chapter VII). Consider the absorption of light of λ 2537 Å by

---

[3] Langer, 115th A.C.S. Meeting, San Francisco, March, 1949.

liquid ethyl iodide, which causes decomposition into ethylene, ethane, iodine, and other minor products. The primary process

$$C_2H_5I \xrightarrow{h\nu} C_2H_5 + I\dagger$$

yields an ethyl radical and an electronically excited iodine atom and corresponds to a potential energy increase of about 90 kcal/mole. The energy of the quantum is, however, about 110 kcal/mole, leaving an excess of approximately 20 kcal/mole to be divided between the separated ethyl radical and iodine atom. Because of the great disparity in masses of the two fragments, the ethyl radical receives most of this energy, making it especially reactive for the first few collisions, or until it has more nearly approached thermal equilibrium with its surroundings.

This type of phenomenon has been postulated in at least two photochemical reactions, the decomposition of hydrogen iodide [4] and of the alkyl iodides.[5] In the latter case the decomposition by ionizing radiations appears to be very similar to the photolysis, and a similar "hot radical" mechanism is presumed.

In both radiolysis and photolysis of liquid ethyl iodide,[5] the rate of production of iodine is independent of the amount of iodine produced. On the other hand, the quantum yield (photolysis) is only 0.4, indicating some important reaction reforming ethyl iodide. This reaction is

$$C_2H_5 + I_2 \rightarrow C_2H_5I + I$$

as is shown by rapid isotopic exchange between molecular iodine and ethyl iodide during photolysis (and radiolysis). This apparent paradox is resolved by the postulate that the product-forming steps, such as

$$C_2H_5 + C_2H_5I \rightarrow C_2H_6 + C_2H_4I$$

[4] Ogg and Williams, *J. Chem. Phys.* **13**, 586 (1945).
[5] Hamill and Schuler, 115th A.C.S. Meeting, San Francisco, March, 1949.

occur in the first few collisions of the ethyl radical, while an appreciable portion of its initial excess energy is retained. The back reaction with molecular iodine occurs only after the radical is "cool" and all opportunity for product formation is past. This study emphasizes the similarities to be found between photochemistry and radiation chemistry.

Radiolysis of Organic Compounds. The complicated nature of the molecules in this classification prevents any detailed analysis of the primary reactions, but several enlightening generalities of experimental behavior have been pointed out by Burton,[6] some of which will be summarized here.

Since the ionizing radiations are somewhat indiscriminate in their attack on a molecule instead of concentrating on a particular bond, the composition of the molecule rather than the energy of the radiation will govern the nature of the products. This is in distinct contrast to photochemical effects. Irradiation of hydrocarbons produces, among other products, methane and hydrogen. These two products probably originate in hydrogen atoms and methyl radicals. These, in turn, may be expected to be produced in proportion to the H and CH_3 groups in the molecules. This behavior is illustrated in Fig. 8.1, which shows that the hydrogen-methane varies in approximate proportion to the ratio of these groups in the molecule. Fig. 8.2 shows a similar dependence of the hydrogen-carbon monoxide plus carbon dioxide ratio on the ratio of groups in a series of carboxylic acids.

Any structural effect which tends to increase the stability of an excited molecule (formed by ion discharge) will be expected, in turn, to increase the stability of that molecule toward radiation decomposition into radicals but not necessarily toward intramolecular rearrangement into ultimate molecules. Stabilization of the excited state may permit colli-

---

[6] Burton, *J. Phys. and Colloid Chem.* **52**, 786 (1948).

sional deactivation before bond rupture occurs and would therefore be expected to become especially important in irra-

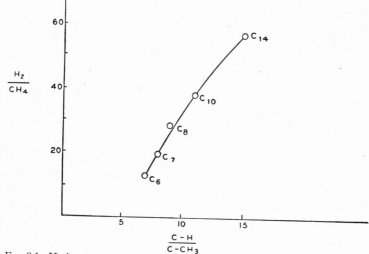

Fig. 8.1. Hydrogen-methane ratio in the radiolysis of normal hydrocarbons.[6]

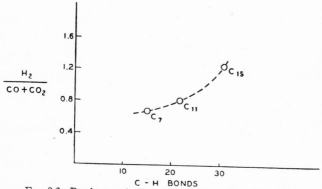

Fig. 8.2. Product ratio in radiolysis of carboxylic acids.[6]

diation of condensed phases, where such deactivation is more probable. Benzene and other highly resonant structures exemplify these principles in their unique stability toward ionizing radiations. Data on the irradiation of several liquid hydrocarbons are given in Table 8.1. The readily recognizable products of the radiolysis (gas and polymer) are reported in terms of molecules of compound decomposed per 100 ev of energy absorbed. The special stability of benzene and toluene may be readily seen in both columns, but the gas yields (hydrogen and methane) are probably low also because of reactions with unsaturated bonds in these compounds. This tendency may also be noted with cyclohexene. Experiments on the radiolysis of benzene vapors have shown much higher yields. Highly resonant molecules like benzene are stabilized in the excited form by virtue of the nonlocal nature of the excitation, which is spread over the whole molecule rather than concentrating in one or a few particular bonds.

TABLE 8.1. FAST ELECTRON IRRADIATION OF LIQUID
HYDROCARBONS [6]

Hydrocarbon	Yield (mol. decomposed/100 ev)	
	Gas	Polymer
Benzene	0.04	0.5
n-Heptane	4.2	1.7
Cyclohexane	4.0	1.2
Cyclohexene	1.0	4.2
Methylcyclohexane	4.5	4.2
Toluene	0.09	0.7

Lind [7] and others have extensively investigated the polymerization of acetylene induced by the gaseous alpha-emitter, radon. They have proposed an ion-cluster mechanism for the reaction, whose principal distinction lies in the idea that the reaction is promoted in clusters of many molecules forming around one or more ionized molecules. This scheme places

[7] Lind, J. Phys. and Colloid Chem. 52, 437 (1948).

the burden on ionization rather than excitation, and the clusters are presumed to account for the high yields per ion pair. Recently, Rosenblum [8] has studied the kinetics of benzene formation in this reaction and has shown that about one-fifth of the reacting acetylene molecules produce this product. Benzene could be formed by a cluster of three acetylene molecules which cyclize, but the over-all yield of decomposition is 21 acetylene molecules per ion pair. Multiplying this figure by 1/5 gives a yield of 4.2 molecules decomposed per ion pair, in contrast with the value of 3.0 which would be expected from the cluster theory. There is a considerable similarity between the radiation-induced reaction and the photochemical reaction which lends positive support to a mechanism involving bimolecular reactions between normal and excited molecules as follows:

$$C_2H_2 \rightarrow C_2H_2{}^+ + e$$

$$e + C_2H_2{}^+ \rightarrow C_2H_2\dagger \ (\text{excited molecule})$$

$$C_2H_2\dagger + C_2H_2 \rightarrow (C_2H_2)_2\dagger \rightarrow (C_2H_2)_3\dagger, \text{ etc.}$$

At the trimer stage, the polymerization may continue, or the trimer may cyclize to form benzene, and no fundamental restrictions are placed on the yields of various products.

Radiolysis of Aqueous Solutions. Pure water is smoothly decomposed by alpha particle bombardment forming hydrogen, oxygen, and hydrogen peroxide. The yield is about 2 molecules of hydrogen per 100 ev of energy absorbed. In contrast, irradiation of very pure water by X-rays and fast electrons produces little or no decomposition, but the decomposition reaction quickly appears upon the addition of traces of almost any solute. It therefore appears that some back-reaction occurs in X-ray and electron bombardment, which is

---

[8] Rosenblum, *J. Phys. and Colloid Chem.* **52**, 474 (1948).

prevented in alpha bombardment and in the presence of solutes.

The active agents in water subjected to ionizing radiation are believed to be the radicals H and OH, which are produced by dissociation of excited water molecules, or in ion reactions such as:

$$e + HOH \rightarrow H + OH^-$$

and

$$H_2O \longrightarrow\!\!\backslash\!\backslash\!\backslash\!\backslash\!\rightarrow H_2O^+ + e$$

followed by

$$H_2O^+ + H_2O \rightarrow H_3O^+ + OH$$

or by

$$H_2O^+ + e \rightarrow (H_2O)\dagger \rightarrow H + OH$$

The ultimate products of the reaction are accounted for by radical-radical reactions such as:

$$H + H \rightarrow H_2$$

and

$$OH + OH \rightarrow H_2O_2$$

Since only hydrogen and hydrogen peroxide are formed in short exposures, oxygen is considered a secondary product.

The low yield of H_2 and H_2O_2 in X-ray and electron bombardment is attributed to reactions such as

$$OH + H_2 \rightarrow H_2O + H$$

$$H + H_2O_2 \rightarrow H_2O + OH$$

Note that these are chain reactions, indicating that the consumption of products will be very efficient. These reactions are less important in alpha particle bombardment because in this case the primary radicals occur in high density along a short path. Thus the radicals can react with each other in preference to reaction with the products, hydrogen and hydrogen peroxide, in the main body of the liquid.

Careful experimentation has served to substantiate the proposal of back-reactions consuming hydrogen and hydrogen peroxide. Allen [9] and others have detected concentrations of these substances of the order of a few micromoles per liter in water irradiated with 1 mev electrons or X-rays. With electrons of lower speeds, where the ions will be formed closer together, a higher steady-state concentration of products is expected. Even with alpha particles, it should be possible to build up a concentration of products sufficient to stop the over-all reaction, although this may be too high for practical realization. Table 8.2 shows data which illustrate this behavior. The proposed mechanism also indicates that the initial yield of the reactions (before appreciable concentrations of the products are built up) should be about the same in all cases, or at least not so greatly different as the final steady states. Data on this point are included in Table 8.2.

TABLE 8.2. DECOMPOSITION OF WATER BY RADIATION [9]

Type	Average Density of Energy Loss (kev./cm air)	Initial Decomposition Yield (molecules H_2/100 ev absorbed)	Steady-state Hydrogen Pressure (cm Hg)
Electrons (1 mev).	3	0.2–0.5	1–2
Betas (0.005 mev).	70	0.1–0.4	10–20
Deuterons (8 mev).	175	0.54	>60
Alphas (5 mev)...	1430	2.0	>>1 atm

The addition of a solute increases the steady-state concentration of products which can be attained and thus permits greater decomposition of the water. Many solutes accomplish this without appreciable change in their concentration and may be effective at extremely small concentrations. Even small amounts of material dissolved from the walls of a container may considerably increase the steady-state product concentrations. This is accomplished by interrupting the chain reactions

[9] Allen, *J. Phys. and Colloid Chem.* **52**, 479 (1948).

which consume products, probably somewhat as follows for bromide ion:

$$OH + Br^- \rightarrow Br + OH^-$$

$$Br + H \rightarrow H^+ + Br^-$$

$$OH^- + H^+ \rightarrow H_2O$$

The essential feature of this series of reactions or those for any similar solute must be the removal of H and OH to form H^+ and OH^- (eventually water) without over-all change in the solute. These reactions might seem to preclude completely the formation of products, but the data of Table 8.2 indicate that most product formation must take place at the end of electron tracks, where the speed is low and the ion density high. In these regions, product formation takes place both in the presence and absence of solutes, but the solutes interrupt the chain reactions which might consume products.

Heavy Particle Bombardment of Solids. The extensive momentum transfer which can occur in collisions between heavy particles and atomic nuclei leads to special dislocation effects in the solid state. The fast neutrons of a chain-reacting pile, whose most important method of energy dissipation is by nuclear interaction, may cause detectable dislocation of atoms in a crystal lattice (Wigner effect). The dislocated atoms may come to rest in a crystal imperfection or an interstitial position. Elevation of the temperature of such a disturbed system should allow a migration of the dislocated atoms to more stable positions or to the exterior of the crystal, with an ease depending on the hardness of the solid structure.

Slow neutrons may also produce similar dislocation reactions in solids by virtue of the highly exothermic character of the neutron capture reaction. The gamma rays ($\sim$5 mev) emitted on capture impart a recoil energy of 100 to 1000 ev to the product nucleus, which will in general suffice to rend it from its normal position in the crystal lattice. If the product nucleus is radioactive, this effect may be susceptible to study at very low neutron intensities.

High-speed ions produced in nuclear reactions such as

$$_3Li^6 + _0n^1 \rightarrow {_2}He^4 + _1H^3 + 4.3 \text{ mev}$$

have been shown to produce coloration effects in crystals similar to those produced by ultraviolet light, X-rays, or electron bombardment. The coloration is presumed to be due to various combinations of electrons and ion vacancies, which would be produced in the travels of the energetic ions formed in the nuclear reaction.

BIOLOGICAL EFFECTS OF NUCLEAR RADIATIONS

The discussions of the previous section have served to indicate the complexity of the reactions induced by nuclear radiations even in the simplest chemical systems. In progressing to biochemical systems the complexity becomes even greater and we must leave even larger gaps between cause and effect. The study is a very important one, however, especially since our own bodies are concerned. Workers in nuclear science must take at least a practical, if not a professional, interest in the biological effects of nuclear radiations.

The more highly developed organisms contain a tremendous variety of cells and tissues, each of which may exhibit a different sensitivity to ionizing radiations. Furthermore, these units are interdependent and a change in any one may affect the functions of another, making the precise measurement of a biological change a very difficult problem. In addition, living organisms possess an ability to repair damage done to them. This ability is manifested in the observation of the ability to recover from certain types of radiation damage and in dependence of some biological effects upon the rate of absorption of radiation.

Radiosensitivity.   The extent or degree of damage to a living organism subjected to ionizing radiations is a difficult quantity to measure.   Perhaps the most definite criterion of effect is the death of the experimental individual, although it is obviously not feasible to adopt this standard in some important cases.   Even when this is done, the sensitivity of a

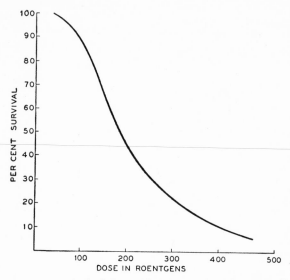

Fig. 8.3. Survival of *drosophila* eggs treated with x-rays.[10]

group of individuals may vary widely as illustrated in Fig. 8.3. It can readily be seen that the "radiosensitivity" of individuals in this case varies by a factor of at least ten.   It is therefore customary to adopt a given percentage survival, say 50%, as representing the criterion of lethal dosage.

The sensitivity to nuclear radiations varies considerably among different types of cells and tissues.   In general, it is found that the greatest sensitivity is associated with the great-

---

[10] Failla, see Supplementary Reading.

est rates of cell division. Thus an organism in the early stages of its development may be much more sensitive than when it has reached adulthood, as is illustrated by Fig. 8.4. Variations of this type can give rise to an apparent delay in the effects of irradiation. A suitable dose of radiation on the testes of the rat will destroy the spermatagonia, which are precursors of the spermatazoa by about thirty days. In this same irradia-

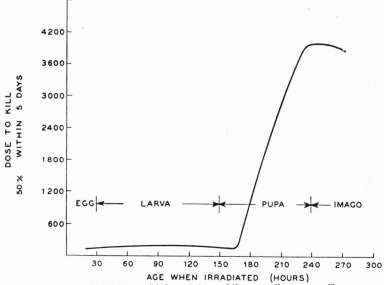

FIG. 8.4. Radiosensitivity of *drosophila* according to age.[10]

tion other cells which represent intermediate stages of development and the spermatazoa themselves are apparently not damaged. Therefore sterility (failure to produce spermatazoa) does not appear until the growth cycle is complete. The sterility may or may not be permanent, depending on the dose.

This so-called "latent period" appears in many other types of radiation damage, such as the reddening or "erythema" in the skin. The "threshold erythema" dose, or that required to produce a barely noticeable reddening of the skin, is around 100-1000 roentgens of X-radiation, depending on the energy, and the effect is noted from two to four weeks after administration of the dose. This latent period is probably due to the greater sensitivity of the rapidly dividing cells in the lower layers of the epidermis. A certain ability to "recover" from the irradiation is exhibited in this case in that the dose required to produce the threshold effect is larger when administered in two portions separated by a few hours. Thus, while 600 roentgens may be sufficient to produce the effect in a single administration, 450 roentgens may be required in each of two administrations when separated by 24 hours, the total dose being 900 roentgens in the latter case. Although a generalization in this matter is not entirely justified, the experimental evidence indicates that rate of administration as well as total dose must be considered in many types of radiation damage.

The administration of a single dose of radiation as large as 500 r to a small volume of tissue such as the human forearm may produce no detectable effect, but, if the same intensity of irradiation is applied to the whole body, death is almost certain. Whereas the energy expended per unit weight of tissue is approximately the same in both cases, the great difference in effect may be attributed to variations in radiosensitivity among various organs and to the interdependence of these units. The most sensitive criterion of radiation damage in whole-body irradiation of humans appears to be a decrease in the white blood cell count, which appears about eight days after exposure. This response indicates that the white blood cells and the system in which they are formed must have an especially high radiosensitivity. A whole-body irradiation of about 50 r, delivered in a single day, is required to produce a significant response. Chronic irradiation at much lower intensities may also produce this response. Data obtained in the radium and X-ray industries have resulted in the acceptance of 0.1 r per day as the "tolerance" dose for whole-body irradiation. This figure represents a dose well below that known to cause any detectable effect and has been generally used in the atomic energy industry. Somewhat higher intensities can be tolerated in exposures of limited regions of the body, such as the skin of the hands, and tolerance levels as high as 1 r per day have been accepted in such cases.

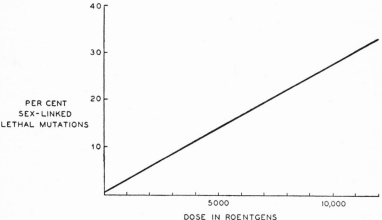

FIG. 8.5. Radiation-induced mutations in *drosophila*.[10]

Genetic Effects. The types of biological responses so far mentioned have represented lethal effects or obvious physical damage, either to whole organisms or individual types of tissues. They are lost with the death of the individual. However, much more subtle and perhaps more important changes may occasionally be produced. Damage to the germ cells of an organism, and in particular to the chromosomes and their genes, may result in an inheritable change in the organism. Such mutations occur spontaneously at a small rate in nature, and this rate can be increased by ionizing radiations, as shown in Fig. 8.5. This type of damage shows no threshold or recovery effect. Apparently the number of individuals affected is directly proportional to the radiation dose. It is interesting to note that the extrapolation of the line in Fig. 8.5 to a dose corresponding to that experienced by an individual due to cosmic radiations and natural radioelements gives a mutation rate much smaller than that actually observed, indicating that the "natural" rate cannot be attributed to nuclear radiations.

Mutations represent a very small fraction of the total response to ionizing radiations, but their importance lies in the fact that such changes, which are generally unfavorable, may be transmitted to succeeding generations. Dominant changes, which can appear in any of the progeny, may be removed by natural selection, but recessive changes, which appear only when two such individuals are mated, may remain in the population for some time. However, as long as only a small fraction of the population is subjected to irradiation at a low level, the rate of congenital anomalies will not seriously increase. Evans [11] has calculated that if as much as 5% of the population received a dose of 280 r before childbearing, the increase of congenital anomalies over the spontaneous rate after several thousand years would be only about 8%.

HEALTH PHYSICS

The increasing use of radioactive substances and other sources of ionizing radiations, as well as the particularly insidious nature of the associated hazards, has resulted in the development of a specialty known as health physics. This subject deals with the protection of personnel from radiation damage and is aptly named, since the protective and measurement procedures are essentially physical, but must be based on an adequate understanding of the physiological effects of the hazardous agents. Experience in radium and X-ray work and, more recently, in connection with the development of the chain-

---

[11] Evans, see Supplementary Reading, Chapter V.

reacting pile, has resulted in the formulation of extensive recommendations for safe practice in this field.[12, 13] This literature should be carefully considered by workers in nuclear science.

Hazards. The various types of radiations and particles vary considerably in their effectiveness in producing biological changes by external application. Alpha particles, because of their very small penetrating power, are effective only on the outermost layers of the skin, and a light covering will serve to shield an individual completely. The increased penetrating ability of beta particles makes a somewhat heavier covering desirable, but again the protection problem is not severe. In contrast, energetic electromagnetic radiation distributes ionization and excitation fairly uniformly throughout tissue and is able to reach and affect deep-seated, radiosensitive organs. The protection problem is correspondingly severe.

Ingestion and inhalation of radioactive materials roughly reverses the importance of the three types of radiations and in addition the biochemical behavior of the ingested activity must also be considered. If its chemical form is such that it is rapidly eliminated, the exposure will be less severe than if the activity accumulates in a particular organ. Unfortunately, some of the long-lived alpha-emitters such as radium, polonium, and plutonium tend to concentrate in the bone, in the region of the blood-forming tissues. This, coupled with the highly localized nature of their energy dissipation, makes them especially dangerous, giving rise to anemia and other blood disturbances. The accepted limit for radium deposition in the body is 0.1 microgram ($\sim 10^6$ alpha d/m), and the most important means of entrance into the body seems to be inhalation of active dust. Beta-emitters, although perhaps

---

12 Natn'l. Bureau of Standards, *X-Ray Protection*, HB20 and *Radium Protection*, HB23.

13 A.E.C., *Safe Handling of Radioisotopes*, Provisional Draft. Jan. 1948.

not so effective in terms of energy concentration, will never-theless expend a good fraction of their decay energy within the body. Internal sources of energetic gamma radiation are comparatively less effective, since only a small fraction of the decay energy will normally be absorbed by the body.

Measurements. The measurement of the radiation exposure to which personnel may be exposed has two general objec-tives: (1) the prevention of hazardous exposures and (2) the accumulation of data on actual exposures, which, when correlated with medical records, will increase the presently inadequate data on this subject. The instruments used for the first function should give a direct indication of the radiation field intensity. Geiger tubes with count rate meters have been used for their simplicity and great sensitivity, but it must be remembered that they count all particles which create an ion pair in the sensitive volume, regardless of particle type or energy. Thus they must be calibrated for each activity or radiation to be measured. Ionization chambers arranged to give a continuous indication of the ion current are less sensi-tive than Geiger tubes to most radiations, but still respond to radiation fields well below the tolerance levels. When properly constructed, such devices yield a response more nearly proportional to the biological effectiveness of the field. The detection of dangerous concentrations of alpha-emitters which might be ingested or inhaled over long periods of time is somewhat more difficult than guarding against simple ex-ternal exposure. The very short range of the alpha particles makes it necessary to employ special techniques for collecting samples from the air, air-borne dust and work surfaces, which are then examined by ordinary alpha-counting devices.

Devices designed to record the radiation exposure to which personnel have actually been subjected must be capable of being worn during work and are usually of the integrating type. Small, pencil-shaped ionization chambers, in which the degree of discharge is measured after a day's use, have been widely used to indicate the daily exposure of individuals. The photographic emulsion, worn in a small badge or in a finger ring, is a less sensitive but highly satisfactory monitoring device. The degree of darkening, when measured under controlled and calibrated conditions, indicates the total exposure during the period of use. Various clinical tests, chief among which is inspection of the blood, are used as indicators of radiation damage. A progressive decline in white blood cell count is taken as an indication of overexposure. Activity measurements on exhaled air, urine, etc., may be used as indications of internal activities.

Protection. Protection from overexposure to external sources of radiation is achieved by two means, distance and shielding. Laboratory operations with very active materials are frequently accomplished with long-handled tongs and other such devices. The precautions necessary will depend on the type of activity encountered. Alpha radiation requires little concern as far as external exposure is concerned, and most beta radiations will be highly absorbed by the glass walls of reaction vessels. However, direct exposure of the hands to beta radiations is a frequent hazard in high-activity work. Penetrating gamma radiations represent the greatest external hazard and may require the use of remote control procedures, with the operator shielded by great amounts of lead or other materials.

Protection from overexposure to internal sources rests largely on preventing the inhalation or ingestion of dangerous amounts of active materials. Clean, dust-free laboratories with liberal ventilation in rooms and in fume hoods is the best protection in this matter. In addition, individuals who work with very active materials must adopt many precautions, such as wearing gloves and special clothing, to avoid introducing active materials into their bodies.

SUPPLEMENTARY READING

"Symposium on Radiation Chemistry and Photochemistry," *J. Phys. and Colloid Chem.* **52**, 437-611 (1948).

Burton, "Radiation Chemistry," *J. Phys. and Colloid Chem.* **51**, 611 (1947).

Failla, "Biological Effects of Ionizing Radiations," *J. App. Physics* **12**, 279 (1941).

Parker, "Health Physics, Instrumentation and Radiation Protection," *Advances in Biological and Medical Physics*, Academic Press, New York, 1948.

Sullivan, "Control of Radioactivity Hazards," *Chem. Eng. News.* **25**, 1862 (1947).

CHAPTER IX

APPLIED NUCLEAR CHEMISTRY

THERE HAS been reserved for treatment here a large variety
of material in which phenomena associated with nuclear properties are employed in the study of problems arising in chemistry and allied sciences. In such applications, the methods and
principles of nuclear chemistry are used in analytical fashion,
frequently offering unique advantages in varying degrees and
sometimes permitting the study of otherwise undetectable
phenomena.

The examples selected for treatment here were chosen from
a large and rapidly increasing number of very diversified
studies. The choice is based on a desire to illustrate the
variety of applications and the various techniques involved,
but the critical assessment of the contribution to a particular
subject is left to the specialists in the various fields.

GEOCHEMISTRY

As mentioned in earlier chapters, the relative abundance
of the isotopes (both stable and radioactive) of an element
varies noticeably with the source of the element. Several
causes of such variations which have been recognized and
employed to yield information about the manner and time
of deposition of the material are briefly described here.

Age of Rocks. The radioactive decay of uranium and thorium yields, ultimately, helium and lead. (See Fig. 4.16.) With
an accurate knowledge of the decay constants of the semi-

stable nuclides, plus some assurance that none of the critical substances have been lost in the course of time, it is possible to estimate the age of rocks.[1]

The chemical atomic weight of lead isolated from nonradioactive ores is 207.22, which may be compared with the values found for lead isolated from the radioactive ores listed in Table 9.1. The thorium ores are seen to show an abnormally high atomic weight, owing to the presence of the decay product Pb^{208}, whereas uranium ores show an abnormally low value, owing to the presence of the decay products Pb^{206} and Pb^{207}. One method of estimating the age of the ore involves comparison of the excess amount of these isotopes with the uranium or thorium content. It is apparent that any selective leaching of lead or the radioactive elements will invalidate this method. In uranium-bearing ores, where U^{235} and U^{238} give rise to Pb^{207} and Pb^{206}, a less objectionable method is available. Because of the different rates of decay of the two uranium isotopes, the ratio of the two lead isotopes will change with time. Since this method depends only on the knowledge of the two abundance ratios and the decay constants, chemical action is not likely to alter the result.

TABLE 9.1. ATOMIC WEIGHT OF LEAD

Uranium Minerals	
Cleveite, Norway	206.08
Bröggerite, Norway	206.01
Pitchblende, Katanga	206.05
Kolm, Sweden	206.01
Thorium Minerals	
Thorite, Ceylon	207.77
Thorite, Norway	207.9

Although the highly radioactive minerals cannot be expected to retain the relatively large amounts of helium generated in

[1] Goodman and Evans, *Bull. Geol. Soc. America* **52** (491), 1941.

radioactive decay, the small uranium and thorium content of many other rocks yields amounts of helium which can be retained over long periods of time. Age measurements based on helium content extend the method to the large variety of deposits containing only traces of uranium and thorium, but this method is again subject to the uncertainties arising from possible helium losses. However, the "natural" helium content is very small, and therefore the method yields minimum ages.

C^{14} **Time Scale.** Libby [2] and others have recently sought and found extremely small amounts of radioactive C^{14} in those carbonaceous materials which are part of the present life cycle. This is ascribed to continuous neutron bombardment of nitrogen in the upper atmosphere by neutrons of cosmic origin, which produces C^{14} (5700-year) at a rate estimated to be about 3×10^{20} atoms per minute. If the neutron flux on the earth has remained constant for several C^{14} half-lives, an equal carbon disintegration rate will be found distributed among all the forms of carbon which are in equilibrium with atmospheric CO_2 on a 5000-year scale. The total amount of carbon in the atmosphere, the biosphere, and ocean carbonate is about 8×10^{13} metric tons. If the radiocarbon is uniformly distributed, a specific activity of about 4 disintegrations per minute per gram should be observed.

Because of the very low energy of the C^{14} beta radiations, such a small specific activity is difficult to measure directly, and early measurements were made on samples enriched by a thermal diffusion process (see Chapter II). A Geiger counter filled with enriched methane from recently living organisms (sewage) showed a higher count rate than the same counter filled with enriched methane from long-dead organisms (petroleum), and the difference, assuming no radiocarbon in petro-

---

[2] Libby, *Phys. Rev.* **69**, 671 (1946) ; Libby, Anderson, and Arnold, *Science* **109**, 227 (1949).

leum, corresponded to a specific activity of 10 ± 1 disintegrations per minute per gram of carbon in the "fresh" sample.

Later improvements in technique have permitted direct measurement of the radiocarbon content of samples of living matter from all over the world, and the results indicate that the activity is quite uniformly distributed. An average specific activity of 12.5 ± 0.2 disintegrations per minute per gram has been found. Assuming that this specific activity has been constant throughout recent geologic time, the date of removal of a sample from the life cycle may be estimated from its present specific activity and the known half-period of C^{14}. Samples of wood from ancient Egyptian tombs estimated to be about 4600 years old have been found to have a specific activity of 7.04 ± 0.20 disintegrations per minute per gram of carbon, in good agreement with the expected value of 7.15 ± 0.15. Isotopic enrichment should permit dating of samples as old as 25,000 years.

Paleo-temperatures.   Variations in the abundance ratios of the stable isotopes of elements such as oxygen are well known (see Chapter II) and may be ascribed to the existence of isotope separation effects among the various forms of combinations. As indicated in equation 2.16, the equilibrium constants for such exchange reactions are temperature-dependent. It has been proposed [3] that this effect may be used to estimate the temperature at which certain geologic deposits were formed.

Assuming that the abundance ratio of the oxygen isotopes has remained constant in the air and in sea water, the abundance ratio of these isotopes in deposited carbonates will differ by approximately the amount indicated in Table 2.3, the exact value depending upon the temperature of the environment in which the deposition occurred. Fig. 9.1 indicates

---

[3] Urey, *Science* **108**, 489 (1948).

the observed variation in the abundance ratio as a function of environment temperature among some modern samples. The small variation indicated, approximately 4 parts per thousand per degree in the abundance ratio O^{18}/O^{16}, indicates the extreme precision required in the measurements. Comparison of the isotope ratio in properly selected ancient deposits with the empirical curve thus established should permit estimation of the temperature at the time of deposition.

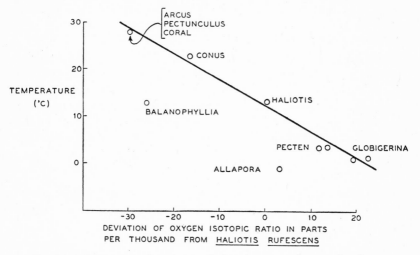

FIG. 9.1. Temperature-dependent variations in oxygen isotope abundance.

ISOTOPIC EXCHANGE

Isotopic exchange has been previously described (see Chapters II and VI) in terms of the generalized equation

$$AX^* + BX = AX + BX^*$$

where X^* denotes an atomic type distinguishable from X by virtue of its nuclear properties. The equilibrium state in such a reaction corresponds to a practically uniform distribution of the isotopes X and X^* in the several chemical forms. Large variations from the chemical identity of isotopes implied in this definition of isotopic exchange equilibrium are observed only with the lightest elements, particularly hydrogen.

Experimental test for isotopic exchange is fundamentally the same whether radioactive or stable isotopes are used. The compounds AX* and BX are prepared from samples of X having different isotopic compositions—perhaps different stable isotope abundances—or by use of a radioactive isotope of X in one sample. After mixing AX and BX, the isotopic composition of X in the two compounds is again examined to determine the extent of exchange. The results of some representative experiments are shown in Table 9.2, condensed from a review by Haissinsky and Dandel.[4]

TABLE 9.2. ISOTOPIC EXCHANGE [4]

A. Hydrogen

System	Result
H_2O—NH_4^+, aqueous solution	+, rapid, all H's
H_2O—Co amine	+, rate increases with Ph
H_2O—CH_3COCH_3, 1 hour-acid, neut. or alk	+
H_2O—$CH_3COCH_2COCH_3$	+, rapid
H_2O—C_2H_5CHO	+, slow
H_2O—$C_2H_5OC_2H_5$	—
H_2O—$CHCl_3$	—
H_2O—C_6H_6	—
H_2O—C_2H_5OH OH	+, rapid
C—H	+, very slow

B. Carbon

System	Result
CO—CO_2, gas at 200° C, 1.5 hr	—
$(CH_3CO)_2O$—CH_3COONa, 2-phase, 20 min	+, 55% exchange
$CO_3^=$—$C_2O_4^=$	—
$Fe(C_2O_4)_3^=$—$C_2O_4^=$, 25° C	+
$Co(C_2O_4)_3^=$—C_2O_4, 25° C	—

---

[4] See Haissinsky and Daudel, Supplementary Reading.

TABLE 9.2. (*Continued*)

C. Oxygen

System	Result
H_2O—BO_2^-, $BO_3^\equiv$, $B_4O_7^=$, $SiO_3^=$, $SO_3^=$, $SeO_3^=$, $AsO_3^\equiv$, $AsO_4^\equiv$, $MoO_4^=$, $WO_4^=$, $CrO_4^=$, $Cr_2O_7^=$, 100° C, neutral or acid, for some anions alkaline	+
H_2O—$CO_3^=$, $BrO_3^=$, IO_3^-	+, slow
H_2O—$PO_4^\equiv$, $SO_4^=$, $SeO_4^=$, acid solution only	+
H_2O—ClO_3^-, ClO_4^-, NO_3^-, NO_2^-, acid, neutral or alkaline	—
H_2O—CH_3OH, C_2H_5OH, C_6H_5OH, glycerine, several hours at 100° C	—
H_2O-aldehydes, 25° C—24 hr	+
H_2O-acetone, alkaline solution	+
CO_2—$CO_3^=$	+

D. Sulfur

System	Result
S—S_2Cl_2	+, rapid at 100° C
S—CS_2, 100° C, 68 hr	—
$S^=$—$SS^=$, 100° C, 1 hr	+, rapid
$S^=$—$SO_4^=$, 100° C, 36 hr	—
$SO_3^=$—$SO_4^=$, 100° C, 36 hr	—
S, $S^=$—$S_2O_3^=$, 100° C, 24 hr	+, one S in $S_2O_3^=$ exchanges

E. Halogens (X)

System	Result
X_2—X^-	+, extremely rapid
X^-—XO_3^-, neut. and alk.	—
X_2—XO_3^-, acid solutions	+, (?)
HCl—PCl_3	+, rapid
HCl—$POCl_3$	+, slow
HCl—$AsCl_3$, 60° C	+, rapid
HCl—$SiCl_4$, 60° C	+, very slow
HCl—CCl_4	—
Cl_2—PCl_3, PCl_5 in $CHCl_3$	+, rapid
Br_2, HBr—Al_2Br_6 solid	+, rapid
Br_2—PBr_3, $AsBr_3$, $SnBr_4$ in CCl_4	+, rapid
Br_2—$SeBr_4$ in CS_2	+
I^-—$TeI_6^=$, $HgI_4^=$, BiI_4^-, $PbI_4^=$	+, rapid
I_2—SbI_3 in pentane, 37°	+, rapid

TABLE 9.2. (*Continued*)

F. Metals

System	*Result*
Cu^{++}—$CuBr_4^=$	+, rapid
Cu^{++}—$Cu(NH_2CH_2COO)_2$	+
Cu^{++}—Cu acetylacetonate, in $CHCl_3$	+, rapid
Cu acetate—Cu salicylaldehyde, other chelates	+
Mn^{++}—MnO_2, neutral or acid solution	+
Mn^{++}—MnO_4^-	—
Mn^{++}—$Mn(C_2O_4)_2^=$	+
Mn^{++}—acetylacetonate, benzoylacetonate in CH_3OH	+
MnO_4^-—MnO_2	—
MnO_4^-—$MnO_4^=$, alkaline solution	+, rapid
Fe^{+++}—Fe^{++}6NHCl	+, rapid
Fe^{++}—$Fe(CN)_6^{\equiv}$	+, rapid
Fe^{+++}—$Fe(CN)_6^=$	—
$Fe(CN)_6^=$—$Fe(CN)_6^{\equiv}$	—
Fe^{+++}—iron hemoglobin, weak acid solution	+, slow
Co^{++}—$Co(CN)_6^=$	—
Co^{++}—$Co(NH_3)_6(NO_3)_3$ and other Werner complexes	—

Dynamic Equilibrium. The exchange of one or more atoms between two chemical forms without alteration of the total amount of either form follows from the concept of dynamic equilibrium, which was first tested experimentally by the use of tracer techniques.[5] Arsenate and arsenite ions exchange arsenic atoms at a measureable rate only in the presence of iodine or iodide ion, presumably through the reversible oxidation-reduction reaction

$$AsO_4^{\equiv} + 2I^- + 2H_3O^+ = AsO_3^{\equiv} + I_2 + 3H_2O$$

The rate of oxidation of arsenite by iodine and the rate of reduction of arsenate in nonequilibrium systems may be measured by ordinary chemical methods. In the equilibrium state these rates may be measured by the introduction of a chemically negligible quantity of radioactive atoms in one valence state, followed by periodic analysis of the rate of transfer to the other state. These rates agree well with the values pre-

---

[5] Wilson and Dickinson, *J. Am. Chem. Soc.* **59**, 1358 (1937).

dicted from the nonequilibrium measurements. The observation of a rapid isotopic exchange reaction between two chemical forms of an element therefore corresponds to the establishment of a rapid and reversible reaction involving the two states.

In many cases, the nature and rate of such a reaction may be predicted from macroscopic equilibrium studies. The great rapidity and reversibility of proton transfer reactions indicates that hydrogen exchange between water and the ionizable protons of acids will be very rapid, through equilibria such as

$$HCl + H_2O = H_3O^+ + Cl^-$$
$$NH_4^+ + H_2O = H_3O^+ + NH_3 \text{ (all H's)}$$
$$RCOOH + H_2O = H_3O^+ + RCOO^- \text{ (one H)}$$
$$RNH_2 + H_2O = OH^- + RNH_3^+ \text{ (both H's)}$$

Similar ease of exchange is to be anticipated in all cases where an electrolytic dissociation reaction connects the two forms in question, as in the cases

$$CuBr_4^= = Cu^{++} + 4Br^-$$
$$Mn(C_2O_4)_2^= = Mn^{++} + 2C_2O_4^=$$

and in the case

$$AgCl(s) = Ag^+(aq.) + Cl^-(aq.)$$

although slow diffusion of ions in the solid will permit rapid exchange only with the outermost layers of the solid phase. This phenomenon has been used as a method of estimating the surface area of crystalline precipitates by use of radioactive tracers.

The rapid exchange between I_2 and I^- is undoubtedly due to the reversible association reaction

$$I_2 + I^- = I_3^-$$

and a similar equilibrium

$$NO(g) + NO_2(g) = N_2O_3(g)$$

is responsible for nitrogen exchange between gaseous NO and NO_2. Other reversible gas phase equilibria such as

$$N_2O_4(g) = 2NO_2(g)$$

and

$$PCl_5(g) = PCl_3(g) + Cl_2(g)$$

also give rise to rapid exchange reactions, but exchange between gaseous hydrogen or nitrogen and ammonia is observed only in the presence of ammonia-synthesis catalysts.

Exchange Mechanisms. In many cases, the existence of a rapid isotopic exchange reaction may require the postulation of a reaction intermediate of a transient nature which may or may not have been anticipated in previous studies. Hydrogen exchange between ketones and water undoubtedly proceeds through the enol form

$$\overset{\text{keto}}{CH_3COCH_3} = \overset{\text{enol}}{CH_2{=}\underset{\underset{OH}{|}}{C}{-}CH_3}$$

previously anticipated but difficult to isolate. Such a mechanism is indicated by the lack of hydrogen exchange between water and paraffin hydrocarbons and the ready exchange with hydroxyl hydrogens.

Hydrogen exchange between concentrated sulfuric acid and hydrocarbons is a particularly interesting problem. Ethylene and other olefins seem to exchange by a reversible addition-subtraction mechanism

$$C_2H_4 + H_2SO_4 \rightleftharpoons CH_3{-}CH_2OSO_3H$$

since the exchange is always accompanied by some addition. On the other hand, hydrogen exchange between benzene and sulfuric acid can be accomplished with practically no simultaneous sulfonation. Substituents on the benzene ring affect the rate and orientation of the exchange reaction in a fashion very similar to that expected of an electrophilic substitution reaction. Ingold and Wilson [6] have proposed a reaction intermediate of the type

forming at points of high electron density. The deuterating ability of various acids decreases in order of decreasing acid strength, i.e.,

$$H_2SO_4 > H_2SeO_4 > H_3O^+ > CH_3COOH > H_2O$$

and substituents on the benzene ring increase the rate of deuteration (in the ortho and para positions) in order of increasing electron-donating ability in a series such as

$$O^- > NR_2 > OCH_3 > H > SO_3H$$

Exchange reactions which appear to involve simple electron transfer, such as that between Cu^+ and Cu^{++} or Fe^{++} and Fe^{+++}, certainly cannot occur by direct approach of two ions of like charge. Rather, it must be assumed that a complex with oppositely charged ions, such as

$$\begin{array}{c} Cl^- \\ Cu^+Cl^-Cu^{++} \\ Cl^- \end{array}$$

is the intermediate in such reactions. Heterogeneous exchange, perhaps even on the surface of a precipitate use to separate the two forms, could also account for these reactions.

Molecular Structure and Exchange. The influence of molecular structure on the rate of exchange may be exemplified by the exchange of bromine between bromide ions and alkyl bromides, which apparently takes place through the mechan-

---

[6] See Supplementary Reading.

ism of Walden inversion, since the rate of isomerization of active halides is found equal to the rate of exchange. The relative rates of exchange of molecules with increasingly complex organic radicals is shown in Table 9.3. The increased steric hindrance offered to the approach of a bromide ion is clearly illustrated.

TABLE 9.3. RELATIVE EXCHANGE RATE OF ALKYL BROMIDES [7]

Radical	Relative Rate
Methyl	17.6
Ethyl	1.0
Propyl	0.28
Isobutyl	0.03
Neopentyl	0.000

The exchangeability of oxygen in oxygenated anions with oxygen of water has been correlated with bond character by Haissinsky and Dandel.[4] These authors point out that when the electronegativity difference (Pauling scale) between oxygen and the central atom is 1.0 or greater, the exchange takes place readily in neutral or acid solutions. This may be exemplified by the cases $AsO_4^\equiv$ (difference, 1.7), $MoO_4^=$ (1.4), $CrO_4^=$ (1.4), $PO_4^\equiv$ (1.4), MnO_4^- (1.2), $CO_3^=$ (1.1), $SO_3^=$ (1.0). The ions BrO_3^- and IO_3^- (difference, 0.7 and 1.0, respectively) exchange oxygen very slowly with water. The ions NO_3^-, NO_2^-, ClO_4^-, ClO_3^- where the electronegativity difference is 0.5 do not exchange oxygen with water. An electronegativity difference of 1.0 or more corresponds, according to Pauling, to 20% or more ionic character in the bond, whereas a difference of 0.5 corresponds to about 5% ionic character in the bond.

As a final example of the influence of molecular structure on isotopic exchange, we may note the case of exchange of

[7] Ingold, Conference of the Faculty of Sciences, Paris, 1946.

sulfur between sulfide ion and thiosulfate ion. Only one of the sulfur atoms in the latter exchanges, indicating that the two sulfur atoms in the ion are not equivalent. This may be further demonstrated by preparing thiosulfate from sulfite and tracer sulfur, followed by acid decomposition of the thiosulfate into sulfur dioxide and sulfur.

$$S^* + SO_3^= \rightarrow S^*SO_3^= \xrightarrow{H^+} S^* + SO_2$$

The labeled sulfur is found entirely in the sulfur rather than in the sulfur dioxide, again demonstrating the nonequivalence of the sulfur atoms in thiosulfate.

Reaction Mechanisms and Exchange. The Walden inversion mechanism mentioned previously for iodine exchange between iodide ions and alkyl iodides indicates that the rate of exchange should be equal to the rate of isomerization or, conversely, that inversion should be accompanied by exchange. This equality has been confirmed for a number of optically active compounds,[8] including sec-octyl iodide and α-bromo-propionic acid. In all cases studied, the rates of inversion and of exchange were equal within experimental error.

A mechanism similar to the Walden inversion was at one time proposed for the iodine atom catalyzed cis-trans isomerization of diiodoethylene. This would require an equal rate of iodide exchange, which however proved to be at least one hundred times as fast as the isomerization but showed the same dependence on concentration of reactants.[9] The activation energy for the exchange is about 8 kcal/mole, whereas that for the isomerization is about 12 kcal/mole. A mechanism involving addition of an iodine atom to the double bond to form the radical $CHI\text{-}CHI_2$ was proposed. Restricted rota-

---

[8] Hughes, Juliusberger, Masterman, Topley, and Weiss, *J. Chem. Soc.* **1935**, 1525; Cowdrey, Hughes, Nevell, and Wilson, *ibid.* **1938**, 209.
[9] Noyes, Dickinson, and Schomaker, *J. Am. Chem. Soc.* **67**, 1319 (1945).

tion about the single bond was taken to account for the higher activation energy of the isomerization process.

The catalytic hydrogenation and exchange of olefins may be taken as an interesting example of the application of exchange studies to a heterogeneous process. With ethylene the two processes occur simultaneously on nickel, hydrogenation predominating at lower temperatures ($\sim 20°$ C.) and the exchange at higher temperatures ($\sim 120°$ C). Exchange equilibrium is attained only when the exchange reaction is rapid compared to hydrogenation, since the hydrogen-ethane exchange is not observed on this catalyst. Greenhalgh and Polanyi [10] have discussed two alternative mechanisms for these reactions, the first of which postulates different mechanisms for the exchange and hydrogenation reactions. Exchange is presumed to proceed by a dissociative addition of the olefin to the catalyst (K) followed by recombination with a hydrogen or deuterium atom.

Exchange:

$$RH_2 + K \to RH\text{---}K + H$$
$$RHK + D \to RHD + K$$

Hydrogenation:

$$RH_2 + H_2\text{---}K \to RH_4 + K$$

Hydrogenation is presumed to proceed by addition of adsorbed hydrogen to the olefin. In the alternate mechanism, both exchange and hydrogenation reactions begin with the formation of an absorbed radical, followed by further addition or by reformation of the olefin, resulting in exchange. Com-

$$RH_2 + K\text{---}D \to RH_2D\text{---}K$$

followed by

$$RH_2D\text{---}K \to RHD + K + H$$

or

$$RH_2D\text{---}K + H \to RH_3D + K$$

[10] Greenhalgh and Polanyi, *Proc. Roy. Soc. London* **35**, 520 (1939).

parison of the two mechanisms indicates that the essential difference is the proposal in the first case that the exchange reaction is unique in that an adsorbed ethylene radical is the intermediate.

The second mechanism given above, in which a common intermediate is formed for hydrogenation and exchange, is favored by Greenhalgh and Polanyi. They emphasize the very slow exchange rate of saturated hydrocarbons with hydrogen, whereas the both saturated and unsaturated hydrocarbons exchange at about the same rate with water (nickel catalyst).

Presumably this latter exchange, as well as the hydrogen-alkane exchange, proceed by a dissociation mechanism, which may also contribute to the olefin-hydrogen exchange, but the greater exchange rate with olefins must be due to some unique mechanism such as the atom addition. Migration of double bonds, observed on hydrogenation catalysts, also supports the second mechanism.

TRACER STUDIES

The isotopic tracer technique consists in the use of an artificial and abnormal isotope (stable or radioactive) distribution to "label" one or more atoms of a given element in a molecule or system containing many such atoms. The method may be illustrated by the classic and relatively simple studies of the hydrolysis of esters and the esterification reaction,[11] in which oxygen enriched in the heavy isotope, O^{18}, was used. Primary amyl acetate was hydrolyzed in heavy water (abnormally high O^{18} content) ; the amyl alcohol produced in this reaction proved to contain only the "natural" abundance of O^{18}, while the acetic acid contained the abnormal abundance of O^{18}. This

---

[11] Polanyi and Szabo, *Trans. Far. Soc.* **30**, 508 (1934). Roberts and Urey, *J. Am. Chem. Soc.* **59**, 2391 (1939).

proved conclusively that the hydrolysis proceeds according to
the mechanism

$$CH_3C \overset{O}{\underset{OC_5H_{11}}{\diagup}} + H_2O^{18} \longrightarrow C_5H_{11}OH + CH_3CO_2^{18}H$$

An equivalent result was obtained in the esterification of
benzoic acid with heavy methanol. In this case the product
water was "normal," and the O^{18} tracer was found in the
ester, according to the mechanism

$$C_6H_5COOH + HO^{18}CH_3 \longrightarrow C_6H_5COO^{18}CH_3 + H_2O$$

In experiments of this sort isotopic exchange of the critical
element between the various reactants and products is undesirable lest the "label" be lost by equal distribution in
the various forms. Earlier experiments using mercaptans,
where the sulfur atom is taken as an oxygen "tracer," indicated
the foregoing mechanisms but, of course, could not be regarded
as conclusive.

General Principles. As indicated in the example, the essential steps in a tracer experiment are three: first, the preparation
of the labeled reagent; second, the accomplishment of the
reaction under study; and, third, the separation and analysis
of the products.

Processes for the production of both radioactive and enriched stable isotopes usually yield a rather simple form of
the element involved. Since the great advantage of the tracer
method is most evident in complicated systems, a rather difficult synthesis may be required. This is especially true in the

case of the element carbon, and a considerable variety of synthetic methods has already been developed.[12] Such methods differ from ordinary synthetic procedures in that the amount of material treated is unusually small and the methods must provide a good yield of the desired product. Both of these features are a consequence of the limitations on the supply of isotopic tracers.

If the reaction under consideration is already well known and relatively simple, no special procedures may be necessary, except perhaps the necessity for operating on a rather small scale to conserve the tracer. The possibility of an isotopic exchange reaction which might dilute the tracer or confuse the results must also be considered. In using the isotopes of hydrogen, differences in reaction rate and equilibrium distribution may be significant. In complex reactions, especially biochemical reactions, the products may be numerous and complex. If the product of interest occurs in small yield, or may already be present in the system, considerable dilution of the tracer by ordinary isotopes may occur. Such a situation calls for a high concentration of the tracer in the starting material, in order that its presence may be detected in the product.

Analysis of the products may require only the establishment of the presence of the tracer in some product or may further require that the exact position of the tracer in the product molecule be established. In the latter case the use of established degradation reactions will be necessary.

Radioactive and Stable Tracers. For many elements the properties of the available isotopes dictate the choice between radioactive and stable tracer technique. Some important elements, such as sodium, phosphorus, and iodine, have only one stable isotope, precluding the possibility of stable tracer tech-

---

[12] Calvin, Heidelberger, Reid, Tolbert, and Yankwich, *Isotopic Carbon*, John Wiley & Sons, New York, 1949.

niques. With other elements, such as nitrogen, oxygen, and magnesium, the radioactive isotopes are so short-lived that only the simplest experiments are possible. The element aluminum falls in both of these classes.

When a choice of stable and radioactive tracer techniques is available, as in the case of carbon or sulfur, the comparative advantages of each must be considered in the light of the experiments contemplated. The major advantage of radioactive tracers lies in their detectability at extremely small concentrations. Even with a nuclide as long-lived as C^{14}, the specific activity of the undiluted nuclide is about 10^{10} disintegrations per minute per milligram, and, after a million-fold dilution by stable carbon, the specific activity is still well above the minimum measurable value. In contrast, a similar dilution of pure C^{13} by ordinary carbon would reduce the concentration of C^{13} to a value indistinguishable from the natural value (1%). This property of radioactive tracers makes them especially useful in biochemical systems, where the tracer may be widely distributed, or where the study of a minor product is desired.

The half-life and decay energy of a radioactive isotope may limit its use. An extremely long half-life may make it difficult to produce a high specific activity, especially when the nuclear bombardment involves no change in atomic number (n, γ and d,p). A small activation cross section is likewise unfortunate. At the other extreme, a short half-life may seriously limit the duration of the experiments.

The energy and type of decay shown by a radioactive tracer are important chiefly in regard to the ease of analysis. An energetic beta radiation, such as emitted by Na^{24}, is, in general, the most satisfactory for tracer analysis. An extremely weak radiation, as in the case of H^3, makes detection very difficult. The external nature of the detection devices in activity determinations makes activity analysis somewhat easier than mass analysis. In the former case, the radioactive tracer may be detected in a gaseous, liquid, or solid sample, frequently without isolation of a pure form. Mass spectroscopy, however, ordinarily requires a gaseous sample, and in the course of analysis the sample is normally altered or lost. On the other hand, activity analyses are, in general, less precise than mass spectrographic analyses.

Organic Reactions. One application of the tracer technique to the study of the mechanism of organic reactions has already been mentioned, but the discussion cannot be complete without some mention of the application of carbon tracers. Both stable and radioactive forms are available, and the techniques of synthesis and analysis have been intensively developed.

The study of rearrangement reactions with isotopic tracers has been especially profitable, since the migration of atoms or groups can be unequivocally established. For instance, the Willgerodt reaction has been studied [13] with acetophenone in which the carbonyl carbon was labeled with C^{14}. Treatment of this compound with ammonium sulfide in pyridine yields an amide ($\sim 65\%$ yield) and an acid ($\sim 14\%$ yield) as indicated below. However, the mechanism of formation of the two compounds is apparently quite different, since the labeled carbon is no longer adjacent to the benzene ring in the acid. Apparently the amide is formed by oxidation and reduction along the chain, whereas the acid represents a more violent rearrangement.

An especially interesting rearrangement reaction has been noted with propane in the presence of aluminum bromide catalyst.[14] Propane—1—C^{13} was synthesized from normal

[13] Dauben, Reid, Yankwich, and Calvin, *J. Am. Chem. Soc.* **68**, 2117 (1946).
[14] Beek, Otvos, Stevenson and Wagner, *J. Chem. Phys.* **16**, 255 (1948).

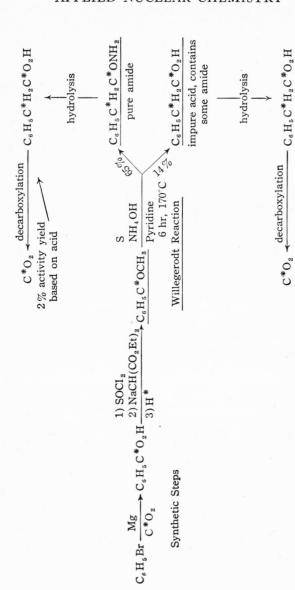

Synthetic Steps

$C_6H_5Br \xrightarrow[C^*O_2]{Mg} C_6H_5C^*O_2H \xrightarrow[\substack{1)\ SOCl_2 \\ 2)\ NaCH(CO_2Et)_2 \\ 3)\ H^*}]{} C_6H_5C^*OCH_3 \xrightarrow[\substack{NH_4OH \\ Pyridine \\ 6\ hr,\ 170°C \\ \underline{Willegerodt\ Reaction}}]{S}$

$\xrightarrow{65\%}$ $\underset{\text{pure amide}}{C_6H_5C^*H_2C^*ONH_2} \xrightarrow{\text{hydrolysis}} C_6H_5C^*H_2C^*O_2H \xrightarrow[\substack{2\%\ activity\ yield \\ based\ on\ acid}]{decarboxylation} C^*O_2 \ C_6H_5C^*H_2C^*O_2H$

$\xrightarrow{14\%}$ $\underset{\substack{\text{impure acid, contains} \\ \text{some amide}}}{C_6H_5C^*H_2C^*O_2H} \xrightarrow{\text{hydrolysis}} \underset{\text{pure acid}}{C_6H_5C^*H_2C^*O_2H} \xrightarrow[\substack{75\%\ activity\ yield \\ based\ on\ acid}]{decarboxylation} C^*O_2 \ C_6H_5C^*H_2C^*O_2H$

ethyl bromide and potassium cyanide containing 16.7 atom per cent C^{13}. In the mass spectrometer, the ionic types $C^{12}C^{13}H_5{}^+$ (mass 30) and $C_2{}^{12}H_5{}^+$ (mass 29) appeared in the ratio 0.106 in the propane as synthesized. This ratio is slightly greater than that computed from the C^{13} content, indicating that the $C^{12}-C^{12}$ bond is broken more frequently than the $C^{12}-C^{13}$ bond. After equilibration with the catalyst for 1074 hr. at 25° C, the ratio 30/29 is found to be 0.133, corresponding to statistical distribution of C^{13} among the three positions of the propane molecule.

Before:

$$C^{12}-C^{12}-C^{13} \text{ and } C^{13}-C^{12}-C^{12}$$

After:

$$C^{12}-C^{12}-C^{13}, \; C^{12}-C^{13}-C^{12}, \; C^{13}-C^{12}-C^{12}$$

The ratio of masses 46 and 44 ($C_2{}^{13}C^{12}H_8$ and $C_3{}^{12}H_8$) has a small value initially due to the natural presence of C^{13}, but this does not change during the course of the experiment, indicating that no intermolecular reactions occur. The reaction proceeds as though the carbon atoms of propane were completely separated by the catalyst and then the same atoms came together again in a random fashion. Similar rearrangements have been observed with more complicated hydrocarbon molecules such as butane and iso-butane.

Metabolism Studies. Tracer techniques are proving to be especially useful in the study of the extremely complicated and important reactions of plant and animal metabolism. As early as 1935, Schoenheimer and Rittenberg[15] began a series of tracer experiments which served to contradict previous con-

---

[15] Schoenheimer and Rittenberg, *J. Biol. Chem.* **111**, 175 (1935).

cepts of the static nature of living tissues. Dietary studies show that the composition of tissues remains remarkably constant whereas excretion of metabolic products closely parallels intake of foods. This led to the assumption of direct and immediate utilization of foods. However, when mice were fed partially deuterated linseed oil, a fat substitute, about 50% of the ingested fat was found in the fatty deposits of the body, in spite of the fact that the diet was insufficient to maintain the weight of the animal. More fat was being burned than ingested, but apparently the dietary fat was directly utilized only in part, the remainder coming from the fat deposits. These experiments indicate a rather rapid turnover of an apparently static tissue. Constancy of composition must therefore be attributed to a balanced rate of consumption and replacement, rather than lack of reaction.

Prior to the use of tracer techniques, many hypotheses concerning the biosynthesis of important biological compounds were based on the "balance method." Increased production of a compound following administration of some suspected precursor was taken as evidence of conversion. Among the objections to this method is the necessity of performing the experiments under somewhat abnormal conditions. Unusually large amounts of the experimental substances in the diet may be degraded and then utilized, or may stimulate changes in the body reactions without being directly utilized. Tracer techniques make it possible to follow the course of a synthetic reaction under normal conditions, and the precursors of several important compounds have been established. For instance, the synthesis of creatine has been clearly outlined by such methods. Through use of N^{15} tracer,[16] glycine has been shown to be the source of α-amino acid group, and arginine the source of the source of the guanido group. Use of methionine with

[16] Block and Schoenheimer, *J. Biol. Chem.* **138**, 167 (1941); Du Vigneaud, Cohn, Chandler, Schenck, and Simmonds, *J. Biol. Chem.* **140**, 625 (1941).

deuterium in the terminal methyl group demonstrated that this compound is the source of the methyl group in creatine.

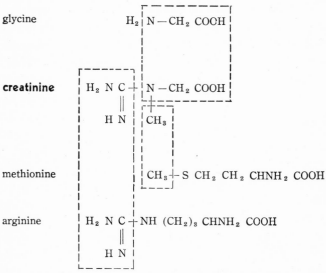

The very difficult study of photosynthesis has been considerably advanced through the use of radioactive carbon tracer.[17] Early work by Ruben and others was performed with the 20-min C^{11}, later work with 5700-year C^{14}. It is only in the last few years, since this material became available, that the tremendous gap between the reactants, carbon dioxide plus water, and the products, oxygen plus carbohydrates, has been noticeably closed. The subject is much too complicated for discussion here, but a few outstanding points may be mentioned. Using carbon dioxide containing radiocarbon, it has been demonstrated that the absorption of carbon dioxide is not a photochemical process; rather, that the absorption of light serves to produce some active form of hydrogen which reduces absorbed carbon dioxide. Carbon dioxide is absorbed in the absence of light and may be later converted to carbohydrates

[17] See Calvin, Supplementary Reading.

by illumination. In addition, the photochemical activation may be stored, permitting later dark absorption and reduction of carbon dioxide. Several of the intermediate forms of absorbed carbon dioxide, principally dicarboxylic acids, have been isolated and examined for carbon distribution. Stable oxygen tracer has been used to demonstrate that photosynthetic oxygen arises from water rather than carbon dioxide.

Calvin and his associates have developed a very useful analytical technique in connection with their studies of photosynthesis.[18] It represents an extension of the methods of paper chromatography, which are especially adaptable to the analysis of complex biochemical mixtures. After exposure of a plant to carbon dioxide containing a high specific activity of C^{14}, a measured quantity of plant extract is placed at the corner of a rectangular piece of filter paper. The spot is "developed" along one edge of the paper by solvent flow, and then in a direction at right angles to the first by flow of a second solvent. Various active compounds may be characterized by their position in this two coordinate system, as registered by the blackening of a photographic emulsion placed next to the paper chromatogram (see Fig. 9.2). The various active spots may be cut out of the chromatogram, and, with the addition of suitable carriers for suspected compounds, the nature of the compound and the position of the active carbon may be determined.

ANALYTICAL APPLICATIONS

Tracer techniques have been useful in testing many analytical procedures through study of coprecipitation, solvent extraction, and in the measurement of the solubility of very sparingly soluble substances. In addition, the use of radioactive materials has been suggested as a rapid analytical

---

[18] Calvin and Benson, *Science* **109**, 140 (1949).

method for use in chemical process control.[19] If a radioactive tracer for an impurity is added to the crude material, subsequent analyses for this substance consist simply of activity measurements. Several specialized applications are discussed below.

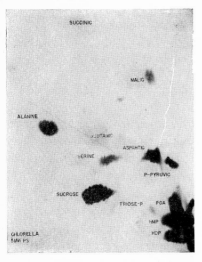 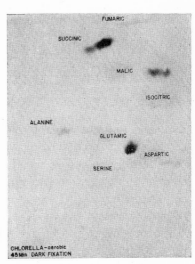

A. Dark fixation of $C^{14}O_2$.   B. Light fixation of $C^{14}O_2$.

FIG. 9.2.   Radiograms of paper chromatograms of algaie extracts after $C^{14}O_2$ absorption.

(Courtesy of M. Calvin, Radiation Laboratories, University of California.)

Surface Area. The determination of the surface area of crystalline precipitates by isotopic exchange between crystal surface and saturated solution was first suggested by Paneth in 1922, but, until artificial radioisotopes became available, the method could be strictly applied only to salts of the heaviest elements.

When a chemically insignificant amount of radioactive tracer is introduced into a saturated solution containing a crystalline

19 Irvine, *Anal. Chem.* **21**, 364 (1949).

solid, a rapid exchange occurs between the ions in solution and those in the surface of the precipitate. Further incorporation by recrystallization and by solid diffusion is usually quite slow, and the initial uptake of activity by the solid may be related to the surface area of the solid through the equation

$$S = A_a \times \frac{A_s}{N}$$

where

S = no. of surface atoms
A_a = adsorbed activity
$\frac{A_s}{N}$ = specific activity of solution in activity per stable atom

This method must be applied with some care, since the character of the surface and, in particular, the surface charge may considerably affect the results. It is most useful as a comparative method applied to similar precipitates under identical conditions.

Isotope Dilution. Quantitative analysis for an organic compound in a mixture of similar substances is frequently next to impossible. Separation by fractionation methods such as crystallization or distillation can yield pure samples, but usually in yields considerably less than 100%. The method of isotope dilution is especially adapted to the analysis of such mixtures.

A weighed amount of the compound to be estimated, containing an abnormal isotope abundance ratio (stable or radioactive) in one of its elements, is added to the mixture. There it is chemically indistinguishable from the compound of interest and is purified with it in subsequent fractionations. The isotope abundance ratio in the isolated compound is compared with that of the initially added material to complete the analysis. The relation

$$b = \left(\frac{A_i}{A_f} - 1 \right) a$$

where

a = weight of added compound
b = weight of compound in mixture

and A_i and A_f are the initial and final specific activities if radiotracers are used. If stable tracers are used, A_i and A_f represent the isotope abundances above the normal value for the element.

Activation Analysis.[20] Activation analysis depends upon the properties of activation cross section and decay reactions of the elements concerned. For extensive use it requires the availability of a rather strong source of neutrons or other activating agent. In a typical application, a small sample of the substance to be analyzed is subjected to neutron bombardment, followed by study of the decay and absorption characteristics of the induced activities. This information, together with quantitative knowledge of the neutron activation cross sections of the elements involved, may permit the estimation of the amount of one or more elements present in the sample. Obviously, the method is most sensitive and useful with those elements which have large activation cross sections, short half-lives, and energetic decay reactions. It has found particular use in the examination of materials intended for use in the chain-reacting pile, where substances with large neutron-capture cross sections are undesirable.

SUPPLEMENTARY READING

Bentley, "Oxygen-18 as a Tracer Element," *Nucleonics*, Feb., 1948.
Calvin, "Investigation of Reaction Mechanisms and Photosynthesis with Radiocarbon," *Nucleonics*, March, 1948.
Flagg and Wiig, "Tracer Isotopes in Analytical Chemistry," *Ind. Eng. Chem. Anal. Ed.* 13, 341 (1941).
Haissinsky and Daudel, "Isotopic Exchange and the Nature of the Chemical Bond," *Bull. soc. chim. France.* 1947, 552 (1947).

---

[20] Boyd, *Anal. Chem.* 21, 335 (1949).

Ingold and Wilson, "Exchange Reactions between Light and Heavy Hydrogen," *Zeits. f. Elecktrochem.* **44**, 62 (1938).

Keston, "Isotopes and their Applications in Biochemistry," *Advances in Nuclear Chemistry and Theoretical Organic Chemistry,* Interscience, New York, 1945.

Radin, "Isotope Techniques in Biochemistry," *Nucleonics*, Sept., Oct., Dec., 1947; Jan., Feb., 1948.

Reitz, "Methods and Results of the Use of Isotopes in Chemistry (with the Exception of Heavy Hydrogen)," *Zeits. f. Elektrochem.* **45**, 100 (1939).

Seaborg, "Artificial Radioactivity," *Chem. Rev.* **27**, 199 (1940).

Taylor, "Applications of Isotopes in Catalytic Reactions at Surfaces," *Advances in Nuclear Chemistry and Theoretical Organic Chemistry,* Interscience, New York, 1945.

Yankwich, "Radioactive Isotopes as Tracers," *Anal. Chem.* 21 318 (1949).

"Symposium on the Use of Isotopes in Biology and Medicine," University of Wisconsin Press, Madison, Wis., 1948.

APPENDIX A

FUNDAMENTAL CONSTANTS [1]

Rest Masses

Neutron	1.6751×10^{-24} gram
Proton	1.6729×10^{-24} gram
Electron	0.1055×10^{-28} gram
Electronic Charge	4.8024×10^{-10} e.s.u.
	1.60213×10^{-20} e. m. u.

Velocity of light in

vacuum (c)	2.99776×10^{10} cm/sec
Planck constant (h)	6.6234×10^{-27} erg sec
Boltzmann constant (k)	1.38032×10^{-16} erg/degree
Avogadro number (N)	6.025×10^{23}
Rydberg constant (R)	$109,737.30$ cm^{-1}

TABLE OF MASS-ENERGY CONVERSION FACTORS

	abs. ev.	ergs	cm^{-1}	cal [15°]	KWH	grams	a.m.u.
1 e. v. =	1	1.60×10^{-12}	8.1×10^3	3.83×10^{-20}	4.45×10^{-26}	1.78×10^{-33}	1.07×10^{-9}
1 erg =	6.24×10^{11}	1	5.04×10^{15}	2.39×10^{-8}	2.78×10^{-14}	1.11×10^{-14}	6.71×10^2
1 cm $^{-1}$=	1.24×10^{-4}	1.99×10^{-16}	1	4.74×10^{-24}	5.51×10^{-30}	2.20×10^{-37}	1.33×10^{-13}
1 cal =	2.61×10^{19}	4.19×10^7	2.11×10^{23}	1	1.16×10^{-6}	4.65×10^{-14}	2.79×10^{10}
1 KWH =	2.25×10^{25}	3.60×10^{13}	1.81×10^{29}	8.55×10^6	1	4.00×10^{-8}	2.41×10^{16}
1 gram=	5.63×10^{32}	9.0×10^{20}	4.53×10^{36}	2.14×10^{14}	2.50×10^7	1	6.02×10^{23}
1 a.m.u.=	9.31×10^8	1.49×10^{-3}	7.51×10^{12}	3.56×10^{-10}	4.15×10^{-17}	1.66×10^{-24}	1

[1] Du Mond and Cohen, *Rev. Mod. Phys.* **20**, 82 (1948).

APPENDIX B

THE ELEMENTS are arranged in a conventional form of the periodic table. The information included for each element includes the atomic number, chemical symbol, chemical atomic weight, electronic structure of the neutral atom, the K and L excitation potentials (in Kv.) and the first ionization potential (in volts). A sample item is given below

At. No.	Symbol	At. Wt.
	Electronic Structure	
K Kv.	L Kv.	1st I.P. v.

	I	II	III	IV	V
I	1 **H** 1,0078 1s¹ K L 1st. I.P. 13.53				
II	3 **Li** 6,940 1s²,2s¹ K L 1st. I.P. 5.36	4 **Be** 9.02 1s²,2s² K L 1st. I.P. 9.28	5 **B** 10,82 1s²,2s²,2p¹ K L 1st. I.P. 0.193 8.25	6 **C** 12,00 1s²,2s²,2p² K L 1st. I.P. 0.285 11.21	7 **N** 14,008 1s²,2s²,2p³ K L 1st. I.P. 0.390 14.47
III	11 **Na** 22.997 Ne core, 3s¹ K L 1st. I.P. 5.11	12 **Mg** 24,32 Ne core, 3s² K L 1st. I.P. 1.31 7.61	13 **Al** 26,97 Ne core, 3s²,3p¹ K L 1st. I.P. 1.56 5.96	14 **Si** 28,06 Ne core, 3s²,3p² K L 1st. I.P. 1.84 8.10	15 **P** 31,02 Ne core, 3s²,3p³ K L 1st. I.P. 2.15 11.0
IV	19 **K** 39.096 A core, 4s¹ K L 1st. I.P. 3.62 4.32	20 **Ca** 40,08 A core, 4s² K L 1st. I.P. 4.05 6.09	21 **Sc** 45,10 A core, 3d¹,4s² K L 1st. I.P. 4.51 6.7	22 **Ti** 47,90 A core, 3d²,4s² K L 1st. I.P. 4.98 6.81	23 **V** 50,95 A core, 3d³,4s² K L 1st. I.P. 5.49 6.76
	29 **Cu** 63,57 A core, 3d¹⁰,4s¹ K L 1st. I.P. 9.01 7.68	30 **Zn** 65,38 A core, 3d¹⁰,4s² K L 1st. I.P. 9.69 9.36	31 **Ga** 69,72 A core, 3d¹⁰,4s²,4p¹ K L 1st. I.P. 10.4 5.97	32 **Ge** 72,60 A core, 3d¹⁰,4s²,4p² K L 1st. I.P. 11.2 8.09	33 **As** 74,91 A core, 3d¹⁰,4s²,4p³ K L 1st. I.P. 11.9 10.5
V	37 **Rb** 85,44 Kr core, 5s¹ K L 1st. I.P. 15.2 2.08 4.16	38 **Sr** 87.63 Kr core, 5s² K L 1st. I.P. 16.2 2.22 5.67	39 **Y** 88,92 Kr core, 4d¹,5s² K L 1st. I.P. 17.1 2.38 6.5	40 **Zr** 91,22 Kr core, 4d²,5s² K L 1st. I.P. 18.1 2.55 6.92	41 **Cb** 92,91 Kr core, 4d⁴,5s¹ K L 1st. I.P. 19.1 2.72
	47 **Ag** 107,880 Kr core, 4d¹⁰5s¹ K L 1st. I.P. 25.6 3.82 7.54	48 **Cd** 112,41 Kr core, 4d¹⁰,5s² K L 1st. I.P. 26.8 4.03 8.96	49 **In** 114,76 Kr core, 4d¹⁰,5s²,5p¹ K L 1st. I.P. 28.0 4.25 5.76	50 **Sn** 118,70 Kr core, 4d¹⁰,5s²,5p² K L 1st. I.P. 29.3 4.48 7.30	51 **Sb** 121,76 Kr core, 4d¹⁰,5s²,5p³ K L 1st. I.P. 30.6 4.72 8.35
VI	55 **Cs** 132,91 Xe core, 6s¹ K L 1st. I.P. 36.0 5.74 3.87	56 **Ba** 137,36 Xe core, 6s² K L 1st. I.P. 37.5 6.02 5.19	RARE EARTHS See below	72 **Hf** 178,6 Xe core, 4f¹⁴,5d²,6s² K L 1st. I.P. 65.3 11.3	73 **Ta** 181,4 Xe core, 4f¹⁴,5d³,6s² K L 1st. I.P. 67.4 11.7
VII	79 **Au** 197,2 Xe core, 4f¹⁴,5d¹⁰6s¹ K L 1st. I.P. 80.9 14.4 9.19	80 **Hg** 200,61 Xe core, 4f¹⁴,5d¹⁰,6s² K L 1st. I.P. 83.4 14.9 10.38	81 **Tl** 204,39 Xe core, 4f¹⁴,5d¹⁰,6s²,6p¹ K L 1st. I.P. 85.9 15.4 6.07	82 **Pb** 207,22 Xe core, 4f¹⁴,5d¹⁰,6s²,6p² K L 1st. I.P. 88.4 15.9 7.38	83 **Bi** 209,00 Xe core, 4f¹⁴,5d¹⁰,6s²,6p³ K L 1st. I.P. 90.8 16.4 7.25
	87 **Fa** Rn core, 7s¹ K L 1st. I.P.	88 **Ra** Rn core, 7s² K L 1st. I.P. 5.25	89 **Ac** Rn core, 6d¹,7s² K L 1st. I.P.	90 **Th** 232,12 Rn core, 5f¹,6d¹,7s² K L 1st. I.P. 110.0 20.6	91 **Pa** Rn core, 5f²,6d¹,7s² K L 1st. I.P.

RARE EARTHS

57 **La** 138,92 Xe core, 5d¹,6s² K L 1st. I.P. 39.0 6.30 5.59	58 **Ce** 140,13 Xe core, 4f¹,5d¹,6s² K L 1st. I.P. 40.5 6.58 6.54	59 **Pr** 140,92 Xe core, 4f²,5d¹,6s² K L 1st. I.P. 42.0 6.86 (5.76)	60 **Nd** 144,27 Xe core, 4f³,5d¹,6s² K L 1st. I.P. 43.7 7.16 (6.31)
65 **Tb** 159,2 Xe core, 4f⁸,5d¹,6s² K L 1st. I.P. 52.1 8.75 (6.74)	66 **Dy** 162,46 Xe core, 4f⁹,5d¹,6s² K L 1st. I.P. 53.9 9.10 (6.82)	67 **Ho** 163,5 Xe core, 4f¹⁰,5d¹,6s² K L 1st. I.P. 55.6 9.44	68 **Er** 167,64 Xe core, 4f¹¹,5d¹,6s² K L 1st. I.P. 9.80

VI · VII · VIII · O

O group

2 **He** 4,002
$1s^2$
K L 1st. I.P.
0.025 · 24.47

Group VI / VII / O

8 **O** 16,0000
$1s^2,2s^2,2p^4$
K L 1st. I.P.
.529 · 13.55

9 **F** 19,000
$1s^2,2s^2,2p^5$
K L 1st. I.P.
0.69 · (18)

10 **Ne** 20,183
$1s^2,2s^2,2p^6$
K L 1st. I.P.
21.46

---

16 **S** 32,06
Ne core, $3s^2,3p^4$
K L 1st. I.P.
2.48 · 10.31

17 **Cl** 35,457
Ne core, $3s^2,3p^5$
K L 1st. I.P.
2.83 · 12.96

18 **A** 39,944
Ne core, $3s^2,3p^6$
K L 1st. I.P.
3.21 · 15.69

---

24 **Cr** 52,01
A core, $3d^5,4s^1$
K L 1st. I.P.
.00 · 6.74

25 **Mn** 54,93
A core, $3d^5,4s^2$
K L 1st. I.P.
6.56 · 7.40

26 **Fe** 55,84
A core, $3d^6,4s^2$
K L 1st. I.P.
7.13 · 7.83

27 **Co** 58,94
A core, $3d^7,4s^2$
K L 1st. I.P.
7.75 · 8.5

28 **Ni** 58,69
A core, $3d^8,4s^2$
K L 1st. I.P.
8.35 · 7.61

---

34 **Se** 78,96
A core, $3d^{10},4s^2,4p^4$
K L 1st. I.P.
2.7 · 9.70

35 **Br** 79,916
A core, $3d^{10},4s^2,4p^5$
K L 1st. I.P.
13.5 · 11.5

36 **Kr** 83,7
A core, $3d^{10},4s^2,4p^5$
K L 1st. I.P.
14.4 · 13.94

---

42 **Mo** 96,0
Kr core, $4d^5,5s^1$
K L 1st. I.P.
0.1 2.89 7.2

43 **Tc**
Kr core, $4d^6,5s^1$
K L 1st. I.P.

44 **Ru** 101,7
Kr core, $4d^7,5s^1$
K L 1st. I.P.
22.2 (7.7)

45 **Rh** 102,91
Kr core, $4d^8,5s^1$
K L 1st. I.P.
23.3 3.43 7.7

46 **Pd** 106,7
Kr core, $4d^{10}$
K L 1st. I.P.
24.4 3.63 8.3

---

52 **Te** 127,61
Kr core, $4d^{10},5s^2,5p^4$
K L 1st. I.P.
1.9 4.95 8.96

53 **I** 126,92
Kr core, $4d^{10},5s^2,5p^5$
K L 1st. I.P.
33.2 5.21 10.5

54 **Xe** 131,3
Kr core, $4d^{10},5s^2,5p^6$
K L 1st. I.P.
34.7 5.46 12.08

---

74 **W** 184,0
Xe core, $4f^{14},5d^4,6s^2$
K L 1st. I.P.
59.6 12.1 8.1

75 **Re** 186,31
Xe core, $4f^{14},5d^5,6s^2$
K L 1st. I.P.
71.5 12.6

76 **Os** 191,5
Xe core, $4f^{14},5d^6,6s^2$
K L 1st. I.P.
74.0 13.0 8.7

77 **Ir** 193,1
Xe core, $4f^{14},5d^9$
K L 1st. I.P.
76.5 13.5

78 **Pt** 195,23
Xe core, $4f^{14},5d^9,6s^1$
K L 1st. I.P.
78.8 13.9 8.88

---

84 **Po**
Xe core, $4f^{14},5d^{10},6s^2,6p^4$
K L 1st. I.P.

85 **At**
Xe core, $4f^{14},5d^{10},6s^2,6p^5$
K L 1st. I.P.

86 **Rn**
Xe core, $4f^{14},5d^{10},6s^2,6p^6$
K L 1st. I.P.
10.70

---

92 **U** 238,14
Rn core, $5f^3,6d^1,7s^2$
K L 1st. I.P.
16.2 21.8

93 **Np**
Rn core, $5f^4,6d^1,7s^2$
K L 1st. I.P.

94 **Pu**
Rn core, $5f^5,6d^1,7s^2$
K L 1st. I.P.

95 **Am**
Rn core, $5f^6,6d^1,7s^2$
K L 1st. I.P.

96 **Cm**
Rn core, $5f^7,6d^1,7s^2$
K L 1st. I.P.

---

61 **Pm**
Xe core, $4f^4,5d^1,6s^2$
K L 1st. I.P.

62 **Sm** 150,43
Xe core, $4f^5,5d^1,6s^2$
K L 1st. I.P.
47.0 7.78 (6.55)

63 **Eu** 152,0
Xe core, $4f^6,5d^1,6s^2$
K L 1st. I.P.
48.6 8.09 5.64

64 **Gd** 157,3
Xe core, $4f^7,5d^1,6s^2$
K L 1st. I.P.
50.4 8.41 (6.65)

---

69 **Tm** 169,4
Xe core, $4f^{12},5d^1,6s^2$
K L 1st. I.P.
59.5 9.82

70 **Yb** 173,04
Xe core, $4f^{13},5d^1,6s^2$
K L 1st. I.P.
61.4 10.56 (6.23)

71 **Lu** 175,0
Xe core, $4f^{14},5d^1,6s^2$
K L 1st. I.P.
63.6 10.91

APPENDIX C

In a series of twelve plates on the following pages various stable and unstable nuclides are arranged in a coordinate system of atomic number vs. mass number. Therefore a series of nuclides parallel to an axis represents an isotopic or isobaric series.

Stable nuclides are indicated by the chemical symbol and mass number in heavy type. This method of designation is also used for the longest-lived isotope of elements having no stable isotope. Symbol and mass number are also given for those unstable nuclides which occur in nature.

The information given for the stable nuclides includes the per cent abundance, the atomic mass (physical scale), and the thermal neutron activation cross section (in units of 10^{-24} cm.^{2}). The arrangement of the data is indicated below. The information given for unstable nuclides includes the half-life, particles and radiations observed in decay, and the energy of these (in units of mev). A predominant mode or energy of decay is indicated by underlining. The arrangement is indicated below.

Data on abundances, half-lives, and decay schemes are taken from the *Table of Isotopes*, Seaborg and Pearlman, *Rev. Mod. Phys.*, 20, 585 (1948), and is limited to those items in class A (element and mass number certain) and class B (element certain, mass number probable). Masses of stable isotopes are quoted from the compilation of Bethe in *Elementary Nuclear Theory*, John Wiley & Sons, New York, 1947. Thermal neutron activation cross sections are quoted from Seren, Friedlander, and Turkel, *Phys. Rev.*, 72, 888 (1947).

Owing to the limitations of space in a tabulation of this sort, numerous simplifications and a few omissions have been necessary, and the reader is referred to these sources when complete information is essential.

ARRANGEMENT OF DATA

Stable	Unstable
Symbol Mass No. Per cent abundance Physical mass Neutron cross section($\times 10^{24}$cm^2)	Half-life Particles and Energies (mev)

ABBREVIATIONS

Half-lives: s = seconds, m = minutes, h = hours, d = days, y = years

α = alpha particle
β^+ = positron, or positive beta particle
β^- = negatron, or negative beta particle
γ = gamma radiation
e^- = conversion electron
I.T. = isomeric transition

Isomeric states of a nuclide are indicated by a subdivision of the appropriate unit. In the case of some naturally unstable nuclides, the half-life and decay data are given in place of mass and cross section.

Nuclide Chart (I)
$_1H^1$ through $_{12}Mg^{25}$

Axes: A (mass number) across the top, Z (element, 12→1) at the left, N at the right.

Nuclide	Half-life / Abundance	Decay & energy (MeV)	Mass / γ / other
Mg 25	10.11%		24.993
Mg 24	78.60%		23.992
Mg 23	11.6 s	β+ 2.8	
Na 25	58.2 s	β− 3.4	γ
Na 24	14.8 h	β− 1.4	γ 1.4, 2.8
Na 23	100%		22.9962, 0.63
Na 22	2.6 y	β+ 0.58	γ 1.3
Na 21	23 s		
Ne 23	40 s	β− 4.1	
Ne 22	9.21%		21.9984
Ne 21	0.28%		20.9996
Ne 20	90.51%		19.9987
Ne 19	20.3 s	β+ 2.2	
F 20	12 s	β− 5.0	γ 2.2
F 19	100%		19.0045, 10^{-3}
F 18	112 m	β+ 0.7	no γ
F 17	70 s	β+ 2.1	
O 19	29.4 s	β− 4.5, 2.9	γ 1.6
O 18	0.204%		18.0049, 2×10^{-4}
O 17	0.039%		17.0045
O 16	99.757%		16.0000
O 15	126 s	β+ 1.7	
O 14	76.5 s	β+ 1.8	γ 2.3
N 17	4.14 s	β− 3.7	n 1.0
N 16	7.35 s	β− 4, 10	γ 7
N 15	0.38%		15.0049
N 14	99.62%		14.0075
N 13	9.93 m	β+ 1.24	no γ
C 14	5100 y	β− 0.15	no γ
C 13	1.1%		13.0075
C 12	98.9%		12.0038
C 11	20.5 m	β+ 0.95	no γ
C 10	20 s	β+ ~2	
B 12	0.027 s	β− 12	
B 11	81.17%		11.0128
B 10	18.83%		10.0162
Be 10	2.5×10^6 y	β− 0.56	no γ
Be 9	100%		9.0150
Be 8	VERY SHORT	2α 0.055	
Be 7	52.9 d	K	γ 0.49
Li 8	0.89 s	β− 12, 2α 2.0	
Li 7	92.61%		7.0182
Li 6	7.39%		6.0169
He 6	0.89 s	β− 3.7	no γ
He 4	100%		4.0039
He 3	10^{-4}%		3.0170
H 3	12.1 y	β− 0.018	no γ
H 2	0.02%		2.0147
H 1	99.98%		1.0081

Nuclide Chart (2)

$_{11}$Na^{22} through $_{22}$Ti^{46}

The chart is a Segrè-type grid: the vertical axis gives the element (proton number Z, from 11 Na up to 22 Ti) and the horizontal axis gives the mass number A (22 – 46). Individual boxes are transcribed below.

Nuclide	Half‑life / Abundance	Decay & γ (MeV)	Atomic mass / notes
Ti 46	7.95%		45.966
Ti 45	3.08h	β^{+}1.2	
Sc 46	85d / 20s	β^{-}0.36 γ / I.T. γ,e^{-}	
Sc 45	100%		44.966; 22(85d)
Sc 44	2.44d / 3.92h	I.T.,e,γ / β^{+}1.5,γ	
Sc 43	3.92h	β^{+}1.1 γ1.7	
Sc 41	0.87s	β^{+}4.9	
Ca 46	0.0033%		
Ca 45	152d	β^{-}0.26 no γ	
Ca 44	2.06%		43.972
Ca 43	0.15%		42.972
Ca 42	0.64%		41.971
Ca 40	96.96%		39.975
K 41	6.7%		40.974; 1.0
K 40	0.011%	1.8×10^{9}y β^{-}1.9, K	
K 39	93.3%		38.974
K 38	7.7m	β^{+}2.5 γ2.2	
A 41	110m	β^{-}1.2 γ1.3	
A 40	99.633%		39.975
A 38	0.060%		37.974
A 37	34.1d	K, no γ	
A 36	0.307%		35.978
A 35	1.88s	β^{+}4.4	
Cl 39	1h	β^{-}	
Cl 38	38.5m	β^{-}1.2,5.2 γ1.6,2.1	
Cl 37	24.6%		36.9775; 0.56
Cl 36	2×10^{5}y	β^{-}0.64, β^{+}, K	
Cl 35	75.4%		34.9787; 0.17f(n,p)K
Cl 34	33m	β^{+}2.5 γ3.4	
Cl 33	2.4s	β^{+}4.1	
S 37	5.04m	β^{-}1.6 γ2.6	
S 36	0.016%		35.978
S 35	87.1d	β^{-}0.17	
S 34	4.18%		33.9771; 0.26
S 33	0.74%		32.980
S 32	95.06%		31.9809
S 31	2.6s	β^{+}3.8	
P 32	14.3d	β^{-}1.7 no γ	
P 31	100%		30.984; 0.23
P 30	2.55m	β^{+}3.0	
P 29	4.6s	β^{+}3.6	
Si 31	170m	β^{-}1.8 no γ	
Si 30	3.05%		29.983; 0.12
Si 29	4.67%		28.986
Si 28	92.28%		27.986
Si 27	4.9s	β^{+}3.7	
Al 29	6.7m	β^{-}2.5	
Al 28	2.30m	β^{-}3.0 γ1.8	
Al 27	100%		26.989; 0.21
Al 26	6s	β^{+}3.0	
Al 25	8s	β^{+}	
Mg 27	10.2m	β^{-}0.8,1.8 γ1.0,0.8	
Mg 26	11.29%		25.989; 0.048
Mg 25	10.11%		24.993
Mg 24	78.60%		23.992
Mg 23	11.6s	β^{+}2.8	
Na 24	14.8h	β^{-}1.39 γ1.4,2.8	
Na 23	100%		22.9962; 0.63
Na 22	2.6y	β^{+}0.58 γ1.3	

Chart axes: vertical axis labelled **N**, rows 31 → 20 (element number, Ca = 20 … Ga = 31); horizontal axis labelled **A**, columns 43 → 67 (mass number).

Columns A = 43 – 55

N \ A	43	44	45	46	47	48	49	50	51	52	53	54	55
27 Co													18.2 h / β+1.5 / γ0.16-1.2
26 Fe										7.8 h / β+0.55	8.9 m / β+	Fe 54 / 5.81% / 53.957	4 y / K / no γ
25 Mn									46 m / β+2.0	21 m / β+2.7 / γ; 5.8 d / β+,K / γ1.5		310 d / K / γ0.84	Mn 55 / 100% / 54.957 / 10.7
24 Cr							41.9 m / β+1.5 / γ0.2,1.6	Cr 50 / 4.49% / 11	26.5 d / K / γ0.32 / e-	Cr 52 / 83.78% / 51.956	Cr 53 / 9.43% / 52.956	Cr 54 / 2.30% / 6×10^{-3}	1.3 h
23 V					33 m / β+1.9	16 d / β+0.72 / γ1.0,1.3	600 d / K / no γ		V 51 / 100% / 50.957 / 4.5	3.74 m / β-2.1 / γ1.5			
22 Ti			3.08 h / β+1.2	Ti 46 / 7.95% / 45.966	Ti 47 / 7.75% / 46.964	Ti 48 / 73.45% / 47.963	Ti 49 / 5.51% / 48.964	Ti 50 / 5.34% / 49.9621 / 0.14(6m)					
21 Sc	3.92 h / β+1.1 / γ1.6	2.44 d / I.T. / e-γ; 3.92 h / β+1.5 / γ	Sc 45 / 100% / 44.966 / 22(asd)	85 d / β-0.36 / γ; 20 s / I.T. / γ / e-			2.5 h / β-2.3 / γ0.8						
20 Ca	Ca 43 / 0.15% / 42.972	Ca 44 / 2.06% / 0.63	152 d / β-0.26 / no γ	Ca 46 / 0.0033%		Ca 48 / 0.19%							

Columns A = 56 – 67

N \ A	56	57	58	59	60	61	62	63	64	65	66	67
31 Ga									48 m / β+	15 m / K / e- / γ0.05,0.12	9.4 h / β+3.1	78.3 h / K / γ0.1-0.3 / e-
30 Zn							9.5 h / K	38 m / β+2.3 / K	Zn 64 / 48.89% / 63.955 / 0.51	Zn 65 / 250 d / K,β+0.3 / γ1.1 / e-	Zn 66 / 27.81% / 65.954	Zn 67 / 4.07% / 66.954
29 Cu					24.6 m / β+1.8 / γ1.5	3.4 h / β+1.2 / no γ / K	10.5 m / β+2.6 / γ0.56	Cu 63 / 69.09% / 62.957	Cu 64 / 12.8 h / K,β+0.66 / β-0.57 / γ1.35	Cu 65 / 30.91% / 64.955 / 1.82	5 m / β-2.9 / γ1.3	56 h / β-0.56
28 Ni	3 s	36 h / β+0.67	Ni 58 / 67.76% / 57.9594	5×10^{4} y / K	Ni 60 / 26.16% / 59.9495	Ni 61 / 1.25% / 60.953	Ni 62 / 3.66% / 61.9493	300 y / β-0.05	Ni 64 / 1.16% / 63.947 / 1.96	2.6 h / β-1.9 / γ1.1	56 h / β-	
27 Co	72 d / β+1.5 / γ0.8-3.3 / K	270 d / β+0.3 / γ0.12-0.22	72 d / K,β+0.47 / γ0.8	Co 59 / 100% / 0.86(11m) / 21.7(5y)	5.3 y / β0.31 / γ; 10.7 m / I.T.? / β-							
26 Fe	Fe 56 / 91.64% / 55.956	Fe 57 / 2.21% / 56.957	Fe 58 / 0.34% / 0.36	46.3 d / β-0.3,0.5 / γ1.1,1.1,1.3								
25 Mn	2.59 h / β-1.0,2.8 / γ2.0,0.8											

Nuclide Chart (3)
$_{20}Ca^{43}$ through $_{31}Ga^{67}$

Nuclide Chart (4)

$_{29}Cu^{64}$ through $_{40}Zr^{88}$

Axes: rows labelled **N** (values 40, 39, 38, 37, 36, 35, 34, 33, 32, 31, 30, 29 — giving element rows Y→Cu); columns labelled **A** (mass numbers 88, 87, 86, 85, 84, 83, 82, 81, 80, 79, 78, 77, 76, 75, 74, 73, 72, 71, 70, 69, 68, 67, 66, 65, 64).

Y (Z = 39)

A	Data
87	14h I.T.,γ,e^- / 80h K no γ
88	2.0h β^+1.6 / 1056+ K,γ,β

Sr (Z = 38)

A	Data
84	Sr 84 0.56%
85	70m I.T.,γ,e^- / 65d K,γ 0.8
86	Sr 86 9.86% 1.29
87	Sr 87 7.02% / 2.7h I.T.,γ,e^- 0.122
88	Sr 88 82.56% 0.0050

Rb (Z = 37)

A	Data
84	~40d β^+
85	Rb 85 72.8% 0.72
86	Rb 86 19.5d β^-1.8,0.7 γ1.1
87	Rb 87 27.2% 0.122
88	17.5m β^-4.6

Kr (Z = 36)

A	Data
76	14.7h K no γ
77	1.1h K β^+1.7
78	Kr 78 0.342%
79	34h K,β^+0.9,0.6 γ0.2
80	Kr 80 2.223%
82	Kr 82 11.50%
83	Kr 83 11.48% / 113m I.T.,γ no γ
84	Kr 84 57.02%
85	Kr 85 4.5h β^-1.0,γ / 9.4y β^-0.7 no γ
86	Kr 86 17.43%
87	Kr 87 74m β^-~4
88	Kr 88 3h β^-2.5

Br (Z = 35)

A	Data
75	1.7h β^+1.6 K no γ
76	15.7h β^+3.15 γ2 e^-0.18
77	57.2h β^+ γ
78	6.4m β^+2.3 γ0.8,0.6
79	Br 79 50.5%
80	18m β^-,γ,β^+ / 4.4h I.T.,γ,e^-
81	Br 81 49.5% 2.25
82	34h β^-0.47 γ0.5–1.4
83	2.4h β^-1.0 no γ
84	30m β^-5.3
86	55.6s β^-,n
88	16.0s β^-

Se (Z = 34)

A	Data
74	Se 74 0.87% 22
75	Se 75 127d K γ e^-
76	Se 76 9.02%
77	Se 77 7.58% / 17.5s I.T.,γ,e^-
78	Se 78 23.52%
80	Se 80 49.62%
81	17m β^- no γ / 59m I.T.,e^-
82	Se 82 9.19% 0.050+
83	25m β1.5,γ / 67s β3.4,γ
84	~2.5m β^-

As (Z = 33)

A	Data
71	52m β^+ / 60h K
72	26h β^+2.8 γ2.4
73	90d K e^- γ0.05
74	17.5d β^-0.9,β^+ γ0.6
75	As 75 100% 4.2
76	26.8h β^-1.3–3.0 γ0.5–1.7
77	40h β^-0.8 γ0.27
78	80m β^-1.4 γ0.27

Ge (Z = 32)

A	Data
66	~140m
68	250d K
70	Ge 70 20.55%
71	11d K,e^- / 39.7h I.T.,e^-,γ
72	Ge 72 27.37%
73	Ge 73 7.61%
74	Ge 74 36.74% 0.38
75	89m β^-1.1 γ
76	Ge 76 7.67%
77	12h β^-2.0,γ / 59s β^-2.8
78	2.1h β^-0.9 γ

Ga (Z = 31)

A	Data
64	48m β^+
65	15m K,β^+ e^- γ0.06,0.12
66	9.4h β^+3.1 γ
67	78.3h K e^- γ0.1–0.3
68	68m β^+1.9
69	Ga 69 60.2% 1.40
70	20.3m β^-1.7
71	Ga 71 39.8% 3.4
72	14.3h β^-0.64–3.2 γ0.68–2.5
73	5h β^-1.4 no γ

Zn (Z = 30)

A	Data
64	Zn 64 48.89% 0.51
65	Zn 65 250d K,β^+ γ1.1
66	Zn 66 27.81%
67	Zn 67 4.70%
68	Zn 68 18.61%
69	13.8h I.T.,γ,e^- / 57m β^-0.9
70	Zn 70 0.620%

Cu (Z = 29)

A	Data
64	Cu 64 12.8h K,β^+,β^- γ 0.57 0.66 1.35
65	Cu 65 30.91% 1.82
66	5m β^-2.9 γ1.3
67	56h β^-0.56

Nuclide Chart (5)

$_{36}Kr^{85}$ through $_{47}Ag^{109}$

Z \ A	85	86	87	88	89	90	91	92	93	94	95	96	97	98	99	100	101	102	103	104	105	106	107	108	109
47																						24.5 m $\beta^+_{2.0}$ no γ 8.2 d K, e^-, γ	**Ag 107** 51.35% 44.3 s I.T., γ e^-	2.3 m β^- 2.8	**Ag 109** 48.65% 40.4 s I.T., γ e^-
46																4.0 d K $\gamma_{0.09,1.8}$	9 h K, $\beta^+_{2.3}$ no γ	**Pd 102** 0.8% 101.94	17 d K	**Pd 104** 9.3% 103.94	**Pd 105** 22.6% 104.94	**Pd 106** 27.2% 105.94		**Pd 108** 26.8% 107.94 11.2	13 h β^- 1.03 no γ
45																19.4 h K, $\beta^+_{3.0}$ γ 1.2 e^- 0.6	4.3 d K γ 0.35 e^-	210 d β^+ 1.13 β^- 1.04 γ 0.46	**Rh 103** 100% 57 m I.T., e^-	44 s β^-, γ, e^- 4.2 m I.T., γ, e^-	36.5 h β^- 0.65 γ 0.33 e^-	30 s β 35.5 $\gamma_{0.3-1.3}$			
44											1.65 h β^+ 1.1 γ 0.95	**Ru 96** 5.68%	2.8 d K γ_{e^-} 0.23	**Ru 98** 2.22%	**Ru 99** 12.81%	**Ru 100** 12.70%	**Ru 101** 16.98%	**Ru 102** 31.34% 1.2	42 d β^- 0.3 γ 0.56	**Ru 104** 18.27% 0.67	4.5 h β^- 1.4 γ 0.76	1.0 y β^- ~0.03 no γ			
43								4.5 m β^+ 4.3 γ 1.3		53 m I.T., e^- < 53 m K, β^+, γ	20.0 h K, γ, e^- 56 d K, β^+, γ	4.30 d K $\gamma_{0.3-1.1}$ e^- 0.64	90 d I.T., e^- > 100 y	2.7 d β^- 1.3 γ 0.9	**Tc 99** 9.4×10^5 y $\beta_{0.32}$ no γ 6.0 h I.T., γ, e^-	80 s β^- 2.3 γ 0.6	14.0 m β^- 1.3 γ 0.3				short β^-				
42								**Mo 92** 15.86%	6.7 h $\beta^+_{0.3,0.7}$ γ 1.6	**Mo 94** 9.12% 93.95	**Mo 95** 15.7% 94.95	**Mo 96** 16.5% 95.94	**Mo 97** 9.45% 96.95	**Mo 98** 23.75% 97.94 0.42	67 h β^- 1.3 γ 0.4	**Mo 100** 9.62% 0.48	14.6 m $\beta^-_{1.0,2.2}$ $\gamma_{0.3,0.9}$				short β^-				
41						15.6 h β^+ ~1 γ 1	62 d I.T., γ, e^-	10.1 d $\beta^-_{1.8}$ γ 21.6 h $\beta^-_{1.2}$ γ	**Cb 93** 100% ~1.0↑	6.6 m I.T., e^- > 10^4 y	35 d $\beta^-_{0.15}$ γ e^- 90 h I.T., e^-	2.8 d β^- 1.8 γ 1	68 m β^- 1.4 γ 0.78	30 m β^-											
40					4.5 m I.T., γ, e^- 80.1 h $\beta^+_{1.1}$ no γ	**Zr 90** 51.46%	**Zr 91** 11.23%	**Zr 92** 17.11%		**Zr 94** 17.40% 0.33	65 d $\beta^-_{0.89,1.0}$ $\gamma_{0.73,0.23}$ e^-	**Zr 96** 2.80% 0.032	17.0 h β^- 2.2 γ ~ 0.8												
39			14 h I.T., γ, e^- 80 h K no γ	2.0 h β^+ 1.6 105 d K, γ, β^+	**Y 89** 100% 1.24	62 h β^- 2.3 no γ	57 d β^- 1.53 51.0 m I.T., γ, e^-	3.5 h β^- 3.5 γ ~ 1	10.0 h β^- 3.1 γ 0.7	20 m β^- γ			short β^-												
38	70 m I.T., γ, e^- 65 d K, γ 0.8	**Sr 86** 9.86% 1.29	**Sr 87** 7.02% 2.7 h I.T., γ, e^-	**Sr 88** 82.56% 0.0050	53 d β^- 1.5 no γ	25 y β^- 0.61 no γ	9.7 h $\beta^-_{1.3,3.2}$ γ 1.3	2.7 h β^-	7 m β^-	~ 2 m β^-			short β^-												
37	**Rb 85** 72.8% 0.72	19.5 d β^- γ 1.1	**Rb 87** 27.2% 0.122	17.5 m β^- 4.6	15 m β^- 3.8 γ	short β^-	short β^-		short β^-	short β^-			short β^-												
36	4.5 h $\beta^-_{1.0}$, γ 9.4 y $\beta^-_{0.7}$ no γ	**Kr 86** 17.43%	74 m β^- ~ 4	3 h β^- 2.5	2.6 m β^-	33 s β^-	9.3 s β^-	2.3 s β^-	2.2 s β^-	1.4 s β^-			short β^-												

Chart organized with mass number A across the top (130 → 106) and proton number Z / element down the side (55 → 44).

Mass numbers A = 130 – 118

Z / El.	130	129	128	127	126	125	124	123	122	121	120	119	118
55 Cs	30 m												
54 Xe	Xe 130 4.07%	Xe 129 26.23%	Xe 128 1.90%	75 s I.T.,γ,e^- / 34 d e^-,γ	Xe 126 0.088%		Xe 124 0.094%						
53 I	12.6 h β^-0.6,1.0 γ0.4-0.7	long β^-	24.99 m β^-2.0,1.6 γ0.43	I 127 100% 6.25	13.0 d β^-1.1 γ0.5	56 d K no γ	4.0 d β^+						
52 Te	Te 130 34.46% 0.02↑0.008↑	72 m β^-1.8 γ / 32 d I.T.,e^- 0.016↑	Te 128 31.72% 0.10↑0.07↑	9.3 h β^-0.76↑0.7 / 90 d I.T.,e^-	Te 126 18.72% 0.76↑0.07↑	Te 125 7.01%	Te 124 4.63%	Te 123 0.89%	Te 122 2.49%	143 d I.T.,γ,e^- / 17 d K,γ0.61	Te 120 0.091%	4.5 d K γ1.4 e^-0.2,0.5	6.0 d K no γ
51 Sb		4.2 h β^-		93 h β^-1.2 γ0.72		2.7 y β^-0.8,0.7 γ0.55	60 d β^-0.6,2.8 / 21 m,1.3 m I.T.,I.T.	Sb 123 42.75% 2.5↑	2.8 d β^-1.4,2.0 / 3.5 m I.T.,e^-	Sb 121 57.25% 6.8↑	17 m β^+1.53 / 60 d K,γ,1e^-	39 h K no γ	3.3 m β^+3.1
50 Sn						10 m β~2.2 γ~0.74	Sn 124 6.11% 123.94 0.57	10 d β^-2.6 γ	Sn 122 4.78% 121.95 0.19	28 h β^-0.4 no γ / 36 m β^-1.5	Sn 120 33.03% 119.94 0.22↑0.04↑	Sn 119 8.62% 118.94	Sn 118 23.98% 117.94

Mass numbers A = 117 – 106

Z / El.	117	116	115	114	113	112	111	110	109	108	107	106
50 Sn	Sn 117 7.54% 116.94	Sn 116 14.07% 115.94	Sn 115 0.35% 114.94	Sn 114 0.61%	105 d K γ0.085 e^-	Sn 112 0.90% 1.1						
49 In	117 m β^-1.73 no γ	13 s β^-2.8 no γ / 54.31 m β^-0.8 γ	In 115 95.77% 4.5 h I.T.,γ,e^-	72 s β^+1.98 / 48 d I.T.,e^-	In 113 4.23% 105 m I.T.,γ,e^-	20 m I.T.,γ,e^- / 9 m β^+,β^-	2.7 d K γ0.17,0.25 e^-	65 m β^+1.6	6.5 h K,β^+2 γ			
48 Cd	170 m β^-1.3-1.7	Cd 116 7.58% 1.4	2.33 d β^-0.6,1.58 / 43 d β^-1.86,0.6	Cd 114 28.86% 1,γ0.14	Cd 113 12.26% 2.3 m I.T.	Cd 112 24.07%	Cd 111 12.75% 48.7 m I.T.,e^-	Cd 110 12.39%	330 d K	Cd 108 0.875%	6.7 h K,β^+ 0.84	Cd 106 1.215%
47 Ag					5.3 h β^-2.2 no γ	3.2 h β^-3.6 γ0.86	7.5 d β^-1.04 no γ	24.2 s β^-2.6 γ / 225 d K,γ,e^-,β	Ag 109 48.65% 40.4 s I.T.,γ,e^-	2.3 m β^-2.8	Ag 107 51.35% 44.3 s I.T.,γ,e^-	24.5 m β^+ no γ / 8.2 d K,e^-,γ
46 Pd						21 h β^-0.2 no γ	26 m β^-3.5 0.86	Pd 110 13.5% 109.94 0.39	13 h β^-1.03 no γ	Pd 108 26.8% 107.94 11.2		Pd 106 27.2% 105.94
45 Rh												30 s β^-3.5 γ0.3-1.3
44 Ru												1.0 y β^-0.03 no γ

Sm (62)

Sm 144	3.16%
Sm 147	15.07%
Sm 148	11.27%
Sm 149	13.84%
Sm 150	7.47%, 149.964
Sm 151	~20 y, β⁻0.06, no γ

Pm (61)

Pm 141	2.42 h, K,β⁺0.78, γ1.05, 10.1
Pm 143	200 d, K, γ0.67, e⁻
Pm 147	3.7 y, β⁻0.22, no γ
Pm 148	5.3 d, β⁻2.5, γ0.8
Pm 149	47 h, β⁻1.1, γ0.25

Nd (60)

Nd 142	27.13%
Nd 143	12.20%
Nd 144	23.87%
Nd 145	8.30%, 144.962
Nd 146	17.18%, 145.962
Nd 147	11.0 d, β⁻0.4,0.9, γ0.6, e⁻0.03
Nd 148	5.72%, 147.962
Nd 149	1.7 h, β⁻1.6, γ
Nd 150	5.60%, 149.964

Pr (59)

Pr 140	3.5 m, β⁺2.5
Pr 141	100%
Pr 142	19.3 h, β⁻2.14, γ1.9
Pr 143	13.8 d, β⁻0.95, no γ
Pr 144	17.5 m, β⁻3.07, γ0.135, e⁻

Ce (58)

Ce 136	0.193%
Ce 138	0.250%
Ce 139	140 d, K, γ0.16,1,8, e⁻
Ce 140	88.48%
Ce 141	28 d, β⁻0.60, γ0.21
Ce 142	11.07%
Ce 143	33 h, β⁻1.36, γ0.5
Ce 144	275 d, β⁻0.35, no γ

La (57)

La 137	< 400 y
La 138	0.089%
La 139	99.911%, 138.95, 8.4
La 140	40.4 h, β⁻1.4, γ1.65
La 141	3.7 h, β⁻2.9, no γ
La 143	20 m, β⁻
La 144	short, β⁻

Ba (56)

Ba 130	0.101%
Ba 131	12.0 d, K, γ0.22,0.50, e⁻
Ba 132	0.097%
Ba 133	38.8 h, I.T.,γ,e⁻; >20 y, K,γ,e⁻
Ba 134	2.42%
Ba 135	6.59%
Ba 136	7.81%
Ba 137	11.32%; 2.63 m, I.T., γ, e⁻
Ba 138	71.66%
Ba 139	84 m, β⁻2.27, γ0.16,1
Ba 140	308 h, β⁻1.1, γ0.16,1, e⁻0.53
Ba 141	18 m, β⁻, γ
Ba 143	< 1 m, β⁻
Ba 144	short, β⁻

Cs (55)

Cs 130	30 m
Cs 131	10.2 d, K, γ0.147, e⁻
Cs 132	7.1 d, K, γ0.62, e⁻-0.6
Cs 133	100%
Cs 134	2.3 y, β⁻,γ,e⁻; 3.15 h, I.T.,γ,β
Cs 135	9.2 d, β⁻,γ,e⁻; 15.6 m, I.T., γ, e⁻
Cs 136	13.7 d, β⁻0.28, γ0.9
Cs 137	37 y, β⁻0.55
Cs 138	37 m, β⁻
Cs 139	9.7 m, β⁻
Cs 140	16 s, β⁻
Cs 141	short, β⁻
Cs 143	~1.3 s, β⁻

Xe (54)

Xe 127	75 s, I.T.,γ,e⁻; 34 d, e⁻,γ
Xe 128	1.90%
Xe 129	26.23%
Xe 130	4.07%
Xe 131	21.17%
Xe 132	26.96%
Xe 133	5.3 d, β⁻0.34, γ0.085, e⁻
Xe 134	10.54%
Xe 135	9.2 d, β⁻,γ,e⁻; 15.6 m, I.T., γ, e⁻
Xe 136	8.95%
Xe 137	3.8 m, β⁻4
Xe 139	41 s, β⁻
Xe 140	16 s, β⁻
Xe 141	1.7 s, β⁻

I (53)

I 127	100%, 6.25
I 128	24.99 m, β⁻2.0,1.6, γ0.43
I 129	long, β⁻
I 130	12.6 h, β⁻0.6,1.0, γ0.4-0.7
I 131	8.0 d, β⁻0.60, γ0.37,0.08, e⁻
I 132	2.4 h, β⁻0.9,2.2, γ0.6,1.4
I 133	22 h, β⁻1.4, γ0.55
I 134	54 m, β⁻, γ>1
I 135	6.7 h, β⁻1.4,1.0, γ1.6

Te (52)

Te 127	9.3 h, β⁻; 90 d, I.T., e⁻0.088,0.0
Te 128	31.72%
Te 129	72 m, β⁻1.8, γ; 32 d, I.T., γ
Te 130	34.46%; 30 m, I.T., 0.18,0.08, e⁻
Te 131	25 m, β⁻; 30 h, I.T., e⁻

Sb (51)

Sb 127	93 h, β⁻1.2, γ0.72

Nuclide Chart (8)
₅₈Ce¹⁴⁵ through ₆₉Tm¹⁶⁹

Chart axes: mass number A (columns, 145–169) versus neutron number N (vertical) and element Z.

Tm ($Z=69$)
- Tm 166 — 7.7 h; K, β^+ 2.1; γ 1.5; e⁻ 0.24
- Tm 167 — 9 d; K; γ 0.22, 0.96; e⁻ 0.21
- Tm 169 — 100%; 1×10⁻⁶ s; I.T., γe⁻

Er ($Z=68$)
- Er 162 — 0.1%
- Er 164 — 1.5%
- Er 166 — 32.9%
- Er 167 — 24.4%
- Er 168 — 26.9%
- Er 169 — 9.4 d; β 0.33; no γ

Ho ($Z=67$)
- Ho 163 — 7 d; K; e⁻ 0.4
- Ho 165 — 100%; 59.6
- Ho 166 — 27.0 h; β^- 1.8

Dy ($Z=66$)
- Dy 156 — 0.0524%
- Dy 158 — 0.0902%
- Dy 160 — 2.294%
- Dy 161 — 18.88%
- Dy 162 — 25.53%
- Dy 163 — 24.97%; e⁻ 0.4
- Dy 164 — 28.18%; 2690↓1204 I.T. e⁻
- Dy 165 — 145 m, β^- 0.4+1.2 γ; 1.25 m, I.T., e⁻ 0.1,0.12

Tb ($Z=65$)
- Tb 159 — 100%; 10.7↑
- Tb 160 — 3.9 h, β^-; 73.5 d, β^- 0.6,0.8 γ
- Tb 161 — 5.5 d; β^- 0.5; γ 1.28

Gd ($Z=64$)
- Gd 152 — 0.20%
- Gd 153 — 155 d; K; γ 0.102; e⁻ 0.2,0.4
- Gd 154 — 2.15%; 153.97
- Gd 155 — 14.78%; 154.97
- Gd 156 — 20.59%; 155.97
- Gd 157 — 15.71%; 156.97
- Gd 158 — 24.78%; 157.97
- Gd 160 — 21.79%; 159.97

Eu ($Z=63$)
- Eu 151 — 47.77%; 1380↑
- Eu 152 — 9.2 h, β^+, γe⁻; long, β^- γ e⁻
- Eu 153 — 52.23%
- Eu 154 — >20 y; β^- 0.9; γ 1.1
- Eu 155 — 2–3 y; β^- 0.18; γ 0.084
- Eu 156 — 15.4 d; β^- 0.5,2.5; γ 2.0

Sm ($Z=62$)
- Sm 147 — 15.07%
- Sm 148 — 11.27%
- Sm 149 — 13.84%
- Sm 150 — 7.47%
- Sm 151 — ~20 y; β^- 0.06; no γ
- Sm 152 — 26.63%; 1.0×10¹³ γ e⁻; α 2.14
- Sm 154 — 22.53%; 4.9
- Sm 155 — 25 m; β^- 1.9; γ~0.3
- Sm 156 — ~10 h; β^-~0.8

Pm ($Z=61$)
- Pm 147 — 3.7 y; β^- 0.22; no γ
- Pm 148 — 5.3 d; β^- 2.5; γ 0.8
- Pm 149 — 47 h; β^- 1.1; γ 0.25
- Pm 150 — 1.7 h; β^- 1.6; γ

Nd ($Z=60$)
- Nd 145 — 8.30%; 144.962 145.962
- Nd 146 — 17.18%; 145.962
- Nd 147 — 11.0 d; β^- 0.4,0.9; γ 0.6; e⁻ 0.03
- Nd 148 — 5.72%; 147.962
- Nd 150 — 5.60%; 149.964

Nuclide Chart (9)
65Tb165 through 76Os189

Z \ A	189	188	187	186	185	184	183	182	181	180	179	178	177	176	175	174	173	172	171	170	169	168	167	166	165
76	Os 189 16.1% 189.04	Os 188 13.3%	Os 187 1.64%	Os 186 1.59%	97 d K γ0.75	Os 184 0.018%																			
75		18.9 h β⁻1.48 γ... e⁻0.12	Re 187 62.93% 4×10^{12} y β⁻0.043 γ... e⁻	92.8 h β⁻1.07 no γ	Re 185 37.07% 101	50 d β⁻0.2 K γ0.17,1.00 e⁻		64 h K γ0.22,1.52 e⁻0,1,0.6																	
74			24.1 h β⁻0.6,1.3 γ0.09-0.14 e⁻	W 186 29.17% 34.2	73.2 d β⁻0.43 no γ	W 184 30.68% 2.12	W 183 14.24%	W 182 25.77%	140 d K β⁻0.14,1.88 e⁻	W 180 0.122%															
73								117 d β⁻1.07 e⁻ 16.2 m β⁻0.2 γ	Ta 181 100% 20.6	8.2 h K γ<0.5 e⁻			2.66 d K e⁻0.1	8.0 h K γ1.7 e⁻ d0.12-1.8											
72									46 d β⁻0.46 γ0.48-1.49	Hf 180 35.11% 10.0	Hf 179 13.84%	Hf 178 27.10%	Hf 177 18.47%	Hf 176 5.30%	70 d K γ0.3,1.5 e⁻	Hf 174 0.18%									
71													6.8 d β⁻0.44 γ0.2	Lu 176 2.6% 7.3×10^{10} y β⁻ K γ... Bi 0 no γ 3.67 h	Lu 175 97.5% 15 γ...				9 d K γ0.17,0.7	2.15 d K,β⁺ γ1.5 e⁻0.1	33 d K γ0.2,0.4 e⁻				
70													2.4 h β⁻1.3	Yb 176 13.38%	99 h β⁻0.6,0.18 γ0.35	Yb 174 29.58%	Yb 173 17.02%	Yb 172 21.49%	Yb 171 14.26%	Yb 170 4.21%		Yb 168 0.06%			
69																			500 d β⁻0.1 γ 2.5×10^{-6} s e⁻	127 d β⁻0.98 γ0.83 e⁻	Tm 169 100% γ... 1×10^{-6} s I.T. γ,e⁻		9 d K γ0.24,0.86 e⁻0.21	7.7 h K,β⁺ γ2.1,1.5 e⁻0.24	
68																				Er 170 14.2%	9.4 d β⁻0.33 no γ	Er 168 26.9%	Er 167 24.4%	Er 166 32.9%	
67																								27.0 h β⁻1.8	Ho 165 100% 59.6
66																									145 m β⁻0.4-1.3 γ 1.25 m I.T. γ0.11,0.18
65																									

Nuclide Chart (10) — ₇₄W¹⁸⁶ through ₈₄Po²¹⁰

Columns are mass number A (210 … 186); rows are atomic number Z (element).

Z = 84 (Po)
- Po 210: 138 d; α 5.30; γ 0.77
- (A 208): 3 y; α 5.14; no γ
- (A 207): 5.7 h; K; γ 0.8; α 5.14
- (A 206): 9 d; K; γ 0.8; α 5.2

Z = 83 (Bi)
- RaE 210: 5.0 d; β⁻ 1.17; no γ
- Bi 209: 100%; 209.05; 0.015
- (A 207): K; γ 1.3; α 5.14
- (A 206): 6.4 d; K; γ 0.74; e⁻
- (A 204): 12 h; K; γ; e⁻ 0.2, 0.8
- (A 200): 62 m; α 5.15
- (A 199): 27 m; α 5.47; K

Z = 82 (Pb)
- RaD 210: 22 y; β⁻ 0.025; γ 0.047
- (A 209): 3.32 h; β⁻ 0.70; no γ
- Pb 208: 52.3%; 208.05
- Pb 207: 22.6%; 207.05
- Pb 206: 23.6%; 206.05
- Pb 204: 1.5% / 68 m; I.T., γ, e⁻
- (A 203): 52 h; I.T. or K
- (A 200): 18 h; K
- (A 199): 1–2 h; K

Z = 81 (Tl)
- RaC″ 210: 1.32 m; β⁻ 1.80
- (A 209): 2.2 m; β⁻ 1.8
- ThC″ 208: 3.1 m; β⁻ 1.72; γ 2.62
- AcC″ 207: 4.76 m; β⁻ 1.47
- (A 206): 4.23 m; β⁻ 1.65; no γ
- Tl 205: 70.9%; 205.05; 0.11
- (A 204): 2.7 y; β⁻ 0.80; no γ
- Tl 203: 29.1%; 203.05; 7.5
- (A 202): 11.8 d; K; γ 0.40
- (A 200): 27 h; K; γ⁻ 0.4
- (A 199): 7 h; K; γ 1.5, 0.5; e⁻

Z = 80 (Hg)
- (A 205): 5.5 m; β⁻ 1.62
- Hg 204: 6.7%; 0.34
- (A 203): 52 h; I.T. or K
- Hg 202: 29.6%
- Hg 201: 13.2%
- Hg 200: 23.3%
- Hg 199: 17.0%
- Hg 198: 10.1%
- (A 197): 64 h, K, γ, e⁻ ; 23 h, K, γ, e⁻
- Hg 196: 0.15%

Z = 79 (Au)
- (A 199): 3.3 d; β⁻ 0.38; γ 0.18
- (A 198): 2.69 d; β⁻ 0.96; γ 0.4; e⁻
- Au 197: 100%; K, γ, e⁻ ; 7.5 s, I.T. e⁻
- (A 196): 5.55 d, β⁻, γ, e⁻ K, 96.4 ; 14.0 h, β⁻ I.T. e⁻ 0.1
- (A 195): 185 d; K; γ 0.1,1,6; e⁻ 0.1,1,6
- (A 194): 39.5 h; K; γ 0.3,1,8,2,0; e⁻ 0.3,1,8
- (A 193): 15.8 h; K; e⁻ <0.2
- (A 192): 4.7 h; K; γ 2.3; e⁻ 0.4

Z = 78 (Pt)
- (A 199): 31 m; β⁻ 1.8
- Pt 198: 7.23%; 198.05
- (A 197): 18 h, β⁻ 0.65 ; 80 m, I.T. γ, e⁻
- Pt 196: 25.4%; 196.05
- Pt 195: 33.7%; 195.04
- Pt 194: 32.8%; 194.04
- (A 193): 4.33 d; K; γ 0.1,6,1,6; e⁻ 0.11
- Pt 192: 0.78%
- (A 191): 3.00 d; K; γ 0.6,7,1,6; e⁻ 0.5

Z = 77 (Ir)
- Ir 193: 61.5%; 193.04; 128
- (A 194): 19.0 h; β⁻ 2.2; γ 1.35
- Ir 192: 70 d, β⁻ γ e⁻ ; 1.5 m, I.T. γ, e⁻
- Ir 191: 30.5%; 191.04; 1000+
- (A 190): 10.7 d; K; γ⁻ 0.25

Z = 76 (Os)
- (A 193): 32 h; β⁻ 1.5; γ 1.17
- Os 192: 41.0%; 192.04; 1.6
- (A 191): 15.0 d; β⁻ 0.142; γ 0.04+0.18; e⁻
- Os 190: 26.4%; 190.03; 8.6
- Os 189: 16.1%; 189.04
- Os 188: 13.3%
- Os 187: 1.64%
- Os 186: 1.59%

Z = 75 (Re)
- (A 188): 18.9 h; β⁻ 2.05; γ 0.14+1.48; e⁻ 0.12
- Re 187: 62.93%; 4×10¹² y; β⁻ 0.043; 25.3
- (A 186): 92.8 h; β⁻ 1.07; no γ

Z = 74 (W)
- (A 187): 24.1 h; β⁻ 0.6,1,3; γ 0.4,8+0.14; e⁻
- W 186: 29.17%; 34.2

Nuclide Chart (II) — $_{81}$Tl^{206} through $_{92}$U^{230}

Rows = atomic number Z (element), columns = mass number A.

A	92	91	90	89	88	87 (N)	86	85	84	83	82	81
230	20.8 d / α 5.85	17.7 d / K / β⁻ 1.1	Io 230 / 8×10^{4} y / α 4.66 / γ									
229	58 m / K / α 6.42	1.5 d / K / α 5.69	7000 y / α 5.0									
228	9.3 m / α 6.72 / K	22 h / K / α 6.09 / K	Rd Th 228 / 1.90 y / α 5.4,5.3 / γ	MsTh$_2$ 228 / 6.13 h / β⁻ 1.55 / γ	MsTh$_1$ 228 / 6.7 y / β⁻ 0.016							
227		38 m / α 6.46 / K	Ra Ac 227 / 18.6 d / α 6.0	Ac 227 / 21.7 y / β⁻ <0.01 / α 4.94								
226		1.7 m / α 6.81	30.9 m / α 6.30	22 h / β⁻	Ra 226 / 1622 y / α 4.79 / γ 0.19							
225			7.8 m / α 6.57 / K	10.0 d / α 5.80	14.8 d / β⁻ 0.2							
224			short / α 7.20	2.9 h / K / α 6.17	Th X 224 / 3.64 d / α 5.68							
223				2.2 m / α 6.64 / K	Ac X 223 / 11.2 d / α 6.72,6.61 / γ	Fa 223 / 21 m / β⁻ 1.20 / γ 0.090						
222				short / α 6.96	38 s / α 6.51		Rn 222 / 3.83 d / α 5.49					
221					31 s / α 6.71	4.8 m / α 6.30						
220					short / α 7.49	27.5 s / α 6.69	Tn 220 / 54.5 s / α 6.28					
219					very short / α 7.85	~0.02 s / α 7.30	An 219 / 3.92 s / α 6.82					
218 (A)							0.019 s / α 7.12		RaA 218 / 3.05 m / K/β / α 6.00			
217							~10^{-3} s / α 7.74	0.018 s / α 7.02				
216							very short / α 8.07	3×10^{-4} s / α 7.79	ThA 216 / 0.158 s / α 6.77 / β			
215								10^{-4} s / α 8.00	AcA 215 / 1.83×10^{-3} s / α 7.37 / β			
214								very short / α 8.78	RaC' 214 / 1.6×10^{-4} s / α 7.68	RaC 214 / 19.7 m / β⁻ 3.15 / α 5.5	RaB 214 / 26.8 m / β⁻ 0.65 / γ	
213									4.2×10^{-6} s / α 8.34	47 m / β⁻ 1.3 / α 5.86		
212								0.25 s / α	ThC' 212 / 3.0×10^{-7} s / α 8.78	ThC 212 / 60.5 m / α 6.1,6.0 / β⁻ 2.2	ThB 212 / 10.6 h / β⁻ 0.36 / γ	
211								At 211 / 7.5 h / K / α 5.89	AcC' 211 / 5×10^{-3} s / α 7.43	AcC 211 / 2.16 m / α 6.6,6.3 / β⁻	AcB 211 / 36.1 m / β⁻ 0.5,1.40 / γ 0.8	
210								8.3 h / K / γ	Po 210 / 138 d / α 5.30 / γ	RaE 210 / 5.0 d / β⁻ 1.17 / no	RaD 210 / 22 y / β⁻ 0.025 / γ 0.047	RaC″ 210 / 1.32 m / β⁻ 1.80
209										Bi 209 / 100% / 209.05 / 0.015	3.32 h / β⁻ 0.70 / no γ	2.2 m / β⁻ 1.8
208									3 y / α 5.14 / no γ		Pb 208 / 52.3% / 208.05	ThC″ 208 / 3.1 m / β⁻ 1.72 / γ 2.62
207									5.7 h / K / γ 1.3 / α 5.14		Pb 207 / 22.6% / 207.05	AcC″ 207 / 4.76 m / β⁻ 1.47 / γ
206									9 d / K / α 5.2 / γ 0.8	6.4 d / K / γ 0.74 / e⁻	Pb 206 / 23.6% / 206.05	4.23 m / β⁻ 1.51 / γ

$_{88}$Ra^{221} ——

Nuclide chart region for Z = 88–99 (Ra through Es) and A = 227–251. Columns are the mass number A; rows are the element (Z). Rows Z = 97, 98, 99 and columns A = 243–251 are empty on this page.

Z ＼ A	242	241	240	239	238	237	236	235	234	233	232	231	230	229	228	227
96 (Cm)	Cm 242 / 150 d / α 6.08		26.8 d / α 6.26													
95 (Am)	16 h / β^- 0.8 / γ 400 γ / β 0.5α	Am 241 / 490 y / α 5.48 / γ 0.062	50 h / K / α / γ 1.3	12 h / K / γ 0.3 e^- / α 5.77	~2.5 h / α 6.50											
94 (Pu)		~10 y / β,+.01-.02 / α 5.0		Pu 239 / 2.4×10^4 y / α 5.15 / γ 0.05,0.2 e^-	92 y / α 5.51	40 d / K / no γ	2.7 y / α 5.75		8 h / α 6.2 / K		22 m / α 6.6					
93 (Np)				2.33 d / β^- 0.33,0.88 / γ 0.06,0.28	2.10 d / β^- 0.22,1.28 / γ 0.8,1.2 / γ 0.06,0.28 e^-	Np 237 / 2.20×10^6 y / α 4.77	22 h / β^- 0.5 / γ	435 d / K / α 5.06	4.40 d / K / γ 1.9							
92 (U)				23.5 m / β^- 1.20 / γ 0.076	U$_I$ 238 / 99.28% / 4.51×10^9 y / α 4.18	6.8 d / β^- 0.23 / γ 0.08,0.28 e^-		AcU 235 / 0.71% / 7.1×10^8 y / α 4.4,4.40 γ	U$_{II}$ 234 / 0.0051% / 2.35×10^5 y / γ 0.04,0.8 e^- / α 4.76	1.62×10^5 y / α 4.82 / γ 0.04–0.8 e^-	70 y / α 5.31	4.2 d / K	20.8 d / α 5.85	58 m / K / α 6.42	9.3 m / α 6.72 / K	
91 (Pa)									UZ 234 / 6.7 h / β^- 0.4 ; UX$_2$ 234 / 1.14 m / β^- 2.31	27.4 d / β^- 0.4 / γ 0.1–0.4 e^-	1.32 d / β^- 0.28 / γ 1.06,0.28 e^-	Pa 231 / 3.43×10^4 y / α 5.0,4.7 / γ 0.3 e^-	17.7 d / K / β^-	1.5 d / K	22 h / K / α 6.09	38 m / α 6.46 / K
90 (Th)									UX$_1$ 234 / 24.10 d / β^- 0.11,0.20	23.5 m / β^- 1.2 / no γ	Th 232 / 100% / 1.39×10^{10} y / α 3.98	UY 231 / 25.65 h / β^- 0.21 / γ 0.036 e^-	Io 230 / 8×10^4 y / α 4.66 / γ	7000 y / α 5.0	RdTh 228 / 1.90 y / α 5.4,5.3 / γ	RdAc 227 / 18.6 d / α 6.0 / γ
89 (Ac)															MsTh$_2$ 228 / 6.13 h / β^- 1.55	Ac 227 / 21.7 y / β^- <0.01 γ / α 4.94
88 (Ra)															MsTh$_1$ 228 / 6.7 y / β^- <0.015	

INDEX